A Treatise on Algebra

BY
GEORGE PEACOCK

Vol. I

GEORGE PEACOCK

A TREATISE

ON

ALGEBRA.

VOL. I.

ARITHMETICAL ALGEBRA.

BY

GEORGE PEACOCK, D.D. F.R.S. F.G.S. F.R.A.S.

Reprinted from the 1842 Edition

Published by SCRIPTA MATHEMATICA
YESHIVA COLLEGE
NEW YORK, N.Y.
1940

a

PREFACE.

THE work, the first volume of which is now offered to the public, was designed in the first instance to be a second edition of a Treatise on Algebra, published in 1830, and which has been long out of print; but I have found it necessary, in carrying out the principles developed in that work, to present the subject in so novel a form, that I could not with propriety consider it in any other light than as an entirely new treatise.

I have separated arithmetical from symbolical algebra, and I have devoted the present volume entirely to the exposition of the principles of the former science and their application to the theory of numbers and of arithmetical processes: the second volume, which is now in the press, will embrace the principles of symbolical algebra: it will be followed, if other and higher duties should allow me the leisure to complete them, by other works, embracing all the more important departments of analysis, with the view of presenting their principles in such a form, as may make them component parts of one uniform and connected system.

In the preface to my former Treatise I have given a general exposition of my reasons for distinguishing arithmetical from symbolical algebra, and of my views of the just relations which their principles bear to each other, though I did not then consider it necessary to separate the exposition of one science altogether from the other. A more matured consideration of the subject, however, has convinced me of the expediency of this separation; for it is extremely difficult, when the two sciences are treated simultaneously, to keep their principles and results apart from each other, and to obviate the confusion, obscurity

and false reasoning which thence arises : a short statement
of the distinct and proper provinces of these two sciences
will make this difficulty sufficiently manifest.

In arithmetical algebra, we consider symbols as representing numbers, and the operations to which they are
submitted as included in the same definitions (whether expressed or understood) as in common arithmetic : the signs
+ and − denote the operations of addition and subtraction
in their ordinary meaning only, and those operations are
considered as impossible in all cases where the symbols
subjected to them possess values which would render them
so, in case they were replaced by digital numbers : thus in
expressions, such as $a + b$, we must suppose a and b to be
quantities of the same kind : in others, like $a - b$, we must
suppose a greater than b, and therefore homogeneous with
it : in products and quotients, like ab and $\dfrac{a}{b}$, we must
suppose the multiplier and divisor to be abstract numbers :
all results whatsoever, including negative quantities, which
are not strictly deducible as legitimate conclusions from
the definitions of the several operations, must be rejected
as impossible, or as foreign to the science.

Numerical fractions, which have not a common denominator, are not homogeneous, and are incapable of addition
and subtraction in arithmetic, and therefore in arithmetical
algebra ; and the multiplication and division of a number
or fraction by a fraction is only admissible in arithmetic,
and therefore in arithmetical algebra, in virtue of a con-
vention which assumes the *permanence of forms*[1], which
constitutes the great and fundamental principle of symbolical algebra ; but by thus trenching upon the province of
another and more comprehensive science, we are enabled to
give an extension to our notion of number, which greatly
enlarges the province of arithmetic and arithmetical algebra.
Without the aid of such an extension, the sciences of
arithmetical and symbolical algebra must have long since
been separated from each other.

[1] See Art. 135, 136, 137, 138, 139, 140.

Again, the generalizations of arithmetical algebra are generalizations of reasoning, and not of form. Thus we conclude that $(a + b)^2$ is equivalent to $a^2 + 2ab + b^2$, for all homogeneous values of a and b, inasmuch as it may be easily shewn that their specific magnitudes, if expressible by numbers, (using the term in its largest sense,) cannot in any way affect the formation of the result : but it is only for values of the symbol a which are not less than b, that the product $(a + b)(a - b)$ can be assumed to be equivalent to $a^2 - b^2$; for in no other case can this product be formed consistently with the arithmetical definition of the operation of multiplication. Again, the product of a^m and a^n can be shewn to be equivalent to a^{m+n}, when m and n are integral and abstract numbers, and in no other case ; for no other values are recognized in the definition of the *power* of a symbol, and therefore in no other case can we appeal to it in determining the form of the product : the series for $(a + b)^n$ is also a necessary result of the same definition, and subject therefore to the same limitations : and we conclude generally that all the necessary results of arithmetical algebra must be rigorously restricted to those conditions of value and representation which the definitions require.

But though the rules for performing the operations of symbolical algebra must embody the limitations which the definitions impose, yet it is very difficult, in innumerable cases, to discover the impossibility of the operation or the inadmissibility of the result, before the operation is performed or the result is obtained : thus if we are required to subtract $a + b$ from a, we do not attempt an operation which is as obviously impossible in arithmetical algebra, as it would be, in common arithmetic, to subtract 3 from 2 : but if it was required to subtract from $7a + 5b$, the several subtrahends $a + 3b$, $3a - 2b$ and $3a + 7b$, we should probably proceed without hesitation to apply the general rule of subtraction, which would give us

$$7a + 5b - a - 3b - 3a + 2b - 3a - 7b$$
$$= 7a - a - 3a - 3a + 5b - 3b + 2b - 7b$$
$$= 7b - 9b,$$

a result which indicates that the final operation, to which the application of the rule conducts us, is impossible : we are perpetually encountering, in arithmetical algebra, as it were unconsciously and unawares[1], similar examples of operations which cannot be performed or of results which cannot be recognized, consistently with the definitions upon which that science is founded.

Symbolical algebra adopts the rules of arithmetical algebra, but removes altogether their restrictions : thus symbolical subtraction differs from the same operation in arithmetical algebra in being possible for all relations of value of the symbols or expressions employed : as far as those relations are admissible, therefore, in the latter science, they are in every respect the same : in both sciences also we change the signs of the terms of the subtrahend, and then proceed as in addition : but it is in the former science only that we form and recognize the result, whatever it may be, without any reference to its consistency with the definitions upon which those rules in arithmetical algebra are founded : we are thus enabled to subtract $a + b$ as well as $a - b$ from a, obtaining by the unrestricted rule
$$a - (a + b) = a - a - b = - b$$
in one case, and
$$a - (a - b) = a - a + b = + b$$
in the other : the same observation extends to the rules for performing all the other operations of arithmetical algebra and to the results to which they lead ; adopting also the results themselves, whether common to arithmetical algebra or not, whether negative or positive, as equally the subjects of the fundamental and other operations.

It is this adoption of the rules of the operations of arithmetical algebra as the rules for performing the operations which *bear the same names* in symbolical algebra, which secures the absolute identity of the results in the two sciences as far as they exist in common : or in other words, all the results of arithmetical algebra which are deduced by the application of its rules, and which are general in form, though particular in value, are results

likewise of symbolical algebra, where they are general in
value as well as in form: thus the product of a^m and a^n,
which is a^{m+n} when m and n are whole numbers, and
therefore general in form though particular in value, will
be their product likewise when m and n are general in
value as well as in form: the series for $(a + b)^n$, determined by the principles of arithmetical algebra, when n is
any whole number, if it be exhibited in a general form,
without reference to a final term, may be shewn, upon
the same principle, to be the equivalent series for $(a + b)^n$,
when n is general both in form and value.

This principle, in my former Treatise on Algebra, I denominated the "*principle of the permanence of equivalent
forms,*" and it may be considered as merely expressing the
general law of transition from the results of arithmetical
to those of symbolical algebra: it is this law which secures
the complete identity of the two sciences as far as those
results exist in common, and without which the latter science
would degenerate into a science expressing the arbitrary
combinations of symbols only, whose results would, in the
first instance at least, be altogether separated from arithmetic, and therefore from arithmetical computation.

Upon this view of the principles of symbolical algebra,
it will follow that its operations are determined by the
definitions of arithmetical algebra, as far as they proceed
in common, and by the "principle of the permanence of
equivalent forms" in all other cases, which those definitions
cannot comprehend: it will follow therefore that in all such
cases, *the meaning of the operation or of the result obtained,
whenever such a meaning can be assigned, must be determined
in conformity with the conditions which it must satisfy, and
consequently must vary with every variation of those conditions:*
upon this principle we shall be enabled to give a consistent
interpretation to symbolical expressions or results such as
$+ a$ and $- a$, considered with reference to each other, where
a denotes a line, a force, a period of time, and various other
concrete magnitudes, as well as to the operations called ddi-
tion and subtraction, multiplication and division, denoted by
the usual signs, when applied to such quantities: but in

innumerable other instances, it will be found that the
results obtained will admit of no interpretation whatever,
or have hitherto failed to receive it.

The results therefore of symbolical algebra, which are
not common to arithmetical algebra, are generalizations of
form, and not necessary consequences of the definitions,
which are totally inapplicable in such cases. It is quite
true indeed that writers on algebra have not hitherto
remarked the character of the transition from one class
of results to the other, and have treated them both as
equally consequences of the fundamental definitions of arithmetic or arithmetical algebra: and we are consequently
presented with forms of demonstration, which though really
applicable to specific values of the symbols only, are tacitly
extended to all values whatsoever: such are the usual
proofs which are given of the indifference of the order of
succession of the factors of a product[1], of the rule for
the multiplication and division of fractions[2], of the rule
for finding the greatest common measure of two quantities,
whether numbers or algebraical expressions[3], of the form
of the product of powers of the same symbol[4], as well as
others which might be mentioned: whilst the rules for
performing the fundamental operations[5], for the incorporation of signs[6], and the meaning of fractional powers[7] of
a symbol, are little more than assumptions, of which not
even the form of a demonstration is attempted to be given.
In all such works, some few of very recent date excepted, it
has been presumed that these conclusions could be deduced
or these generalizations made in perfect consistency with
the arithmetical definitions of the operations employed, or,
in other words, without any change in the meaning of
such operations, however different may be the quantities
which are subjected to them: the consequence of this fundamental error has been, that no sufficient demonstration
or adequate exposition has been given of the principles of

[1] Wood's *Algebra*, Art. 75.   [2] Ib. Art. 105 and 108.
[3] Ib. Art. 90, 91, 92, and Example.   [4] Ib. Art. 78 and 108.
[5] Ib. Art. 73, 74, &c.   [6] Ib. Art. 76.
[7] Ib. Art. 57.

that science which is of all others the most general in its applications.

A student who is not only familiar with the results of arithmetical algebra, but likewise with the limitations which it imposes, will be in a condition to comprehend and appreciate the whole extent of the legitimate conclusions which it furnishes : and though he may find himself perpetually brought in contact as it were, by the generality of the form of the symbols which he employs and of the rules of the operations to which they are submitted, with results, which the definitions of arithmetical algebra will not authorize, yet he will thus acquire a habit of observing not merely what is within, but what is without the just and proper boundaries of the science : and what is still more important, as a preparation for the study of symbolical algebra, he will be thus enabled to appreciate at once the origin and the full extent of the "principle of the permanence of equivalent forms," which assumes a knowledge of the rules of arithmetical as the basis of those of symbolical algebra, without which the identity of the results of the two sciences, as far as they proceed in common, could not be secured. I have considered the above mentioned reasons sufficient to justify me in separating the exposition and study of the two sciences from each other : and I feel satisfied that the adoption of such a course will be found materially to contribute to the most secure, if not to the most expeditious acquisition of distinct and general views of the principles of this most important science.

The present volume, though strictly elementary as far as the theory and operations of arithmetical algebra are concerned, will be found to comprehend many other subjects, which cannot be considered as equally necessary as introductory to the study of symbolical algebra : such are some parts of the discussion and exposition of the theory of arithmetical operations, of the theory of continued fractions, of the extraction of simple and compound roots, of the theory of ratios and proportions and various questions of commercial arithmetic connected with them, of the solution of indeterminate problems of the first degree,

b

and of several important propositions in the theory of
numbers. Such an arrangement of subjects is perfectly
consistent with their philosophical order of dependence upon
each other, though it may not be altogether consistent
with their order of difficulty: but I have endeavoured at
the end of the Table of Contents, to point out those
articles which a student, at his first reading of this volume,
may pass over, without any material sacrifice of propositions, the knowledge of which may be necessary to the
complete understanding and demonstration of those which
follow.

CONTENTS.

ADVERTISEMENT.

Though there are few articles in this volume, the subjects of which are not more or less connected with those which follow, yet there are a considerable number of them, which a student, who possesses no previous knowledge of Algebra, may pass over, at his first reading, without any serious sacrifice: they are as follows:

Chapter II. Articles 108–115: 138–141: 158–169: 180 to the end.

Chapter III. Articles 226–232: 239 to the end.

Chapter IV. Articles 268–277: 305–315: 345 to the end.

Chapter VII. Articles 451, 452: 459 to the end.

Chapter IX. The whole chapter.

Chapter X. The whole chapter.

ERRORS.

PAGE	LINE	FROM	ERROR.	CORRECTION.
6	5	bottom	321	323
11	15	top	$a - b - d + c - e$	$a - b - d + c + e$
16	18	—	Art. 10	Art. 9
18	9	—	Art. 15	Art. 16
19	24	—	$a - b + c - d$	$a - b + c + d$
20	8	—	$(a - b)$	$(a + b)$
23	26	—	forth	fourth
33	25	—	63	81
36	last		Art. 15	Art. 16
42	11	top	258	238
—	12	—	258	238
—	13	—	258	238
46	18	—	$\dfrac{b^2 - b^3}{a}$	$b^2 - \dfrac{b^3}{a}$
—	30	—	$\dfrac{b^3}{a^2}$	$\dfrac{b^3}{a}$
49	16	—	$(a + b\,(a - b)$	$(a + b)(a - b)$
53	3	—	228	224
—	4	—	228	224
—	6	—	228	224
55	16	—	by c	by b
—	3	bottom	1519	853
—	last		24827	24834
64	7	top	$b = q\,x,\; c = q\,y$	$b = q\,xz,\; c = r\,yz$
67	2	bottom	8	7
68	2	—	620	630
—	last		300	360
82	7	bottom	by r	by n
84	15	top	only num-	only prime num-
86	18	—	1) 1.00000	7) 1.00000
96	16	—	.7000 ×	7000 ×
—	24	—	56	5.6
107	last		$\dfrac{130}{431}$, we find $\dfrac{130}{431}$	$\dfrac{130}{421}$, we find $\dfrac{130}{421}$
108	6	bottom	$\dfrac{130}{431}$	$\dfrac{130}{421}$

PAGE	LINE	FROM	ERROR.	CORRECTION.
108	7	bottom	$\frac{130}{431}$	$\frac{130}{421}$
117	22	top	$\frac{14.98}{2435}$	$\frac{14.98}{24.35}$
124	20	—	immensurable	innumerable
126	10	—	$+\frac{40}{480}+\frac{14}{480}+\frac{714}{480}=$	$+\frac{40}{480}+\frac{14}{480}=\frac{714}{480}=$
127	20	—	00994318	0099318
—	26	—	11.895	11.875
206	6	—	$4+$	$4x+$
301	10	bottom	$2^{n}+1$	$2^{2^{n}}+1$
—	7	—	$2^{32}+1$	$2^{2^{32}}+1$
321	6	top	$\frac{1}{48}$	$\frac{1}{47}$
330	14	—	$\times 10 \times 6 \times$	$\times 10 + 6 \times$
—	16	—	dele Art. 484	
—	17	—	$754x$	$744x$
—	19	—	754	744
346	5	—	(Art. 190)	(Art. 496)
357	13	—	$\frac{eq}{u}$	$\frac{cq}{u}$
363	3	bottom	1100101110	1100100100

CHAPTER I.

PRINCIPLES OF ARITHMETICAL ALGEBRA.

1. ARITHMETICAL Algebra is the science which results from the use of symbols and signs to denote numbers and the operations to which they may be subjected; those numbers or their representatives, and the operations upon them, being used in the same sense and with the same limitations as in common arithmetic. Arithmetical Algebra.

2. Arithmetical Algebra is not the same science with Symbolical Algebra, the exposition of the principles of which will constitute the chief object of the following Treatise: in this latter science, the symbols which are used are perfectly general in their representation, and perfectly unlimited in their values; and the operations upon them, in whatever manner they are denoted, or by whatever name they are called, are universal in their application: but, since the principles and general conclusions or rules of Arithmetical Algebra will be found to *suggest*, and in a certain sense to *determine*, the assumption of the first principles of Symbolical Algebra, it is expedient to commence with the exposition of the former science, as forming the proper, and, in some respects, necessary introduction to the latter. Not the same science with Symbolical Algebra.

3. In Arithmetical Algebra, the symbols which are employed, whether they be the letters of the same or of different alphabets, are used to denote numbers, or numerical quantities *only*: they may denote concrete as well as abstract numbers, as long as the numerical relations only of such concrete numbers are considered and not the specific properties of the magnitudes which they represent. Those numbers which are actually assigned and given, are expressed by means of the nine digits and zero, by the aid of the artifices of ordinary arithmetical notation*: but, numbers which Symbols in Arithmetical Algebra.

---

* This consists in assigning to each digit its value according to its position with respect to the place of units, supposing them to be severally multiplied by ten, one hundred, one thousand, ten thousand, one hundred thousand, and so on, according as they are placed at the distance of one, two, three, four, five, &c. places to the left of the place of units: if the digits are placed to the right of the place of units, they are supposed to be divided by a similar series of numbers: the entire number, or numerical quantity, denoted by any collection of digits (zero included) is found by

are supposed to be *known*, though not *assigned*; or **which are** subject to conditions by which they may be *determined*, though not *known*; or which are supposed to be perfectly *arbitrary* in their value, whether they be *assignable* or *not*; are, in all cases, denoted by symbols.

Signs of operations not generally required in Arithmetic. 4. In the ordinary processes of Arithmetic, no signs of operation are required: thus, numbers are added and subtracted, multiplied and divided, and their roots extracted, and the final results of those operations are numbers, or numerical quantities, expressed by the common arithmetical notation, without presenting, in those results, any traces whatever of the process or processes by which they are obtained: the following are examples:

Examples. 5. (1) Add together 271, 164, 1023.

$$271$$
$$164$$
$$1023$$

1458   final result.

(2) From 1695 subtract 763.

$$1695$$
$$763$$

932   final result.

(3) Multiply together 191 and 27.

$$191$$
$$27$$

$$1337$$
$$382$$

5157   final result.

adding together the numbers, or numerical quantities, denoted by the several digits in their respective positions: thus, 3456 denotes three thousand four hundred and fifty six; or, the sum of 3 multiplied by one thousand, of 4 multiplied by one hundred, of 5 multiplied by ten and of 6 : 46.189 denotes forty six, together with one tenth, eight hundredth and nine thousandth parts of unity : and similarly in all other cases.

If all arithmetical operations were supposed to be completed, every numerical quantity would be represented either as a whole number or a decimal : in other words, all proper numerical fractions would be represented as the sum of a series of fractions whose denominators are numbers in the series 10, 100, 1000, 10,000, and so on : if such a practice was universally followed, it would be possible to exclude signs of operation altogether from arithmetic.

(4)   Divide 29680 by 112.

$$112) \ 29680 \ (265 \quad \text{final result.}$$
$$\underline{224}$$
$$728$$
$$\underline{672}$$
$$560$$
$$560$$
$$\overline{ \cdots}$$

(5)   Extract the square root of 219961.

$$2\dot19\dot96\dot1 \ (469 \quad \text{final result.}$$
$$16$$
$$\overline{86) \ 599}$$
$$516$$
$$\overline{929) \ 8361}$$
$$8361$$
$$\overline{ \cdots\cdot}$$

(6)   Extract the cube root of 474552.

$$4\dot74\dot55\dot2 \ (78 \quad \text{final result.}$$
$$343$$
$$\overline{147) \ 131552}$$
$$1176$$
$$1344$$
$$512$$
$$\overline{131552}$$
$$\overline{\cdots\cdots}$$

6. The final results, in all the preceding examples, are obtained and exhibited without the use of any sign of operation: but though the use of signs of operation in arithmetical processes may generally be dispensed with, without occasioning any considerable practical inconvenience, yet it by no means follows that they may not be introduced with advantage.   Thus, if we assume the sign

+ to denote the operation of addition.

− .... of subtraction.

× .... of multiplication.

÷ .... of division.

Explanation of signs of operation.

$\sqrt{}$ to denote the operation of extracting the square root.

$\sqrt[3]{}$ .... of extracting the cube root.

$=$ to denote equality, or the result of any operation or operations: then the results of the operations in the examples just given (Art. 5.) may be very briefly and clearly exhibited under the following forms:

Examples of their application.

$$271 + 164 + 1023 = 1458$$
$$1695 - 763 = 932$$
$$191 \times 27 = 5157$$
$$29680 \div 112 = 265$$
$$\sqrt{219961} = 469$$
$$\sqrt[3]{474552} = 78.$$

Their interpretation in words.

7. These examples may be read, and therefore interpreted as follows:

(1) The sum of 271, 164, and 1023, or *the result of the addition of these numbers to each other*, is equal to 1458.

(2) The difference of 1695 and 763, or *the result of the subtraction of the second of these numbers from the first*, is equal to 932.

(3) The product of 191 and 27, or *the result of the multiplication of these numbers into each other*, is equal to 5157.

(4) The quotient of 29680 divided by 112, or *the result of the division of the first of these numbers by the second*, is equal to 265.

(5) The square root of 219961, or *the result of the process for extracting the square root of this number*, is equal to 469.

(6) The cube root of 474552, or *the result of the process for extracting the cube root of this number*, is equal to 78.

Use of signs of operation in arithmetic in superseding the necessity of verbal statements.

8. *Signs of operation*, when thus defined to represent the fundamental operations of arithmetic, may be considered as artifices for superseding the use of ordinary language in describing the nature of the operations to be performed and their connection with the results which are obtained: thus, if it was required to add together, subtract from each other, or multiply together, the numbers 619 and 347, they must be written underneath each other, in all these cases, precisely in the same manner, as follows:

619	619	619
347	347	347
966	272	214793 :

and it becomes necessary therefore to premise a statement in words of the nature of the particular operation to be performed in each case, in order that one operation may not be performed when another is required: but, the use of signs of operation, as in the expressions

$$619 + 347 = 966$$
$$619 - 347 = 272$$
$$619 \times 347 = 214793$$

at once indicates, without any previous verbal statement, the nature of the operations to be performed and their connection with the results obtained, though it does not supersede the necessity of performing the arithmetical operations themselves.

9. Let us now advance a step farther and suppose that the letters of the alphabet, such as a, b, $c \ldots x$, y, z, are used to denote numbers of any kind, whether known or unknown, whole or fractional (Art. 3.); and let us take corresponding examples to those given in Art. 5. *Use of signs of operation applied to numbers expressed by symbols.*

(1) Let it be required to add together the numbers *represented* by the letters a and b. *Addition.*

The result is represented by

$$a + b,$$

which admits of no further simplification or reduction.

(2) Let it be required to subtract the number b from the number a. *Subtraction*

The result is represented by

$$a - b.$$

(3) Let it be required to multiply the number a by the number b. *Multiplication.*

The result is represented by $a \times b$, or more commonly by ab.

(4) Let it be required to divide the number a by the number b. *Division.*

The result is represented by $a \div b$, or more commonly, like an arithmetical fraction, under the form $\dfrac{a}{b}$.

We shall now proceed to make a detailed examination of the preceding and similar results, with a view to the establishment of the fundamental rules of operation, when symbols are employed to represent numbers, which in common arithmetic are expressed by the nine digits and zero.

Rule for
addition of
symbols,
and the
grounds
upon which
it is
founded.

10. The sum of two numbers a and b is represented by

$$a + b:$$

the sum of three numbers a, b, and c, would be represented by

$$a + b + c:$$

the sum of four numbers a, b, c, and d, would be represented by

$$a + b + c + d:$$

and in a similar manner, *the sum of any number of such quantities would be represented by writing them in succession in the same line with the* SIGN *of* ADDITION + placed between the several symbols.

The reason of this rule is obvious, inasmuch as the notation used merely indicates that the several numbers expressed by the symbols are to be added together for the purpose of forming the required sum.

When
symbols are
added to-
gether, it is
indifferent
in what
order they
are taken.

11. When any number of symbols are added together and the result is written down, it is *indifferent* in what order the symbols succeed each other.

Thus $a + b$ is the same quantity or number with $b + a$; or expressed *algebraically.*   (Art. 6.)

$$a + b = b + a.$$

In a similar manner $a + b + c$ is the same quantity with $a + c + b$, or $b + a + c$, or $b + c + a$, or $c + a + b$, or $c + b + a$: or expressed algebraically,

$$a + b + c = a + c + b = b + a + c = b + c + a = c + a + b = c + b + a:$$

and similarly in all other cases: for it is obvious that, when numbers are to be added together, their sums will be the same in whatever order they are taken.

Thus if $a = 117$, $b = 323$, and $c = 211$, and if these numbers be added together, their sum will be the same in whatever order they are placed:

117	117	323	323	211	211
323	211	117	211	117	323
211	321	211	117	323	117
651	651	651	651	651	651

Subtrac-
tion, in
what man-
ner repre-
sented.

12. The result of the subtraction of the number b from the number a, is represented by

$$a - b. \quad \text{(Art. 9.)}$$

In this result, the order of succession of the symbols is essentially dependent upon the particular symbols which are the subject of the operation, and they are therefore not commutable, as in the expression

$$a + b.$$

13. In the expression

$$a - b$$

it is *presumed* that the number denoted by a is greater than the number denoted by b: if this condition be not satisfied, the operation of subtracting b from a could not be performed: under such circumstances, we might call the quantity represented by

$$a - b$$

impossible, if by the use of such a term with such an application, we should merely deny the *possibility* of obtaining any conceivable numerical result, when the number a was less than the number b.

14. When one number is subtracted from another in common arithmetic, the relation of their respective magnitudes is apparent from inspection, and no attempt is made to perform an operation which is visibly impossible: but when numbers are denoted by symbols, there is nothing which is *essentially* included in those symbols by which either their absolute or their relative magnitude can be inferred: it becomes necessary therefore (in arithmetical algebra) when one symbol is subtracted from another or from others, to assume such a *limitation* of its value as may be required for the practicability of the operation to be performed; in other words, symbols in arithmetical algebra are limited in their representation to numbers, and, in their values, by the peculiar circumstances of their application; if we consider symbols as unlimited both in *value* and in *representation*, (and there is nothing in the symbols themselves which can express such limitations either with respect to one or the other) we must necesarily admit the existence of expressions such as

$$a - b,$$

where b is *greater* as well as *less* than a, and where a and b may represent not merely numbers but any quantities whatsoever.

This distinction is extremely important and requires the most careful study and consideration, inasmuch as it is one of the capital points which renders necessary, as will be shewn hereafter, the **separation** of *arithmetical* from *symbolical* algebra.

15. If a number be first added to and then subtracted from, another, or conversely, the result will be identical with the original number: thus if 7 be first added to 10, making 17, and if the same number 7 be then subtracted from 17, the result is 10, which is the original number: or conversely, if 7 be first subtracted from 10, leaving 3, and if the same number 7 be then added to 3, the result is 10, which is the original number. Similarly, if to the number a, we add the number b, making $a + b$, and if the same number b be subsequently subtracted from $a + b$, the result is the number a, which is the original number: or conversely, if the number b be subtracted from the number a, leaving $a - b$, and if the same number b be then added to $a - b$, the result is the number a, which is the original number: or if these operations and results be expressed algebraically, we get

$$a + b - b = a,$$

and also,

$$a - b + b = a.$$

16. The conclusion in the last Article results from the essential relation between the operations of Addition and Subtraction, which are the *inverse* of each other: or in other words, one operation *undoes* the effect of the other, when the number subjected to the two operations is the same: an attention to this relation of these two operations is extremely important, inasmuch as it enables us to obliterate the same symbol when it presents itself twice in the same expression, preceded by the sign − in one case, and by the sign + or by no sign whatever in the other: thus,

$$a - a = 0,$$
$$a - a + b = b,$$
$$a - b + b - a = 0.$$

. 17. The operations of Multiplication and Division are also the *inverse* of each other; and in a similar manner any symbol or number may be obliterated which both multiplies and divides the same symbol or quantity. It is this relation of the operations of Multiplication and Division which leads to some of the most common and most important reductions both of numerical quantities and of symbolical expressions to others, which possess the same import and generally also a more simple or a more manageable form.

18. When numbers in common Arithmetic are added, subtracted, multiplied or divided, we usually obliterate, upon the conclusion of the operation, all traces of the original numbers, and

make use of the final result only expressed by the nine digits and zero: but if we employ symbols to denote numbers, we cannot *generally*, unless in the case of inverse operations with the same symbols, obliterate in the results the particular symbols which are involved in the operation or operations performed upon them: thus if it was required, in arithmetic, to subtract the sum of 67 and 54 from 171, we should proceed as follows:

$$\begin{array}{cc} 67 & 171 \\ 54 & 121 \\ \hline 121 & 50 \end{array}$$

and we should employ the number 50 as the final result, which contains in itself no traces of the numbers 67, 54 and 171, nor of the operations to which they have been subjected: but if we should denote the numbers 171, 67, and 54 by the symbols a, b, and c respectively, the operation of addition by the sign + and the operation of subtraction by the sign −, the result in question would be represented by $a - (b + c)^*$, where the sum $b + c$, of the two numbers b and c to be subtracted, is included between *brackets*, and where the sign − of subtraction is placed before them; and where all the symbols employed in the course of the operations, as well as the signs of the operations themselves, are exhibited in the final result.

19. In the preceding Article, we have used *brackets* to denote that the whole number or quantity expressed by the symbols included between them, connected with their proper sign or signs, is to be subjected to the operation which is denoted by the sign which precedes them. **Use of brackets.**

The use of brackets is very general in Algebra, and is connected with rules both for their introduction or removal, which are of great importance, and which require the most careful attention. The principle of their introduction may be stated generally as follows: *whenever any number of symbols or combination† of symbols which are connected together with the signs + or −, one or both, are required to be considered* COLLECTIVELY *as constituting one quantity or number, which is required to be subjected to any operation or operations, they are included between brackets.‡*

* It will be afterwards shewn (Art. 20.) that $a - (b + c) = a - b - c$.
† This term will be explained hereafter.
‡ The brackets are sometimes replaced by the *vinculum*, which is a line drawn *over* the symbols which are required to be connected together: thus, $\overline{b + c}$ is used instead of $(b + c)$: $a - \overline{b - c}$ instead of $a - (b - c)$: and similarly in other cases.

Rule for
the sub-
traction of
the sum of
any num-
ber of
quantities,
and for the
removal of
brackets in
such cases.

20. In Article 18, the result of the subtraction of $b + c$, or of the sum of two numbers b and c, from a, has been shewn to be represented by

$$a - (b + c): \qquad (1)$$

the same result may be likewise represented by the equivalent expression

$$a - b - c: \qquad (2)$$

for it is obvious that the result of the subtraction of the sum of two numbers b and c, or of $(b + c)$, from the number a, is equivalent to the result of the successive subtraction of the two parts b and c, which together make up that sum, from the same number; a conclusion which is algebraically expressed by the second of the two forms (1) and (2).

In a similar manner, if the operation of subtraction be applied to the sum of any number of quantities or numbers, the result will be equivalent to the application of the same operation to all the numbers or symbols in succession, of which that sum is composed: it thus appears that

$$a - (b + c + d) = a - b - c - d,$$
$$a - b - (c + d + e) = a - b - c - d - e,$$
$$a - (b + c) - (c + d) = a - b - c - c - d,$$

and similarly in all similar cases: we thus arrive at the following general and very simple rule: *whenever any number of symbols connected together with the sign + are to be subtracted from any other symbol or symbols (however connected with each other), we must place before each of the symbols to be subtracted the sign −, and write them in succession after the symbol or symbols which express the number or minuend from which the subtraction is to be made.*

Rule for
the sub-
traction of
numbers
connected
together
with the
sign — as
well as +.

21. In the rule stated in the last Article, the symbols forming the number to be subtracted were all connected together with the sign +: it remains to consider the case where the sign − occurs, connecting some of the symbols which form the subtrahend: thus, let it be proposed to subtract $(b - c)$ or the excess of the number b above the number c, from the number a.

If we subtract b from a, the result is represented by $a - b$ (Art. 9.); but if we subtract $b - c$ from a, the result will obviously be greater than $a - b$ by the number c, inasmuch as the number subtracted in the second case is less by c than the number subtracted in the first: it follows therefore that the result required is correctly represented by $a - b + c$: or, if the question proposed and the result obtained be expressed algebraically, it will follow that

$$a - (b - c) = a - b + c.$$

In a similar manner, we should find that

$$a - (b - c - d) = a - b + c + d:$$

for the number subtracted from a is less than b by the sum of the numbers c and d.

Likewise,

$$a - (b - c + d - e) = a - b + c - d + e:$$

for, inasmuch as $b - c + d - e$ is equal to $b + d - c - e$, it follows that the number subtracted from a is less than the sum of the numbers b and d by the sum of the numbers c and e, which is therefore equal to

$$a - b - d + c - e; \qquad (1)$$

and which becomes, by merely changing the arrangement of the letters,

$$a - b + c - d + e. \qquad (2)^*$$

22. The change in the order of succession of the terms of the expression (1) at the conclusion of the last Article, which enables us to pass to their subsequent arrangement in alphabetical order as in the expression (2), can make no alteration in its value. For, when a series of numbers are to be added to, or subtracted from, another, the same final result will be obtained, in whatever order the required operations succeed each other, so long as the subtrahend, when the operation of subtraction is required to be performed, continues to be less than the minuend†. And if we may

The value of an algebraical expression consisting of several terms is not altered by any change in the order of succession of those terms which are preceded by the signs + and −.

---

* Thus, if $a = 31$, $b = 10$, $c = 9$, $d = 12$, and $e = 3$, the succession of operations as indicated in forms (1) and (2) will be as follows:

For form (1)

$a = 31$	$a - b = 21$	$a - b - d = 9$	$a - b - d + c = 18$
$b = 10$	$d = 12$	$c = 9$	$e = 3$
$a - b = 21$	$a - b - d = 9$	$a - b - d + c = 18$	$a - b - d + c + e = 21.$

For form (2)

$a = 31$	$a - b = 21$	$a - b + c = 30$	$a - b + c - d = 18$
$b = 10$	$c = 9$	$d = 12$	$e = 3$
$a - b = 21$	$a - b + c = 30$	$a - b + c - d = 18$	$a - b + c - d + e = 21.$

† If we had supposed $a = 21$, $b = 10$, $c = 9$, $d = 12$, and $e = 3$, we should have found $b + d = 22$: in this case, the second of the successive operations indicated in form (1) would have been impracticable, inasmuch as it would have required the subtraction of a greater number 22 from a less 21: this difficulty would not have occurred in form (2).

be allowed to suppose that in any succession of operations, all terms preceded by the sign + are added to the first term to form a single *minuend*, and all terms preceded by the sign − are also added together to form a single *subtrahend*, then one operation of subtraction will, in all such cases, produce the correct final result*, *which will clearly be altogether independent of the order of succession of all the terms after the first*, and which will involve no impracticable operation, as long as the single subtrahend, which is thus obtained, is less than the minuend from which it is to be taken.

General rule for performing the operation of subtraction.

23. The observation of the results obtained in the preceding Articles, and of the reasoning employed for that purpose, would shew that in performing the operation of subtraction, all those terms in the subtrahend which were preceded by no sign, or by the sign +, would be preceded in the final result by the sign −; and that all those terms in the subtrahend which were preceded by the sign −,

The sign + is assumed (for the purposes of a rule) to precede a symbol whenever no sign appears.

would be preceded in the final result by the sign +: whilst the terms of the minuend and their antecedent signs would undergo no change. If, therefore, for the sake of greater brevity in the expression of a rule in this and in other cases, we should assume the existence of the sign +, where no antecedent sign appears, whether in the first term of the *minuend* or *subtrahend* or *subtrahends*, the rule for subtraction may be expressed in the following very simple form: *change none of the signs preceding the terms of the minuend: change all the signs preceding the terms of the subtrahend, + into −, and − into +: the final result will be found by writing in the same line all the terms preceded by the signs which thus result, in any order which may be considered most convenient or most symmetrical.*

Alphabetical arrangement of the symbols generally adopted.

In the absence of any other principle of arrangement, the alphabetical order of the symbols or combinations of symbols, which form the several terms, is generally preferred: we say *generally*, for innumerable cases will occur, in which it is convenient to depart from such a final arrangement of the terms.

Examples of addition and subtraction.

24. We will subjoin a few examples, for the purpose of illustrating the rules for addition and subtraction in Algebra, as far as they are derivable from the preceding Articles.

---

* Thus, in the example under consideration, we add c and e to a, making the *minuend* $a + c + e$; and we also add together b and d, making the *subtrahend* $b + d$ and the final result may be represented by

$$a + c + e - (b + d),$$

which is equivalent to both the expressions in forms (1) and (2). Art. 21.

(1)   To $a + b$ add $c - d$.

Summand* $a + b$
Summand $c - d$
Sum...... $a + b + c - d.$

In this example, and generally in all similar cases, we place the *summands* or expressions to be added, underneath each other, as in the addition of numbers in common arithmetic: but if the same operation be exhibited throughout by means of algebraical signs, it will assume the following form:

$$a + b + (c - d) = a + b + c - d ;$$

or if expressed in words, it appears that if the excess of c above d be added to $a + b$, the sum will be equivalent to the sum of a, b and c diminished by d.

(2)   From $a + b$ subtract $c - d$.

Minuend $a + b$
Subtrahend $c - d$
Remainder $a + b - c + d.$

In this example we have placed the *minuend*, *subtrahend* and *remainder* underneath each other precisely in the same manner as in the subtraction of numbers in common arithmetic: if the same operation be exhibited throughout by means of algebraical signs, then it must be written as follows

$$a + b - (c - d) = a + b - c + d.$$

In this second form, the *subtrahend* $c - d$ is included between brackets in order to shew that the whole quantity or number which they include (which is the excess of c above d) is to be subtracted from $a + b$: the rule for removing the brackets when they are preceded by the sign $-$ is in every respect identical with the rule for performing the operation of subtraction. *Rule for removing brackets when preceded by the sign $-$.*

When a quantity or number expressed by more terms than one is included between brackets, which are preceded by the sign $+$, no change whatever takes place in their several signs. *Rule when the brackets are preceded by the sign $+$.*

---

* The use of the *term summand* to express any one of a series of quantities to be added, may be justified by the same analogy which is observable in the formation and use of the terms *minuend*, *subtrahend*, *multiplicand* and *dividend*: a father extension of this analogy has led to the assumption of the terms *radicand* and *logarithmand*, to express the numbers whose roots are to be extracted or whose logarithms are to be taken: See Ohm's Versuch eines vollkommen consequenten system der mathematick, Vol. I.

when the brackets are removed ; it being understood that where no such sign is exhibited as preceding the first term, the existence of the sign + is assumed. (Art. 23.)

Thus, $\qquad a + b + (c - d) = a + b + c - d :$
and $\ a + (b - c) + (d - e) = a + b - c + d - e.$

Rule for addition in algebra. It follows, therefore, that quantities or expressions, whether included between brackets or not, are added together in algebra by merely writing them consecutively in the same line with their proper signs.

(3)   From $a + b + 7$ subtract $b - c + 10$.

Minuend $\qquad a + b + \ 7$

Subtrahend $\quad b - c + 10$

Remainder $\quad a + b + 7 - b + c - 10 = a + c - 3.$

Otherwise,

$$a + b + 7 - (b - c + 10) = a + b + 7 - b + c - 10$$
$$= a + c + 7 - 10 = a + c - 3.$$

For it has been shewn in Art. 15. that $b - b = 0$, and consequently that $a + b - b = a$: and it is obvious that the addition of 7 to, and the subsequent subtraction of 10 from, $a + c$, is equivalent to the subtraction of their difference 3, by a single operation, from $a + c$.

(4)   From $c - 10 + d + 8$, subtract $14 + d - 9 - e.$

Minuend $\qquad c \ - 10 + d + 8$

Subtrahend $\quad 14 + d \ - 9 - e$

Remainder $\quad c \ - 10 + d + 8 - 14 - d + 9 + e = c + e - 7.$

For it is obvious that d must be (or rather may be) obliterated from the final result, (Art. 15.) and that $8 + 9$, or 17 must be added to, and that $10 + 14$, or 24 must be subtracted from, $c + e$: or their difference 7 *subtracted* (for the subtrahend 24 is greater by 7 than the minuend 17) from $c + e$, by one operation.

Or, we may begin by replacing $c - 10 + d + 8$, by its equivalent expression $c + d - 2$, and also $14 + d - 9 - e$ by its equivalent expression $d - e + 5$, when the remaining operations may be exhibited as follows :

$$c + d - 2$$
$$d - e + 5$$
$$\overline{c + d - 2 - d + c - 5 = c + e - 7.}$$

Or, if the operations to be performed and their results, be expressed by symbols, we get

$$c - 10 + d + 8 - (14 + d - 9 - e)$$
$$= c - 10 + d + 8 - 14 - d + 9 + e$$
$$= c + e - 7.$$

Generally, all those terms which consist of numbers expressed by digits and not by general symbols, are combined into one in the final result, by writing the difference of the sums of those terms which are preceded by no sign or by the sign + and of those which are preceded by the sign −, and prefixing to it the sign of the greater.

Rule for the incorporation of terms expressed by digits.

(5) To $c + d - 2$, add $d - e + 5$.

    Summand $c + d - 2$

    Summand $d - e + 5$

    Sum..... $c + d - 2 + d - e + 5 = c + d + d - e + 3.$

In this result, the letter d occurs *twice* preceded by the same sign: in the following Article it will be shewn that $d + d$, may be more conveniently represented by $2d$, by which substitution, the result under consideration becomes $c + 2d - e + 3$.

25. When a number denoted by a is added to itself, the result is algebraically denoted by $a + a$: if the same summand a be repeated three times, the result is denoted by $a + a + a$: if four times, by $a + a + a + a$: and similarly when the same summand a is repeated any number of times whatsoever: in all such cases, it is usual for greater brevity to express the same results by prefixing to the symbol thus repeatedly added, the digit or number which expresses the number of times that the summand is *repeated*:

Rule for the abbreviated representation of the result of the addition of the same symbol or term to itself when repeated several times.

thus, instead of $a + a$,   we write ... $2a.$

.... $a + a + a$ .... $3a.$

.... $a + a + a + a$ .... $4a.$

.... $a + a + a + a + a$ .... $5a.$

and similarly whatever be the number of times that the same summand is repeated in such expressions.

26. The number which is thus prefixed to a symbol, or combination of symbols (for such will hereafter occur) is called the *coefficient* of the term in which it appears, and will clearly in-

Meaning of the term coefficient.

dicate that the symbol (or the number or quantity which it denotes) is multiplied by it: thus $2a$ may be read *twice a*, $3a$ may be read *thrice a*, $4a$ *four times a*, $10a$ *ten times a*, and similarly whatever be the number which forms the coefficient: by this means, expressions which would consist of 10, 100, or any conceivable number of identical terms, will be reduced into one, and the results which involve them will be greatly simplified and abridged in form.

The adoption of coefficients determines the mode of representing the operation of multiplication.

27. When a coefficient precedes a symbol, it means that the symbol is multiplied by it: thus, $5a$, or five times a may be likewise called the product of 5 and of a: if the digital number which forms the coefficient be denoted (as it always may be) by a symbol, then the product of this symbolical coefficient and of the accompanying symbol will be expressed by merely writing one after the other: thus, if the digital coefficient be replaced by a, and if the symbol into which it is to be multiplied (or which is to be repeated in addition as often as *unity* is contained in a) be b, then the product or result will be denoted by ab (Art. 10.): it will necessarily follow therefore that in all cases the product of two numbers a and b will be denoted by ab: if not, then results essentially identical would not be represented by the same symbolical form: for in all cases the symbol a in ab will become a coefficient, if it be replaced by a digital number.

Like and unlike terms.

28. Terms, which involve the same symbol (or symbols) whatever be their coefficients, are called *like* terms: those which involve different symbols, are called *unlike terms*: thus, $3a$ and $5a$, $7b$ and $15b$, $9ab$ and $11ab$, $3abc$ and $121abc$ are pairs of *like* terms respectively: whilst $3a$ and $7b$, $11b$ and $12ab$, $6ab$ and $7abc$ are pairs of *unlike* terms.

Addition of like terms.

29. When like terms are required to be added together and are therefore connected together with the same sign, whether $+$ or $-$, they may be combined into one by adding their several coefficients together, and subjoining the common symbol or combination of symbols: thus, $3a + 5a = 8a$: for it is obvious that the sum of three times a and of five times a, whatever a may denote, is equivalent to eight times a: the same reasoning will be sufficient to prove the correctness of the application of the rule above given, whatever be the number or the coefficients of the *like* terms which are required to be combined into one.

Thus,
$$7\,a + 9\,a = 16\,a.$$
$$3\,b + 7\,b + 19\,b = 29\,b.$$
$$4\,ab + 21\,ab + 100\,ab = 125\,ab.$$
$$c - 2\,d - 3\,d = c - 5\,d.$$

30. If a term appears without a coefficient, *unity* may in all cases be assumed as its coefficient for the purposes of the rule in the last Article: for it is obvious that $1\,a$ and a, or *one times* a and a are identical in signification, and that the formal exhibition of 1 as a coefficient is *unnecessary* (Art. 34.) and *therefore never made:* we are thus enabled to replace expressions such as $a + 2\,a$ by $3\,a$: $x + 7\,x + 9\,x$ by $17\,x$: $ab - cd - 9\,cd$ by $ab - 10\,cd$. Unity may be supposed to be the coefficient of all terms where no other coefficient appears.

31. If two or more like (Art. 28) terms present themselves in a compound expression with different signs before them, they may be combined into one, by adding together respectively the like terms which are preceded by the same signs, whether + or −, subtracting the greater resulting coefficient from the less, prefixing to the remainder the sign of the greater, and subjoining the common symbol or combination of symbols. If the *final* sign be −, and if there be no term preceded by no sign or by the sign +, after which it can be placed, then the required operation is impossible in Arithmetical Algebra. Rule for the combination of like terms connected by different signs into one.

Thus,
$$7\,a - \ 4\,a = 3\,a.$$
$$11\,x - 10\,x = x. \quad \text{(Art. 30.)}$$
$$7\,xy - 4\,xy - 2\,xy + 14\,xy = 21\,xy - 6\,xy = 15\,xy.$$
$$19\,xyz - 20\,xyz + 23\,xyz - 22\,xyz = 0.$$
$$a - 2\,b + 3\,b - 4\,b = a - 3\,b.$$
Examples.

If it was required to subtract $5\,a$ from $3\,a$, the operation, in *Arithmetical* Algebra, would be impossible, inasmuch as it would be required to subtract a greater quantity from a less: in *Symbolical* Algebra, however, as we shall afterwards see, a symbolical result would always be found, and which would, in the case under consideration, be expressed by $-2\,a$.

32. It will be convenient, for the sake of greater brevity in describing operations or in the statement of rules, to call all those terms which are preceded by no sign or by the sign +, *positive* terms; and all those terms which are preceded by the sign −, *negative* terms. It is important however that the student should keep in mind that no meaning is attached to the adjectives *positive* and *negative*, when so used in Arithmetical Algebra, beyond what is distinctly expressed in the definition just given. Positive and negative terms.

33. The rules for the combination of like terms into one, will
enable us to give an increased extent to the application of the rules
for addition and subtraction in Algebra: the following are examples.

EXAMPLES OF ADDITION.

(1)   Summand $a + b - c$

Summand $a - b - c$

$$2a - 2c$$

In the first and unreduced result $a + b - c + a - b - c$, b is
obliterated, (Art. 15.) and $a + a - c - c$ is replaced by $2a - 2c$.
Art. 26.

(2) $a - 3b + 3c - d$

$a + 3b + 3c + d$

$$2a + 6c$$

The first and unreduced result is

$$a - 3b + 3c - d + a + 3b + 3c + d,$$

and the final result is obtained by replacing $a + a$ by $2a$,
$3c + 3c$ by $6c$, and obliterating $3b - 3b$ and $d - d$ respectively.

(3) $7a - 5b + 3c$

$2a - 3b - 7c$

$a + 2b + 3c$

$$10a - 6b - c$$

The like terms $7a$, $2a$ and a are all positive, (Art. 32.) and
their sum is $10a$: of the like terms $5b$, $3b$ and $2b$, the two first
(whose sum is $8b$) are negative, (Art. 32.) and the last positive:
the difference of the sums of the negative and positive terms
is $6b$, which must be preceded by the sign $-$, which is the
sign of the greater coefficient (Art. 31.): of the like terms
$3c$, $7c$ and $3c$, the first and last (whose sum is $6c$) are positive,
and the second negative: therefore the difference of their sums is
$1c$ or c, (Art. 30.) which must be preceded by the sign $-$, since
the single negative term $7c$ is greater than the sum of the
positive terms or $6c$.

(4) $7xy - 6xz + 11yz$

$xy + 13yz - 12xz$

$xz - 2yz + 3xy$

$9yz - 24xz - 10xy$

$$xy - 41xz + 31yz$$

Of the like terms $7\,xy$, xy, $3\,xy$ and $10\,xy$, the three first are positive and the last negative; they are replaced by the single positive term xy: of the like terms $6\,xz$, $12\,xz$, xz and $24\,xz$, the first, second, and last are negative, and the third positive; they are replaced by the single negative term $41\,xz$: of the like terms $11\,yz$, $13\,yz$, $2\,yz$ and $9\,yz$, the first, second, and last are positive, and the third negative: they are replaced by the single positive term $31\,yz$.

Whatever be the order of the terms in the several expressions which are to be added together, it is convenient to arrange them in the final result in alphabetical order; but in all cases it is necessary, *in Arithmetical Algebra*, that a positive term should occupy the first place: when no such term, after the combination of the several sets of like terms into one, is found to exist, the operation is necessarily impossible (Art. 31.): it is not impossible however, as will afterwards be shewn, in Symbolical Algebra.

EXAMPLES OF SUBTRACTION.

$$(5) \qquad a + b - c$$
$$a - b - c$$
$$\overline{2b}$$

The first and unreduced result is $a + b - c - a + b + c$ (Art. 23.): in the final result $b + b$ is replaced by $2\,b$, and $a - a$ and $c - c$ are respectively obliterated. (Art. 26.)

$$(6) \qquad a - b + c - d$$
$$a + b - c - d$$
$$\overline{2c - 2b + 2d}$$

A positive term must occupy the first place in the remainder, a condition which cannot be fulfilled consistently with the alphabetical arrangement of the terms: in *Symbolical* Algebra, the remainder would, or rather might be, written $- 2b + 2c + 2d$, inasmuch as the *independent* existence of negative, as well as of positive terms, as will be seen hereafter, is recognized in Symbolical Algebra.

$$(7) \qquad 2\,(a + b) - 3\,(c - d)$$
$$a + b - 4\,(c - d)$$
$$\overline{a + b + c - d}$$

In this Example, $(a + b)$ and $(c - d)$, when included between brackets, are considered as simple terms, whose coefficients in the minuend are 2 and 3, and in the subtrahend 1 and 4 respectively : or if, for greater clearness we should replace $a + b$ by x, and $c - d$ by y, the example under consideration would stand as follows :

$$\begin{array}{r} 2x - 3y \\ x - 4y \\ \hline x + y \end{array}$$

If we now replace, in the result last obtained, x by $(a-b)$ and y by $(c-d)$, we get

$$x + y = (a+b) + (c-d) = a + b + c - d.$$

(8) To subtract $2x + 3y$ and $5y - 7x$ respectively from $5x - 7y$.

If the operations to be performed be expressed algebraically, we get

$$5x - 7y - (2x + 3y) - (5y - 7x)$$
$$= 5x - 7y - 2x - 3y - 5y + 7x$$
$$= 10x - 15y.$$

By the first line, we signify that the subtrahends $2x + 3y$ and $5y - 7x$ are to be subtracted from the minuend $5x - 7y$: by the second line, we merely remove the brackets from the several subtrahends, in conformity with the rules (Art. 23 and Art. 24, Ex. 2.) : we form the final result in the third line, by collecting severally the like terms into one (Art. 31.).

(9) $a - 2b - (3a - 4b) + (5a - 6b) - (7a - 8b) + (9a - 10b)$
$= a - 2b - 3a + 4b + 5a - 6b - 7a + 8b + 9a - 10b = 5a - 6b$.
Or, we may begin by adding together the expressions which are preceded by the same sign, and subsequently subtract the results from each other, as follows :

$$\begin{array}{rr} a - 2b & \qquad 3a - 4b \\ 5a - 6b & \qquad 7a - 8b \\ 9a - 10b & \qquad \overline{10a - 12b} \\ \hline 15a - 18b & \\ \text{Subtract} \quad 10a - 12b & \\ \hline 5a - 6b & \end{array}$$

(10) $a - (a - b) + (a - b - c) - (a - b - c - d)$
$= a - a + b + a - b - c - a + b + c + d = b + d$.

(11) $a - \{a - (a - b)\} = a - a + (a - b) = a - b$.

In this example, we consider $a - (a - b)$ as one quantity, which becomes, when the brackets are removed, $a - a + b = b$ (Art. 15.); when this reduction is made, we immediately get the final result just given.

$$(12) \quad a - [a - \{a - (a - b)\}]$$
$$= a - a + \{a - (a - b)\}$$
$$= a - a + a - (a - b)$$
$$= a - a + a - a + b = b.$$

In this example, we remove pairs of brackets in succession, and follow the directions of the rule in Art. 24, Ex. 1 and 2.

Much more complicated examples of the use of brackets may be given; but a careful attention to the principles by which the reductions have been effected in the three last and other examples, will be found sufficient to enable the student to obtain, in all cases, the most simple equivalent expressions which result from their removal.

34. The result of the multiplication of two numbers a and b is expressed by $a \times b$, or more simply by writing them consecutively, as ab, without the interposition of any mark or sign between them (Art. 9 and 27.). In some cases a simple dot is placed between the factors, and ab is expressed by $a \cdot b$: but it may be considered as a general principle in Algebra, *amongst different modes of representation which possess the same meaning and which are equally distinct and unambiguous, to adopt, in all cases, that which is most easily written:* and it is for this reason that the sign $\times$ or the equivalent dot are rarely used, except in cases where their omission might lead to confusion or ambiguity. *Different modes of representing the product of two symbols.*

Thus, in representing the product of two digital numbers 37, and 15, we write 37×15 in preference to $37 . 15$ which would denote the number 37 added to the decimal .15: and it is obvious that if we should write these factors consecutively without the interposition of any sign whatever, we should confound their product with the number 3715. The continued product of a series of numbers such as 2, 3, 4, 5 is written $2 \times 3 \times 4 \times 5$, or more simply $2 . 3 . 4 . 5$, as there is no danger, when the dot is thus repeated, of confounding such a product with an ordinary decimal number. *The multiplicand and multiplier are interchangeable without altering the value of the product.*

35. In common Arithmetic, the two factors are distinguished from each other as the *multiplicand* and the *multiplier;* and though

the product is the same* when the multiplicand and multiplier are interchanged, yet the arithmetical operation to be performed, in conformity with the rule, is not the same, when the factors are different from each other. In Algebra, however, the product of two symbols is exhibited only and no operation, like arithmetical multiplication, is performed; and consequently it is not necessary, *in the case of simple symbols or terms*, to distinguish the multiplicand˙from the multiplier: the common term multiplicand may therefore be correctly applied to both the factors of the product upon the same principle that the same denomination *summand* may be applied to both the terms of the expression $a + b$, which are interchangeable with each other, without altering its value.

Digital numbers (or coefficients) in a product always occupy the first place.

36. The expressions ab and ba are therefore in every respect identical in meaning, but the first arrangement of the symbols, as being alphabetical, is generally preferred: if one of the symbols be replaced by a digit or number, it becomes a coefficient (Art. 26. and 27.) of the other, and always occupies the first place: thus, we always write $7a$ and never $a7$. The second form, however, is not incorrect, though never used: for if it were so, it might be confounded, when written indistinctly, with a^7, an expression which possesses, as will be seen in Art. 38, a totally different meaning.

Mode of representing the product of any number of factors; indifference of the order in which they are written in the product.

37. If three factors or multiplicands, represented by a, b, c, be multiplied together, their product is represented by abc: and though they are generally written in alphabetical order, the same reasoning which proves that ab is identical with ba, would prove that abc is identical with acb, or bac, or bca, or cab, or cba. The same observation may clearly be extended to any number of factors whatsoever: thus, the product a, b, c and x is represented by $abcx$: the product 7, x and y is represented by $7xy$: the product of $7x$ and $9y$ is represented by $7 \times 9xy$, or $63xy$: the product of $7x$, $9y$, and $11z$ is represented by $7 \times 9 \times 11xyz$, or $7 \cdot 9 \cdot 11xyz$, or $693xyz$: and similarly in other cases.

Rule for the abbreviated representation of the result which arises from the same factor or multiplicand repeated any number of times.

38. When a factor or multiplicand a is repeated *twice*, the product is represented by $a \times a$ or aa: if *three* times by aaa: if

* In other words, if m be the multiplicand and n the multiplier, n times m is equal to m times n: for m is equal to $1 + 1 + 1 + ...$ to m terms, and n times m is therefore equal to $1 \times n + 1 \times n + 1 \times n + ...$ to m terms, or to $n + n + n + ...$ to m terms which is clearly equal to m times n. It is however very difficult in the case of very simple and nearly self-evident propositions, like the one under consideration, to add to their evidence by any attempt to subject them to the form of a regular and systematic proof.

four times by *aaaa*: and similarly whatever be the number of times that the same factor or multiplicand is repeated. In all such cases it is usual, for greater brevity, to express the same products by writing the repeated symbol *once* only with a digit or digital number above it to the right hand, expressing the whole number of times that it presents itself in the product when written in the ordinary manner: thus,

$$\begin{aligned}
\text{instead of} \quad & aa \quad \text{we write } a^2 \\
\ldots\ldots\ldots \quad & aaa \quad \ldots\ldots\ldots \ a^3 \\
\ldots\ldots\ldots \quad & aaaa \quad \ldots\ldots\ldots \ a^4 \\
\ldots\ldots\ldots \quad & aaaaa \quad \ldots\ldots\ldots \ a^5:
\end{aligned}$$

and similarly whatever be the number of times that the same factor or multiplicand is repeated in the product.

39. The number which is thus written above the symbol to its right hand is called the *index* or *exponent*, as expressing the number of times that the symbol is repeated in the product written at full length: and the entire number or quantity which is expressed by the symbol with its *index*, is called generally a *power* of that symbol: thus, a^2 is called the *second power* of a, or more generally the *square* of a, from an analogy in the relation which exists between a^2 and a, with that which exists between a square in geometry and the line upon which it is described: a^3 is called the *third power* of a, or more generally the cube of a, from an analogy in the relation which exists between a^3 and a, with that which exists between a *cube* in geometry and one of its edges: a^4 is called the *forth* power of a: a^{10} the *tenth* power of a: a^{100} the *hundredth* power of a; and similarly whatever be the value of the index.

Meaning of the term index or exponent and power.

Square.

Cube.

40. Most important and remarkable consequences will follow from the use of these and other indices: but in arithmetical algebra we shall have occasion to consider such indices only, as those which we have just described and which are always positive whole numbers.

Integral and positive indices alone considered in arithmetical algebra.

41. When a^2 is multiplied into a^3, the result $a^2 \times a^3$ is identical with $aa \times aaa$, or $aaaaa$, or a^5, since a is repeated five times in the product when written at full length. The index 5 is the *sum* of the indices 2 and 3 of the two factors, a^2 and a^3, of the product. In the same manner when a^4 is multiplied into a^7 the result $a^4 \times a^7$ is identical with a^{11}, since a is repeated 4 times in

Rule for the incorporation of powers of the same symbol.

one factor, and 7 times in the other, and therefore $(4 + 7)$, or 11 times in their product written at full length. In a similar manner, if any *powers* (Art. 39.) whatever of a are multiplied together, their product will be equal to the continued product of the symbol a repeated as often as unity is contained in the sum of the indices (Art. 39.) of all the factors which are multiplied together, and it will therefore be correctly represented by a single *power* of a, whose *index* is equal to the sum of the *indices* of all the component factors of the product: for it is obvious that the entire product written out at full length, without the abbreviation of indices, would exhibit the symbol a repeated as often as unity is contained in the sum of the indices of all the powers which are incorporated into one term.

A symbol without an index may be supposed to have an index 1. 42. If one of the factors be a symbol without an *index*, we may assume it to possess an index 1, for the purposes of the rule stated in the last Article: for a^1 is clearly identical with a, inasmuch as it indicates that the symbol a presents itself *once only* in the *power* expressed by a^1.

Examples. 43. The following are examples of the incorporation of powers of the same symbol, in conformity with the rule which has just been established.

(1) $a \times a^2 = a^1 \times a^2 = a^{1+2} = a^3$: attaching to the symbol a an index 1, (Art. 42.) in order to bring the exhibition of the product of a and a^2 under the operation of the rule in Article 41.

(2) $x^{11} \times x^{12} = x^{11+12} = x^{23}$.

(3) $7 a^3 \times 8 a^7 = 7 \times 8 \times a^3 \times a^7 = 56 a^{3+7} = 56 a^{10}$:

changing the order of succession of the factors, so as to make the numerical, precede the symbolical, factors. (Art. 36.)

(4) $a^4 \times a^5 \times a^6 = a^{4+5+6} = a^{15}$. (Art. 41.)

(5) $7 a^7 \times 8 a^8 \times 9 a^9 = 7 . 8 . 9 \times a^7 a^8 a^9$
$$= 504 a^{7+8+9} = 504 a^{24}. \quad (\text{Art.} 36. \text{and} 41.)$$

Like powers. (6) $a b \times a^2 b^3 = a a^2 b b^3 = a^{1+2} b^{1+3} = a^3 b^4$,

changing the order of succession of the factors, so as to bring powers of the same symbol or *like* powers together.

(7) $a^2 b^3 \times a^4 b^5 \times a^6 b^7 = a^2 a^4 a^6 b^3 b^5 b^7$
$$= a^{2+4+6} b^{3+5+7} = a^{12} b^{15}.$$

(8) $10\,abc \times 11\,a^4\,b^6\,c^8 \times 12\,a^7\,b^9\,c^{15}$

$$= 10\,.\,11\,.\,12\,a\,a^4\,a^7\,b\,b^6\,b^9\,c\,c^8\,c^{15}$$
$$= 1320\,a^{1+4+7}\,b^{1+6+9}\,c^{1+8+15}$$
$$= 1320\,a^{12}\,b^{16}\,c^{24}.$$

44. If we denote the indices of any two powers of a by the symbols m and n, it will appear from the proposition investigated in Art. 41, that $a^m \times a^n = a^{m+n}$: it is this proposition which becomes, when the indices m and n are generalized in Symbolical Algebra, the general principle of indices, from which innumerable important consequences will be found to follow. General principle of indices.

45. Let a, b and c be numbers, and let it be required to multiply the sum of a and b by c. Result of the multiplication of a symbol into the sum of two others.

The product of the sum of a and b multiplied by c will be expressed by $ac + bc$: or if the same proposition be represented throughout algebraically (Art. 34.),

$$(a + b)\,c = ac + bc.$$

For it is obvious that the product of $a + b$ by c, will exceed the product of a by c, by the product of b by c.

46. Let a, b and c be numbers, where a is greater than b: and let it be required to multiply the excess of a above b by c. Result of the multiplication of a symbol into the difference of two others.

The product of the excess of a above b by c, will be expressed by $ac - bc$: or if the same proposition be represented algebraically,

$$(a - b)\,c = ac - bc.$$

For it is obvious that the product of $a - b$ by c, will be less than the product of a by c, by the product of b by c.

47. The propositions in the two last Articles constitute the most general form of the rules for the combination of *like* terms into one, which are given in Arts. 29. and 31: for if we consider a and b as the coefficients (Art. 36.) of the terms ac and bc, (which when so considered become *like* terms, inasmuch as they differ from each other in their coefficients only, Art. 28.) then $a + b$ will become the coefficient of their sum $ac + bc$ (Art. 45.) and $a - b$ will become the coefficient of their difference $ac - bc$ (Art. 46.): or in other words, $ac + bc$ may be replaced by $(a + b)\,c$, and $ac - bc$ may be replaced by $(a - b)\,c$, or conversely. The propositions in the two last Articles constitute the most general expression of the rule for the combination of like terms into one.

48. The same propositions are of the greatest importance in Algebra, inasmuch as they form the foundation of the rules for Fundamental propositions in

symbolical
multiplica-
tion. symbolical multiplication in all cases: the mode in which those rules are deduced from them will be seen from the following Articles.

Investi-
gation of
rule for the
multiplica-
tion of
a single
term into
an express-
ion consist-
ing of any
number of
terms. 49. Let it be required to multiply a single symbol or term into an expression consisting of any number of terms connected by the signs + and −, one or both. The examination of the results obtained in a few cases will readily lead to the establishment of a general rule.

(1)   Let it be required to multiply x into $a + b + c$.
$$(a + b + c)\, x = ax + bx + cx.$$

For if we express $a + b$ by a single symbol s, and therefore $a + b + c$ by $s + c$, we shall find

$$(a + b + c)\, x = (s + c)\, x = sx + cx, \quad \text{(Art. 45.)}$$
$$= ax + bx + cx : \text{ for } sx$$
$$= (a + b)\, x = ax + bx, \quad \text{(Art. 45.)}$$

and therefore $sx + cx = ax + bx + cx.$

(2)   Let it be required to multiply x into $a + b + c + d$.
$$(a + b + c + d)\, x = ax + bx + cx + dx.$$

For if we express $a + b + c$ by s, and therefore $a + b + c + d$ by $s + d$, we shall find

$$(a + b + c + d)\, x = (s + d)\, x$$
$$= sx + dx = ax + bx + cx + dx,$$
$$\text{since } sx = ax + bx + cx ; \text{ (Ex. 1. Art. 49.)}$$

and therefore $sx + dx = ax + bx + cx + dx.$

The same reasoning may be applied successively to the product of a single symbol or term into an expression consisting of five, six, seven, &c., or any number of terms: and it will follow that the product is found by "multiplying the single term successively into every term of the compound multiplicand, and connecting the several results together with their proper signs."

(3)   Let it be required to multiply x into $a + b - c$.
$$(a + b - c)\, x = ax + bx - cx.$$

For if we express $a + b$ by s, and therefore $a + b - c$ by $s - c$, we shall find

$$(s - c)\, x = sx - cx, \quad \text{(Art. 46.)}$$
$$= ax + bx - cx : \text{ for } sx = (a + b)\, x = ax + bx, \quad \text{(Art. 45.)}$$

and therefore $sx - cx = ax + bx - cx.$

(4) Let it be required to multiply x into $a - b + c - d$.

$$(a - b + c - d)\,x = a\,x - b\,x + c\,x - d\,x.$$

For if we express $a + b$ or the sum of the positive terms by s, and $b + d$ or the sum of the negative terms by t, then

$$a - b + c - d = s - t,$$

and therefore

$$(a - b + c - d)\,x = (s - t)\,x = s\,x - t\,x$$
$$= a\,x + c\,x - b\,x - d\,x = a\,x - b\,x + c\,x - d\,x :$$

for $s\,x = (a + c)\,x = a\,x + c\,x$, and $t\,x = (b + d)\,x = b\,x + d\,x$; and therefore

$$s\,x - t\,x = a\,x + c\,x - (b\,x + d\,x) = a\,x + c\,x - b\,x - d\,x$$
$$= a\,x - b\,x + c\,x - d\,x.$$

And generally, if we express the sum of the positive terms of any compound multiplicand by s, and the sum of its negative terms by t, the product of this multiplicand and of x will be, in a similar manner, expressed by $s\,x - t\,x$: we must then multiply x into every term of s, and also into every term of t, and afterwards subtract the resulting products from each other, in order to obtain the complete product required: the terms of this final product may then be arranged, without any alteration of its value (Art. 22.), in any order, whether alphabetical or not, which may be considered most convenient or most symmetrical.

50. We thus have arrived at the following simple and general rule for finding the product of a single term and of a compound multiplicand. *General rule in all such cases.*

Multiply the single term successively into every term of the compound multiplicand, and connect the several results together with their proper signs, which are those of the several terms of the multiplicand.

51. The following are examples of the preceding rule: *Examples.*

(1) $(7\,a - 5\,b + 4\,c)\,d = 7\,a\,d - 5\,b\,d + 4\,c\,d.$

(2) $(a^2 - a\,b + a\,c)\,a\,d = a^3 d - a^2 b\,d + a^2 c\,d.$ (Art. 41. and 42.)

(3) $(10\,x - 11\,y + 12\,z) \times 4\,t = 40\,t\,x - 44\,t\,y + 48\,t\,z.$

(4) $(3\,x\,y - 4\,y^2 - 6\,y\,z) \times 7\,x\,y\,z$
$$= 21\,x^2 y^2 z - 28\,x\,y^3 z - 42\,x\,y^2 z^2.$$

(5) $(a^4 - a^3 b + a^2 b^2 - a\,b^3 + b^4)\,a^2 b^2$
$$= a^6 b^2 - a^5 b^3 + a^4 b^4 - a^3 b^5 + a^2 b^6$$

Product of
two factors
when both
of them are
compound.

52. We shall now proceed to investigate the rules for the multiplication of two factors, both of which are compound: for this purpose we shall commence with the examination of the more simple cases, and advance from them to others which are more complicated and which are adequate to form the foundation of a general rule.

Product
of $a + b$
and $c + d$.

53. Let it be required to multiply $a + b$ into $c + d$.

If we express the multiplicand $a + b$ by x, we shall find

$$(a + b)(c + d) = x(c + d) = cx + dx \quad \text{(Art. 45.)}.$$
$$= (a + b)c + (a + b)d = ac + bc + ad + bd$$
$$= ac + ad + bc + bd.$$

Or in other words, we multiply successively each term of the multiplier into every term of the multiplicand, and connect all the results together with their proper signs, and place them in their proper order.

The common mode of exhibiting this process is as follows:

$$a + b$$
$$c + d$$
$$\overline{ac + bc}$$
$$+ ad + bd$$
$$\overline{ac + ad + bc + bd.}$$

That is, we write the multiplicand $a + b$, and the multiplier $c + d$, underneath each other, precisely as in the multiplication of numbers in common arithmetic: we then multiply successively each term c and d of the multiplier into every term of the multiplicand $a + b$, placing the partial products $ac + bc$, and $ad + bd$ underneath each other as in common arithmetic: we then add the partial products together, forming the final product

$$ac + ad + bc + bd,$$

which we have arranged, as is most commonly done, in alphabetical order.

In compound multiplication the multiplicand and multiplier are interchangeable: but the partial products which are obtained are not the same in both cases, though the final and entire product is so.

54. Let it be required to multiply $a + b$ into $c - d$.

$(a + b)(c - d) = x(c - d)$, making $x = a + b$,

$= cx - dx = (a + b)c - (a + b)d$

$= ac + bc - ad - bd = ac - ad + bc - bd.$

Or thus,

$$
\begin{array}{l}
a + b \\
c - d \\
\hline
ac + bc \\
\quad - ad - bd \\
\hline
ac - ad + bc - bd.
\end{array}
$$

55. It appears from this example, that if a negative (Art. 32.) term such as $-d$ be multiplied into a positive term such as a or $+b$, the product will be a negative term, such as $-ad$ or $-bd$: it is convenient to distinguish positive from negative terms by writing the first with no sign or with the sign $+$, and the second always with the sign $-$: by prefixing such signs to terms, when referred to *apart* from their connexion with others, we merely indicate the signs by which those terms are to be connected with the others, when the complete product is written down in the same line, with all its terms in their proper order.

It is for this reason, or rather with a view to this convenience, that we write the second of the partial products in the example under consideration $-ad - bd$, merely indicating that the two terms ad and bd will be preceded by the sign $-$ in the complete and final product.

56. Let it be required to multiply $a - b$ into $c - d$.

$(a - b)(c - d) = x(c - d)$, making $x = a - b$

$= cx - dx = (a - b)c - (a - b)d$

$= ac - bc - (ad - bd)$

$= ac - bc - ad + bd$

$= ac - ad - bc + bd.$

For $(a - b)c = ac - bc$, (Art. 46.) and $(a - b)d = ad - bd$, and if the second of these expressions be subtracted from the first, we get

$$ac - bc - (ad - bd)$$
$$= ac - bc - ad + bd. \quad \text{(Art. 21.)}$$

The preceding process is most commonly exhibited as follows:

$$a - b$$
$$c - d$$
$$\overline{ac - bc}$$
$$- ad + bd$$
$$\overline{ac - bc - ad + bd}, \text{ or } ac - ad - bc + bd.$$

Signs of the products of positive and negative terms.

57. From the preceding example, it appears that the product of the two *positive* terms a and c is the *positive* term ac: the product of the *positive* term c into the *negative* term $-b$ is the *negative* term $-bc$: the product of the *negative* term $-d$ into the *positive* term a is the *negative* term $-ad$: and the product of the *negative* term $-d$ into the *negative* term $-b$ is the *positive* term bd.

Rule for the concurrence of like and unlike signs in multiplication.

The observation of these results leads to the following very important general rule for the concurrence of positive and negative terms in multiplication: or if we may be allowed, as is commonly done, to separate the signs which precede or which are presumed to precede (Art. 23. and 55.) the terms, from the terms themselves, the rule under consideration may be properly denominated the rule for the *concurrence of like or unlike signs* in multiplication.

The product of two POSITIVE *or of two* NEGATIVE *terms is positive: the product of a* NEGATIVE *and a* POSITIVE *or of a* POSITIVE *and a* NEGATIVE *term is negative.*

Or in other words, *if two* LIKE *signs, whether $+$ and $+$ or $-$ and $-$, concur in multiplication, the resulting sign, which precedes the resulting term, is $+$: if two* UNLIKE *signs, whether $+$ and $-$ or $-$ and $+$, concur in multiplication, the resulting sign is $-$.*

Rule for the concurrence of like and unlike signs in the operations of addition and subtraction.

58. The same rule for the concurrence of *like* and *unlike* signs in Algebra is not confined to their concurrence in multiplication, but in a certain sense also applies in the operations of addition and subtraction: for if we suppose the sign which precedes a bracket enclosing two or more terms to be placed successively before every term which those brackets include, *like* or *unlike* signs will *concur*, and will be replaced by single signs in accordance with the general rule stated in the last Article: thus

$$a + (b + c) = a + b + + c = a + b + c,$$
$$a - (b - c) = a - b - - c = a - b + c,$$
$$a + (b - c) = a + b + - c = a + b - c,$$
$$a - (b + c) = a - b - + c = a - b - c.$$

59.   The preceding view of the concurrence of like signs in the operations of addition and subtraction, though foreign to the principles of Arithmetical Algebra, is perfectly conformable, as will be afterwards seen, to the principles of Symbolical Algebra: if it be considered, however, as merely another mode of presenting the rules which have been strictly demonstrated (Arts. 20. and 21.) for performing the operations of addition and subtraction in Arithmetical Algebra, it will lead to no error, and will enable us to give increased generality to the expression of the rule of signs which we have just been considering: assuming, therefore, that the same rule will be true for the concurrence of signs in the operation of division, though no proper examples of such concurrence, different from those which occur in multiplication, will present themselves in this operation in Arithmetical Algebra, it may be stated in the following form: *whenever two like signs concur in any one of the fundamental operations of Algebra, whether + and + or − and −, they may be replaced by the single sign +: and whenever two unlike signs concur, whether + and − or − and +, they may be replaced by the single sign −.*

In what sense the rule for the concurrence of signs may be extended to all the fundamental operations of Algebra.

60.   Let it be required to multiply together

$$a - b + c, \text{ and } d - e + f.$$

$a - b + c = s - b$, if we make $s = a + c$.

$d - e + f = t - e$, if we make $t = d + f$.

$$(a - b + c)(d - e + f) = (s - b)(t - e)$$
$$= st - bt - es + be. \quad (\text{Art. 56.})$$
$$= (a + c)(d + f) - b(d + f) - e(a + c) + be, \text{ (replacing } s \text{ and } t \text{ by their values)}$$
$$= ad + af + cd + cf - bd - bf - ae - ce + be,$$
$$= ad - ae + af - bd + be - bf + cd - ce + cf.$$

The final product consists therefore of 9 terms, which is equal to the product 3 and 3 of the number of terms in the multiplicand and multiplier: it is arranged in alphabetical order.

The ordinary mode of exhibiting this process is as follows:

$$a - b + c$$
$$d - e + f$$
$$\overline{}$$
$$ad - bd + cd$$
$$- ae + be - ce$$
$$+ af - bf + cf$$
$$\overline{ad - ae + af - bd + be - bf + cd - ce + cf.}$$

The three partial products $ad - bd + cd$, $- ae + be - ce$, $af - bf + cf$, are obtained by multiplying successively d, $- e$, and f into the several terms of the multiplicand, in conformity with the rule for the concurrence of signs (Art. 57.): having once explained the sense in which $+$ and $-$ are allowed to be placed before *positive* and *negative* terms independently (that is, without another term preceding them, Art. 55.), the rule for the concurrence of signs admits of immediate application, and the several partial products may be arranged underneath each other, precisely as in compound multiplication in arithmetic, without occasioning any difficulty or doubt in the determination of the final product: if any such difficulty or doubt should present itself to the mind of the student, it will disappear upon writing the several partial products successively in the same line, as in the first form which is given of the example under consideration.

61. The process which has been followed in the last example may obviously be extended to the multiplication of two factors consisting of any number of terms whatsoever, connected with the signs $+$ and $-$, one or both: when stated in words at full length, it will become the following general rule:

General rule for the multiplication of polynomials.

Write the two factors underneath each other, as in the multiplication of numbers in common arithmetic: multiply successively every term of one factor into every term of the other, the signs of the resulting terms being determined in conformity with the rule for the concurrence of like or unlike signs (Art. 57.); and write the several partial products either in the same line or underneath each other, as in the multiplication of numbers in arithmetic: and, lastly, add the several partial products together, combining the like terms severally into one, if any such occur.

If there be three factors, multiply the third into the product of the two first: if four factors, multiply the fourth into the product of the three first: and similarly whatever be the number of factors which are required to be multiplied together.

In writing the PARTIAL *products underneath each other, it is usual to place, as much as possible, like terms (when such occur) under like terms, inasmuch as such an arrangement greatly facilitates the combination of like terms into one, by thus presenting them to the eye in immediate connection with each other.*

The examples which follow will farther illustrate the application of this rule: many of them will be found to express important general theorems, to which very frequent reference will hereafter be made, and which will require to be very carefully studied and remembered.

62. To form the product of $a + b$ into $a + b$, or the square (Art. 39.) of $a + b$.

Square of $a + b$.

$$
\begin{array}{l}
a \ + b \\
a \ + b \\
\hline
a^2 + \ \ ab \\
\ \ \ + \ \ ab + b^2 \\
\hline
a^2 + 2\,ab + b^2 = (a + b)^2
\end{array}
$$

Or the square of the sum of two numbers is equal to the sum of the squares of those numbers together with twice their product.

$$\text{Thus,} \ \ (5 + 3)^2 = 25 + \ \ 9 + 2 \times 3 \times 5 = \ \ 64$$
$$(7 + 9)^2 = 49 + 63 + 2 \times 7 \times 9 = 256.$$

In writing down the partial products in this Example, the *like* terms ab are placed underneath each other (Art. 61.)

The rule for the formation of the square of the sum of two numbers will be found to be the foundation of the rule for the inverse operation of extracting the square root.

Foundation of the rule for the inverse operation.

63. To form the square of $a + b + c$.

Square of $a + b + c$.

$$
\begin{array}{l}
a \ + b + c \\
a \ + b + c \\
\hline
a^2 + \ \ ab + ac \\
\ \ \ + \ \ ab + b^2 + \ \ bc \\
\ \ \ \ \ \ \ \ \ + ac + \ \ bc + c^2 \\
\hline
a^2 + 2\,ab + b^2 + 2\,ac + 2\,bc + c^2 = (a + b + c)^2
\end{array}
$$

Or the square of the sum of three numbers is equal to the sum of the squares of those numbers, together with twice the sum of all the different products which can be formed by combining them two and two together.

The same rule may be extended to the formation of the square of $a + b + c + d$ and of the sum of any number of symbols whatsoever.

64. To form the square of $a - b$.

$$
\begin{array}{l}
a - b \\
a - b \\
\hline
a^2 - ab \\
 - ab + b^2 \\
\hline
a^2 - 2ab + b^2 = (a - b)^2
\end{array}
$$

Or the square of the difference of two numbers is equal to the excess of the sum of the squares of those numbers above twice their product.

Thus, $(5 - 3)^2 = 2^2 = 4 = 25 + 9 - 2 \times 5 \times 3$
$(11 - 4)^2 = 7^2 = 49 = 121 + 16 - 2 \times 11 \times 4.$

65. The following propositions are immediate corollaries from the two last Articles.

$(a + b)^2 + (a - b)^2 = a^2 + 2ab + b^2 + a^2 - 2ab + b^2 = 2a^2 + 2b^2$
$(a + b)^2 - (a - b)^2 = a^2 + 2ab + b^2 - (a^2 - 2ab + b^2) = 4ab.$

Or the sum of the squares of the sum and difference of two numbers is equal to twice the sum of their squares : and the difference of the squares of the sum and difference of two numbers, is equal to four times their product.

66. To form the product of $a + b$ and $a - b$.

$$
\begin{array}{l}
a + b \\
a - b \\
\hline
a^2 + ab \\
 - ab - b^2 \\
\hline
a^2 - b^2
\end{array}
$$

Or the product of the sum and difference of two numbers is equal to the difference of their squares.

Thus, $(5 + 3)(5 - 3) = 8 \times 2 = 25 - 9 = 16$
$(11 + 4)(11 - 4) = 15 \times 7 = 121 - 16 = 105.$

67. To form the cube of $a + b$. (Art. 39.)

$$a + b$$
$$a + b$$

$$a^2 + 2ab + b^2 = (a + b)^2 \quad \text{(Art. 62.)}$$
$$a + b$$

$$a^3 + 2a^2b + ab^2$$
$$+ \quad a^2b + 2ab^2 + b^3$$

$$a^3 + 3a^2b + 3ab^2 + b^3 = (a + b)^3$$

Or the cube of the sum of two numbers is equal to the sum of their cubes, together with three times the two products which are formed by multiplying one of them into the square of the other.

This rule, for the formation of the cube of the sum of two numbers, will be found to be the foundation of the rule for the inverse operation of extracting the cube root.

68. To form the cube of $a - b$.

$$a - b$$
$$a - b$$

$$a^2 - 2ab + b^2 = (a - b)^2 \quad \text{(Art. 64.)}$$
$$a - b$$

$$a^3 - 2a^2b + ab^2$$
$$- \quad a^2b + 2ab^2 - b^3$$

$$a^3 - 3a^2b + 3ab^2 - b^3 = (a - b)^3$$

Or the cube of the difference of two numbers is equal to the difference of the cubes of those numbers diminished by the excess of three times the product of the square of the first into the second above three times the product of the square of the second into the first.

The examples given in the six last Articles form important Arithmetical as well as Algebraical theorems; and we have written out their interpretation in words at full length for the purpose of familiarizing the student with the translation of symbolical results into ordinary language: the following are miscellaneous examples, where such translations are not given.

69   (1) Multiply $x + 7$ into $x + 10$.

$$
\begin{array}{l}
x + 10 \\
x + \ 7 \\
\hline
x^2 + 10x \\
\quad\ + \ 7x + 70 \\
\hline
x^2 + 17x + 70
\end{array}
$$

- The like terms $10x$ and $7x$ are placed underneath each other and subsequently combined into one term, which is $17x$.

(2) Multiply $x - 7$ into $x - 10$.

$$
\begin{array}{l}
x - 10 \\
x - \ 7 \\
\hline
x^2 - 10x \\
\quad\ - \ 7x + 70 \\
\hline
x^2 - 17x + 70
\end{array}
$$

(3) Multiply $x - 7$ into $x + 10$.

$$
\begin{array}{l}
x + 10 \\
x - \ 7 \\
\hline
x^2 + 10x \\
\quad\ - \ 7x - 70 \\
\hline
x^2 + \ 3x - 70
\end{array}
$$

(4) Multiply $x + 7$ into $x - 10$.

$$
\begin{array}{l}
x - 10 \\
x + \ 7 \\
\hline
x^2 - 10x \\
\quad\ + 7x - 70 \\
\hline
x^2 - 3x - 70
\end{array}
$$

(5) Multiply $x^2 + ax + a^2$ into $x - a$.

$$
\begin{array}{l}
x^2 + ax + a^2 \\
x - a \\
\hline
x^3 + ax^2 + a^2x \\
\quad\ - ax^2 - a^2x - a^3 \\
\hline
x^3 - a^3
\end{array}
$$

The terms ax^2 and a^2x are obliterated. (Art. 15.)

(6)   Multiply $x^3 - ax^2 + a^2x - a^3$ into $x + a$.

$$x^3 - ax^2 + a^2x - a^3$$
$$x + a$$
$$\overline{}$$
$$x^4 - ax^3 + a^2x^2 - a^3x$$
$$+ ax^3 - a^2x^2 + a^3x - a^4$$
$$\overline{}$$
$$x^4 - a^4$$

The terms ax^3, a^2x^2 and a^3x are obliterated.

(7)   Multiply $x^2 + 4x + 8$ into $x^2 - 4x + 8$.

$$x^2 - 4x + 8$$
$$x^2 + 4x + 8$$
$$\overline{}$$
$$x^4 - 4x^3 + 8x^2$$
$$+ 4x^3 - 16x^2 + 32x$$
$$+ 8x^2 - 32x + 64$$
$$\overline{}$$
$$x^4 + 64$$

The terms involving x^3, x^2 and x are obliterated.

(8)   Multiply together $x + 3$, $x + 5$ and $x + 7$.

$$x + 3$$
$$x + 5$$
$$\overline{}$$
$$x^2 + 3x$$
$$+ 5x + 15$$
$$\overline{}$$
$$x^2 + 8x + 15$$
$$x + 7$$
$$\overline{}$$
$$x^3 + 8x^2 + 15x$$
$$+ 7x^2 + 56x + 105$$
$$\overline{}$$
$$x^3 + 15x + 71x + 105$$

(9)   Multiply together $3a^2 + 2ab - b^2$ and $3a^2 - 2ab + b^2$.

$$3a^2 + 2ab - b^2$$
$$3a^2 - 2ab + b^2$$
$$\overline{}$$
$$9a^4 + 6a^3b - 3a^2b^2$$
$$- 6a^3b - 4a^2b^2 + 2ab^3$$
$$+ 3a^2b^2 + 2ab^3 - b^4$$
$$\overline{}$$
$$9a^4 - 4a^2b^2 + 4ab^3 - b^4$$

70. In the operation of Multiplication, *two factors* are given to find their *product;* whereas in the operation of Division, the *product* or what is *presumed* to be the *product* and one of the two *factors* are given, to find the other. With reference to this operation, this product or this presumed product is called the *Dividend,* and the given factor is called the *Divisor:* whilst the factor or presumed factor whose value is required to be found, is called the *Quotient.*

Thus, if the *dividend* be 96 and the *divisor* 8, the *quotient* is 12 : for the dividend 96 is the product of the divisor 8 and of the quotient 12: or in other words, 8 is said to be contained in 96, 12 times. If the dividend be ab and the divisor a, the quotient is b: for the dividend ab is the product of the divisor a and of the quotient b: or in other words, a is said to be contained in ab, b times. Again, the dividend $a^2 - b^2$ and the divisor $a + b$, give the quotient $a - b$: for the dividend $a^2 - b^2$ is the product of the divisor $a + b$ and of the quotient $a - b$, (Art. 66.): or in other words, $a + b$ is said to be contained in $a^2 - b^2$, $a - b$ times.

71. The operation of division is denoted by the sign $\div$, or more commonly by simply writing the divisor beneath the dividend with a line between them, as in the case of numerical fractions, (Art. 9.): thus the quotient of a divided by b, is denoted by $\frac{a}{b}$, in the same manner that the quotient of a digital number 3 divided by 4 becomes or is represented by, the numerical fraction $\frac{3}{4}$.

72. The operation of division is the *inverse* of that of multiplication, by which it is meant that if a number be first *multiplied* and then *divided* by the *same* number, its value is not altered. Thus, if the number 12 be first multiplied by 4, and if their product 48 be then divided by 4, the result will be the original number 12: and *conversely*, if the number 12 be first divided by 4, and if their quotient 3 be then multiplied by 4, the result will be the same original number 12. More generally if a number denoted by a be multiplied by a number denoted by b, and if their product ab be then divided by the same number b, the result will be the original number a: and conversely, if the number a be first divided by b, and if their quotient $\frac{a}{b}$, (Art. 71.) be subsequently multiplied by b, the result is the original number a: or if these

processes be exhibited throughout algebraically, it will follow that

$$a \times b \div b = \frac{a \times b}{b} = \frac{ab}{b} = a,$$

$$a \div b \times b = \frac{a}{b} \times b = \frac{ab}{b} = a.$$

73. It is this relation of the operations of multiplication and division, which enables us either to introduce or to obliterate numbers or symbols, which are common to the dividend and the divisor, and which becomes the foundation of innumerable changes of form of expressions both numerical and symbolical, to others, whether more complex or more simple, which are of equal import and value: we shall have frequent occasion to refer to it in the subsequent articles.

Important consequences which follow from it.

74. The quotient of a number or quantity divided by itself is *unity*.

Thus, $\dfrac{a}{a} = 1:$ $\quad \dfrac{ab}{ab} = 1:$ $\quad \dfrac{a^2}{a^2} = 1:$ $\quad \dfrac{axyz}{axyz} = 1:$ $\quad \dfrac{10}{10} = 1:$

$$\frac{100}{100} = 1: \quad \frac{54\,x^2 y^2}{54\,x^2 y^3} = 1.$$

The quotient of a magnitude (however represented) divided by itself is unity.

This proposition is only another form of the principle enunciated in the last article: it is equally true whether *a* represents a number or a concrete quantity: it is equivalent to saying that every magnitude is contained *once* in itself, and that therefore *unity* is the quotient which results from the division of any magnitude by itself.

75. When one number or expression is divided by another, all those factors which are *common* to both the dividend and divisor, may be struck out or exterminated without altering the value of the quotient which results from their division: and conversely, the dividend and divisor may be both of them multiplied by any common factor or factors, without altering the value of the quotient which results from their division.

Factors common to the dividend and divisor may be obliterated or introduced without affecting the value of the quotient.

Thus if we represent the dividend and divisor by A and B respectively, and if we suppose $A = aD$ and $B = ad$, where a is a factor common to both A and B,

Proof.

then we have $\dfrac{A}{B} = \dfrac{aD}{ad} = \dfrac{D}{d}$, (by Art. 72):

and it is obvious that whatever be the quotient (q), the same quantity or number (q), which, when multiplied into d produces the dividend D, will, when multiplied into ad, produce the dividend aD or A: and conversely, the same quantity or number which multiplied into ad produces the dividend aD or A, will, when multiplied into d alone, produce the dividend D.

Factors in the divisor which are not common to the dividend must be retained in the denominator of the quotient.

76. It will follow as a corollary from the proposition in the last article, that when *all* the factors of the divisor are common to the dividend, that they may be *entirely* obliterated, and that the product of the remaining factors of the dividend will constitute the *quotient:* and that if there exist any factors in the divisor which are not likewise *common* to the dividend, they cannot be obliterated, and their product must remain as a divisor in the quotient, which will retain therefore a fractional form. The following are examples.

Examples.

77. (1) The quotient of $4ax$ divided by $2a$, is $2x$: or written algebraically,

$$\frac{4ax}{2a} = 2x.$$

(2) The quotient of $12a^2x^2$ divided by $3ax$, is $4ax$: or written algebraically,

$$\frac{12a^2x^2}{3ax} = 4ax.$$

(3) The quotient of $72abxyz$ divided by $12axz$, is $6by$: or written algebraically,

$$\frac{72abxyz}{12axz} = 6by.$$

(4) The quotient of a^5 divided by a^3, is a^2: or written algebraically,

$$\frac{a^5}{a^3} = a^2 : \text{ for } \frac{a^5}{a^2} = \frac{aaaaa}{aaa} = aa = a^2.$$

(5) The quotient of a^{11} divided by a^4, is a^7: or

$$\frac{a^{11}}{a^4} = a^7.$$

When powers of the same symbol are divided by each other, we obliterate the lowest of the two powers, and diminish the index of the highest of the two powers by that of the lowest: the remaining power with its diminished index will present itself in the quotient: but if the highest index is found in the divisor, this diminished power will be found in the denominator of the quotient.

Rule for the division of powers of the same symbol by each other.

Thus,

$$\frac{a^3}{a^2} = a \qquad\qquad \frac{3^3}{3^2} = \frac{27}{9} = 3$$

$$\frac{a^3}{a^3} = 1 \quad \text{(Art. 74.)} \quad \frac{3^3}{3^3} = \frac{27}{27} = 1$$

$$\frac{a^3}{a^4} = \frac{1}{a} \qquad\qquad \frac{3^3}{3^4} = \frac{27}{81} = \frac{1}{3}$$

$$\frac{a^3}{a^5} = \frac{1}{a^2} \qquad\qquad \frac{3^3}{3^5} = \frac{27}{243} = \frac{1}{9} = \frac{1}{3^2}$$

$$\frac{a^4}{a^9} = \frac{1}{a^5} \qquad\qquad \frac{3^4}{3^9} = \frac{81}{19683} = \frac{1}{243} = \frac{1}{3^5}.$$

(6) The quotient of $100\,a^4 b^5 c^7$ divided by $25\,a^3 b^4 c^6$, is $4\,abc$:

or, $\dfrac{100\,a^4 b^5 c^7}{25\,a^3 b^4 c^6} = 4\,a\,b\,c.$

(7) The quotient of $63\,a^2 x^3 y z^5$ divided by $27\,a^4 x^2 y^3 z^4$, is $\dfrac{7\,x\,z}{3\,a^2 y^2}$:

or, $\dfrac{63\,a^2 x^3 y z^5}{27\,a^4 x^2 y^3 z^4} = \dfrac{7\,x\,z}{3\,a^2 y^2}.$

70. The preceding examples and the principles upon which their reduction is founded, will at once lead us to the following rule for the division of *mononomials* by *mononomials*.

Rule for the division of mononomials by mononomials.

Omit all the quantities, whether digital or literal, which are common to the divisor and dividend; underneath what remains of the dividend write what remains of the divisor, and the resulting expression is the quotient required.

If no part of the divisor remains except *unity*, the remaining part of the dividend is the quotient.

When we speak of the omission of common factors in the dividend and divisor, we mean that they are severally replaced by *unity*, which is not exhibited, when it is followed or preceded by other factors (Art. 30), or when it is the only divisor.

Thus,
$$\frac{abc}{ac} = \frac{1 \times b \times 1}{1 \times 1} = \frac{b}{1} = b.$$

Common digital factors are sometimes concealed by their incorporation with others.

79. The application of this rule, as we have already seen, is immediate as far as all common literal factors are concerned: with respect, however, to common digital factors, they may be so masked by their incorporation with others, as not to be easily discoverable without the aid of the ordinary arithmetical rule for finding the greatest common divisor of two numbers, which is given in all books of arithmetic: unless such common factors, wherever they exist, are found out and obliterated, the quotient which is obtained will not be presented under its most simple form.

Examples.

80. Thus the quotient of $391\,a^2x^3$ divided by $258\,a^3x^2$ is $\dfrac{391\,x}{258\,a}$, which is reducible to the more simple form $\dfrac{23\,x}{14\,a}$, if the common factor 17 of the numbers 391 and 258 be detected and obliterated. The quotient of $12987\,a^4b^5c^6$ divided by $13209\,a^6b^5c^4$, which is first found, is $\dfrac{12987\,c^2}{13209\,a^2}$, which is reducible to the more simple form $\dfrac{117\,c^2}{119\,a^2}$, if the common factor 111 of the digital coefficients be struck out.

Rule for the division of a polynomial by a monomomial.

81. If the divisor only be a mononomial and the dividend consist of two or more terms, the quotient may be found by the following rule:

Divide successively every term of the polynomial dividend, by the monomial divisor, by the rule given in Art. 78, and connect together with their proper signs the several partial quotients for the complete quotient required.

It will obviously follow, from this process, that the dividend will be the product which arises from multiplying the mononomial divisor into the quotient which is thus obtained, which is the only condition which the quotient is required to satisfy.

Examples.

82. The following are examples of the rule in the last Article.

(1) The quotient of $ax + bx$ divided by x is $a + b$, or if expressed algebraically,
$$\frac{ax + bx}{x} = a + b.$$

For the product of the divisor x and of the quotient $a + b$, is the dividend $ax + bx$. (Art. 45.)

(2) The quotient of $ax^3 + a^2x^2 + a^3x$ divided by ax, or

$$\frac{ax^3 + a^2x^2 + a^3x}{ax} = x^2 + ax + a^2.$$

For the product of the divisor ax and of the quotient $x^2 + ax + x^2$ is the dividend $ax^3 + a^2x^2 + a^3x$.

(3) The quotient of $12x^2 + 20ax + 32a^2$ divided by $4ax$,

$$\text{or,} \quad \frac{12x^2 + 20ax + 32a^2}{4ax} = \frac{3x}{a} + 5 + \frac{8a}{x}.$$

(4) The quotient of $8a^2 - 6ab + 4c + 1$ divided by $4a^2$, or

$$\frac{8a^2 - 6ab + 4c + 1}{4a^2} = 2 - \frac{3b}{2a} + \frac{c}{a^2} + \frac{1}{4a^2}.$$

(5) The quotient of $156a^4 - 204a^3x + 228a^2x^2$ divided by $48a^2x^2$, or,

$$\frac{156a^4 - 204a^3x + 228a^2x^2}{48a^2x^2} = \frac{156a^2}{48x^2} - \frac{204a}{48x} + \frac{228}{48}$$

$$= \frac{13a^2}{4x^2} - \frac{17a}{4x} + \frac{19}{4},$$

reducing the several fractions

$$\frac{156}{48}, \quad \frac{204}{48} \quad \text{and} \quad \frac{228}{48}$$

to their most simple equivalent forms.

83. The third and most important case of the operation of division, is that in which the divisor consists of more terms than one. *Third case where the divisor is a polynomial.*

We possess no means of ascertaining, antecedently to the application of the rule for division itself, whether there exists any definite quotient which multiplied into a *given* divisor will produce a *given* dividend: it is for this reason that the rule for performing this operation must be framed so as to furnish this definite quotient whenever it exists, and to exhibit a quotient under all circumstances which will produce, when multiplied into the divisor, a dividend which differs, by remainders which are greater or less, from the given dividend which is under consideration. *The practicability of resolving the dividend into two factors of which the divisor is one, is not known before the operation is performed.*

84. The following is the rule for performing the operation of division with a polynomial divisor.

Arrange the divisor and dividend according to the powers of some one symbol, or, as much as possible, according to the same order of succession, whether alphabetical or otherwise, and place them in one line in the same manner as in long division of numbers in arithmetic: find the quantity which multiplied into the first term of the divisor will produce the first term of the dividend; this is the first term of the quotient: multiply this term into all the terms of the divisor and subtract the resulting product from the dividend: consider the remainder, if any, as a new dividend and proceed as before, continuing the process until no remainder exists, or until it becomes obviously interminable.

If there is any mononomial, whether literal or digital, which is common to both the divisor and dividend, it is *generally* most convenient to strike it out in the first instance, and afterwards to proceed with the reduced divisor and dividend according to the preceding rule.

85. By the preceding process we subtract *successively* the product of the divisor and of the several terms of the quotient which are obtained, which is obviously equivalent to the subtraction of the entire product of the divisor and of all the terms of the quotient, by one operation: the remainders, therefore, whether zero or not, will be the same in both cases: if the remainder be zero, the *quotient* obtained is *complete,* and the dividend is resolved into two factors, which are the divisor and the quotient; but as long as a remainder exists, the quotient is *incomplete:* and in those cases in which the remainder can never disappear, however often the operation is repeated, the quotient is necessarily *incomplete* and *interminable,* as there is no algebraical expression consisting of a finite number of terms which multiplied into the divisor can produce the dividend. We shall have occasion to notice all these circumstances, and many others, in the discussion of the following examples.

86. (1) Divide $6a^2 - 9ab$ by $2a - 3b$.

$$2a - 3b) \; 6a^2 - 9ab \; (3a, \text{ the quotient,}$$
$$\underline{6a^2 - 9ab}$$

or $\dfrac{6a^2 - 9ab}{2a - 3b} = 3a.$

The divisor and dividend are arranged in the same order: and the quotient, which is a mononomial, is obtained by dividing $6a^2$, the first term of the dividend, by $2a$ the first term of the divisor: (Art. 84. Rule.) there is no remainder and the quotient is therefore complete. (Art. 85.)

(2) Divide $ax + bx$ by $a + b$.

$$a + b\,)\ ax + bx\ (x, \text{ the quotient,}$$
$$\underline{ax + bx}$$

or $\dfrac{ax + bx}{a + b} = x$. (Art. 45.)

(3) Divide $20\,x^3y - 28\,x^2y^2 + 16\,xy^3$ by $5\,x^2 - 7\,xy + 4\,y^2$.

$$5\,x^2 - 7\,xy + 4\,y^2\,)\ 20\,x^3y - 28\,x^2y^2 + 16\,xy^3\ (4\,xy, \text{ the quot.}$$
$$\underline{20\,x^3y - 28\,x^2y^2 + 16\,xy^3}$$

(4) Divide $a^2 + 2\,ab + b^2$ by $a + b$.

$$a + b\,)\ a^2 + 2\,ab + b^2\ (a + b.\ \text{ (Art. 62.)}$$

Multiply $a + b$ into a, $\quad \underline{a^2 +\ \ ab}$

$$ab + b^2$$

Multiply $a + b$ into b, $\quad \underline{\ \ \ ab + b^2}$

By the first operation, we take away the product of a and $a + b$ from the dividend: by the second, we take away from the remainder the product of b and $a + b$: we have thus taken away altogether from the dividend the entire product of $a + b$ and $a + b$, and there is no remainder: consequently $a + b$ is the *complete* quotient of $a^2 + 2\,ab + b^2$ divided by $a + b$.

If we reverse the order of the letters in the divisor and dividend, as follows,

$$b + a\,)\ b^2 + 2\,ab + a^2\ (b + a$$

we should find $b + a$ for the quotient, by a process similar to the preceding: the arrangement in this case, as in the former, being alphabetical, although in an inverse order: but if we pay no attention to the alphabetical arrangement of the terms of the dividend and divisor, though we may sometimes find the *complete* quotient after a greater number of operations than are otherwise necessary, yet in most cases the process will never terminate, and consequently the complete quotient will never be determined.

For suppose the divisor and dividend arranged as follows:

$$a + b \,) \; 2\,ab + a^2 + b^2 \;\; (\, 2\,b + a - b = a + b$$
$$2\,ab + 2\,b^2$$
$$\overline{\hphantom{2\,ab + 2\,b^2}}$$
$$a^2 - b^2$$
$$a^2 + a\,b$$
$$\overline{\hphantom{a^2 + a\,b}}$$
$$-\,a\,b - b^2$$
$$-\,a\,b - b^2$$
$$\overline{\hphantom{-\,a\,b - b^2}}$$

We thus obtain the quotient $2\,b + a - b$, which is equivalent to $a + b$, after three operations instead of two. But if we place them in the following order, and adhere to it throughout, the process will never terminate:

$$a + b\,) \; 2\,ab + b^2 + a^2 \;\; \left(\, 2\,b - \frac{b^2}{a} + \frac{b^3}{a^2} -,\ \&\text{c.}\right.$$
$$2\,ab + 2\,b^2$$
$$\overline{\hphantom{2\,ab + 2\,b^2}}$$
$$-\,b^2 + a^2$$
$$-\,b^2 - b^3$$
$$\overline{\hphantom{-\,b^2 - b^3}}$$
$$a$$
$$\overline{\hphantom{aa}}$$
$$\frac{b^3}{a} + a^2$$
$$\frac{b^3}{a} + \frac{b^4}{a^2}$$
$$\overline{\hphantom{\frac{b^3}{a} + \frac{b^4}{a^2}}}$$
$$-\frac{b^4}{a^2} + a^2.$$

The second term $\dfrac{-b^2}{a}$, in the quotient, is the quantity which, when multiplied into a, produces $-\,b^2$:[*] the third term $\dfrac{b^3}{a^2}$, is the quantity which, when multiplied into a, produces $\dfrac{b^3}{a^2}$:[†] and

---

[*] For $a \times -\dfrac{b^2}{a} = -\dfrac{a\,b^2}{a} = -\,b^2$, (Art. 72): when we admit the existence of the negative term $-\dfrac{b^2}{a}$, we have reference to other terms with which it is connected by the sign $-$.

[†] For $a \times \dfrac{b^2}{a^2} = \dfrac{a\,b^2}{a^2} = \dfrac{b^2}{a}$. (Art. 72 and 77.)

so on, the terms of the quotient, according to the rule, being such quantities as, when multiplied into the *first* term of the divisor, necessarily produce in succession the *first* terms of the remainders: it is quite clear that by this process the remainder can never disappear, and consequently that the quotient can never become complete.

(5)   Divide $x^2 + (a + b) x + ab$ by $x + a$.

$$x + a \,)\; x^2 + (a + b)\, x + ab \;(\, x + b, \text{ the quotient,}$$
$$\underline{x^2 + a x}$$
$$bx + ab; \text{ for } (a+b)x - ax = bx. \text{ (Art. 49. Ex. 3.)}$$
$$\underline{bx + ab}$$
$$\cdot \qquad \cdot$$

(6)   Divide $x^2 - (a - b) x - ab$ by $x + b$.

$$x + b \,)\; x^2 - (a - b)\, x - ab \;(\, x - a$$
$$\underline{x^2 + b x}$$
$$-ax - ab; \text{ for } -(a - b)\, x - bx = -ax$$
$$\underline{-ax - ab}$$
$$\cdot \qquad \cdot$$

(7)   Divide $x^2 + 3 x - 28$ by $x - 4$.

$$x - 4 \,)\; x^2 + 3 x - 28 \;(\, x + 7$$
$$\underline{x^2 - 4 x}$$
$$7 x - 28$$
$$\underline{7 x - 28}$$
$$\cdot \qquad \cdot$$

(8)   Divide $x^3 - 86 x - 140$ by $x - 10$.

$$x - 10 \,)\; x^3 - 86 x - 140 \;(\, x^2 + 10 x + 14$$
$$\underline{x^3 - 10 x^2}$$
$$10 x^2 - \ 86 x$$
$$\underline{10 x^2 - 100 x}$$
$$14 x - 140$$
$$\underline{14 x - 140}$$
$$\cdot \qquad \cdot$$

In this case it is not necessary to bring down -140 to form a part of the first remainder, as it would not be affected by the second operation: it is omitted, therefore, to save superfluous writing.

(9)   Divide $x^4 - 4x^3 - 34x^2 + 76x + 105$ by $x - 7$.

$$x - 7 \,)\ x^4 - 4x^3 - 34x^2 + 76x + 105\ (\,x^3 + 3x^2 - 13x - 15$$

$$\underline{x^4 - 7x^3}$$

$$3x^3 - 34x^2$$
$$\underline{3x^3 - 21x^2}$$

$$-13x^2 + 76x$$
$$\underline{-13x^2 + 91x}$$

$$-15x + 105$$
$$\underline{-15x + 105}$$

$$. \qquad .$$

If the complete remainders were brought down after each subtraction, the process would stand as follows:

$$x - 7\,)\ x^4 - 4x^3 - 34x^2 + 76x + 105\ (\,x^3 + 3x^2 - 13x - 15$$

$$\underline{x^4 - 7x^3}$$

$$3x^3 - 34x^2 + 76x + 105$$
$$\underline{3x^3 - 21x^2}$$

$$-13x^2 + 76x + 105$$
$$\underline{-13x^2 + 91x}$$

$$-15x + 105$$
$$\underline{-15x + 105}$$

$$. \qquad .$$

(10)   Divide $3a^5 + 16a^4b - 33a^3b^2 + 14a^2b^5$ by $a^2 + 7ab$.

In the first place, it is evident from inspection that a is common to every term of the divisor and dividend: we begin therefore by dividing them both by a, and we then proceed with the results as follow:

$$a + 7b\,)\ 3a^4 + 16a^3b - 33a^2b^2 + 14ab^3\ (\,3a^3 - 5a^2b + 2ab^2$$

$$\underline{3a^4 + 21a^3b}$$

$$-5a^3b - 33a^2b^2$$
$$\underline{-5a^3b - 35a^2b^2}$$

$$2a^2b^2 + 14ab^3$$
$$2a^2b^2 + 14ab^3$$

(11) $\dfrac{a^2 + ab + 2ac - 2b^2 + 7bc - 3c^2}{a + 2b - c} = a - b + 3c.$

(12) $\dfrac{x^6 - 140x^4 + 1050x^3 - 3101x^2 + 3990x - 1800}{x^3 + 12x^2 - 43x + 30}$

$= x^3 - 12x^2 + 47x - 60.$

(13) Divide $x^4 - \dfrac{19a^2x^2}{6} + \dfrac{a^3x}{3} + \dfrac{a^4}{6}$ by $x^2 - 2ax + \dfrac{a^2}{2}.$

$$x^2 - 2ax + \frac{a^2}{2} \Big) \, x^4 - \frac{19a^2x^2}{6} + \frac{a^3x}{3} + \frac{a^4}{6} \, \Big(x^2 + 2ax + \frac{a^2}{3}$$

$$x^4 - 2ax^3 + \frac{a^2x^2}{2}$$

$$\overline{\qquad\qquad 2ax^3 - \frac{11a^2x^2}{3} + \frac{a^3x}{3}}$$

$$2ax^3 - 4a^2x^2 + a^3x$$

$$\overline{\qquad\qquad\qquad\qquad \frac{a^2x^2}{3} - \frac{2a^3x}{3} + \frac{a^4}{6}}$$

$$\frac{a^2x^2}{3} - \frac{2a^3x}{3} + \frac{a^4}{6}$$

$$\overline{\qquad\qquad\qquad\qquad\qquad \cdot\qquad\cdot\qquad\cdot}$$

(14) Divide $x^3 - 2ax^2 + (a^2 - ab - b^2)\,x + a^2b + ab^2$ by $x - a - b.$

$x - a - b\,)\,x^3 - 2ax^2 + (a^2 - ab - b^2)\,x + a^2b + ab^2\,(\,x^2 - (a-b)\,x - ab$

$\qquad x^3 - (a+b)\,x^2$

$\qquad\overline{\quad -(a-b)\,x^2 + (a^2 - ab - b^2)\,x}$; for $(a+b) - 2a = b - a = -(a-b),$

$\qquad\underline{\quad -(a-b)\,x^2 + (a^2 - b^2)\,x}$; for $(a + b\,(a-b) = a^2 - b^2$ (Art. (66).

$\qquad\qquad -abx + a^2b + ab^2$

$\qquad\qquad \underline{-abx + a^2b + ab^2}$

$\qquad\qquad\qquad \cdot\qquad\cdot\qquad\cdot$

The divisor and dividend being arranged according to powers of x, the divisor must be considered as a binomial, under the form $x - (a + b).$

(15) $\dfrac{y^6 + (a^2 - 2b^2)\,y^4 - (a^4 - b^4)\,y^2 - a^6 - 2a^4b^2 - a^2b^4}{y^2 - a^2 - b^2}$

$= y^4 + (2a^2 - b^2)\,y^2 + a^4 + a^2b^2.$

(16) $\dfrac{x^3 - a^3}{x - a} = x^2 + ax + a^2.$

(17) $\quad \dfrac{x^3 + a^3}{x + a} = x^2 - ax + a^2.$

(18) $\quad \dfrac{x^4 - a^4}{x - a} = x^3 + ax^2 + a^2 x + a^3.$

(19) $\quad \dfrac{x^5 - a^5}{x - a} = x^4 + ax^3 + a^2 x^2 + a^3 x + a^4.$

Examples of incomplete and interminable quotients.

87. In the preceding examples, the quotients obtained have been *complete*, (Art. 85.); in that which follows, the quotient is *incomplete* and *interminable*.

To divide $x^3 - a^3$ by $x + a$.

$$x + a \,)\, x^3 - a^3 \,\big(\, x^2 - ax + a^2 - \dfrac{2a^3}{x} + \dfrac{2a^4}{x^2} - \,\&\text{c.}$$

$$x^3 + ax^2$$
$$\overline{\qquad\qquad}$$
$$- ax^2 - a^3$$
$$- ax^2 - a^2 x$$
$$\overline{\qquad\qquad}$$
$$a^2 x - a^3$$
$$a^2 x + a^3$$
$$\overline{\qquad\qquad}$$
$$- 2a^3$$
$$- 2a^3 - \dfrac{2a^4}{x}$$
$$\overline{\qquad\qquad}$$
$$\dfrac{2a^4}{x}$$
$$\dfrac{2a^4}{x} + \dfrac{2a^5}{x^2}$$
$$\overline{\qquad\qquad}$$
$$- \dfrac{2a^5}{x^2}.$$

The remainder after the third operation is $-2a^3$, and the next term in the quotient is therefore $-\dfrac{2a^3}{x}$, since $-\dfrac{2a^3}{x} \times x = -2a^3$; or the product of the new term in the quotient and of the first term of the divisor, is the first, and, in this case, the only term, in the remainder: the next remainder is $\dfrac{2a^4}{x}$, and the corresponding term in the quotient is therefore $\dfrac{2a^4}{x^2}$, since $\dfrac{2a^4}{x^2} \times x = \dfrac{2a^4}{x}$: as the nature of the process in this case leaves necessarily a new remainder after every operation, the quotient may evidently be continued without limit, and will consist of a series of terms alternately positive and negative, the index of a in the numerator and of x in the denominator, increasing by unity in every successive term. (See Example 2, Art. 86.)*

88. We have here an example of an indefinite quotient, and the theory of its formation may be easily understood, by reference to the rule for division. (Art. 84.) As the terms in the quotient are successively determined by finding a quantity, which multiplied, in conformity with the rule of signs, (Arts. 55 and 57,) into the first term of the divisor produces the first term of the remainder (Art. 84), it is evident that the process may be continued as long as the remainder exists, and consequently may be continued *indefinitely*, when the remainder never disappears, which must always be the case when the divisor is not a *factor* (Art. 76.) of the dividend: such quotients, therefore, may be considered as originating in the rule for division, which is equally adapted to all cases, and whose application is not limited by the practicability of determining the quotient in any finite number of terms.

Theory of their formation.

89. Incomplete and indefinite quotients present themselves in arithmetic as well as in arithmetical algebra, when the decimal scale is supposed to be extended indefinitely, both ascending and descending, by means of the use of decimals. In the following chapter we shall discuss at considerable length, the theory of arithmetical operations, and their relation to the corresponding operations conducted by general symbols: and we shall reserve to that occasion the further consideration of the series which these quotients form, when they possess a character which is capable of being explained and understood, without the aid of the more general views which will be hereafter supplied by symbolical algebra, properly so called.

Incomplete and indefinite quotients in arithmetic.

* In the course of this example and in those given in the preceding articles, we are more or less compelled to consider the sign — as existing independently, (Art. 55.) and thus to advance beyond the proper limits of arithmetical algebra: the fact is, that the mere use of general symbols and of signs to connect them, however strictly limited in their primitive meaning and application, conducts us almost insensibly to a science of pure symbols, presenting forms of combination and processes which are both unintelligible and impracticable when considered solely with reference to their simple arithmetical usage.

CHAPTER II

ON THE THEORY OF THE FUNDAMENTAL OPERATIONS
IN ARITHMETIC.

Numbers abstract and concrete become identified by arithmetical notation.

90. THE numbers which are the objects of Arithmetical Operations, are considered as *abstract* so long as no specific properties are assigned to the units of which they are composed and *concrete* under all other circumstances. The notation, however, which we adopt for the purpose of representing numbers, generally suppresses all consideration of the specific properties of their component units, and consequently indicates no distinction in the operations to be performed upon them, whether they be abstract or concrete: it is only when we come to the details of commercial arithmetic, that we are compelled in general to take into account the specific properties of the units which compose our numbers, inasmuch as they are connected with the customary subdivisions of them, to which names are attached, which are very rarely adapted to the decimal scale, requiring therefore for their reduction and calculation, the application of rules which vary with almost every species of magnitude and which greatly interfere with the uniformity which might otherwise be made to prevail in nearly all the processes of arithmetic.

The operations of addition and subtraction are confined to numbers whose units are identical.

91. The operations of addition and subtraction can only be conceived to take place between numbers which are abstract, or whose units represent magnitudes of the same kind, whether they be specified or not: in all other cases, there can be no results of such operations. It is true that magnitudes of different natures may be connected with the algebraical signs + and −, but the operations which are indicated will continue to be impossible, until such previous reductions are effected, when such are practicable, as will restore the required identity of the units which compose the numbers which are the subjects of the operations: thus the sum of 2 cwt. 3 qr. and 14 lb. may be represented by 2 cwt. + 3 qr. + 14 lb. or more commonly by

$$\begin{array}{ccc} \text{cwt.} & \text{qr.} & \text{lb.} \\ 2 & . \quad 3 & . \quad 14 \end{array}$$

and the operation indicated, as long as the units of the numbers to be added together continue to be different in their value, will be impossible: but if we replace 2 cwt. by 228 lb., 3 qr. by 84 lb., then the units of the numbers 228, 84 and 14 to be added together, become identical with each other, and their sum (326 lb.) is obtained precisely in the same manner as in the addition of abstract numbers: but, if it had been required to add together 7 feet and 4 lb. whose units are not merely different but irreducible to others of the same nature, the operation to be performed might be represented by connecting 7 feet and 4 lb. with the sign +, but no result, in which they are collected into one term, would be obtainable *.

In conformity with the preceding observations it will be found that fractions, whose denominators are different, and whose numerators express therefore units of a different kind, are incapable of addition, until they have been reduced to the same denominators, or in other words, until we have obtained the required identity of the units of the numbers which are the subjects of these operations.

92. The operations of multiplication and division are the inverse of each other, and so far as the numbers which form the multiplier or divisor are concerned, they must be considered as perfectly abstract, representing as they do, the number of times that the multiplicand, whatever it may be, whether abstract or concrete, is contained in the product and the quotient in the dividend: it will follow likewise, that the units of the multiplicand will be identical with those of the product, and the units of the quotient identical with those of the dividend. If, however, the divisor is not contained a certain number of times exactly in the dividend, and if a remainder, less than the divisor, is found to exist, the operation of division cannot be extended to the units of that remainder, unless we conceive them to be concrete: for, if we form a fraction, to be added to the integral quotient previously obtained, of which the

In the operations of multiplication and division, the multiplier and the divisor are generally abstract numbers.

Origin and meaning of fractions in quotients.

* In Algebra, symbols or combinations of symbols are connected together with the signs + or −, without any immediate reference to the identity or diversity of the quantities which are thus connected together, whether in their specific nature or in the units of the numbers which express them: it is only when the quantities thus connected together possess the same symbolical part, with or without numerical coefficients, that results are obtained of the operations denoted by the signs + and −, by the reduction of all such terms into one.

numerator is the remainder and the divisor is the denominator, it will signify, that unity (that is, the primary unit) is divided into as many equal parts as there are units in the divisor or denominator and that as many of these subordinate units are taken as there are units in the numerator: it is for this reason that we are compelled, under such circumstances, to consider the units of the original dividend to be concrete, inasmuch as the mind cannot conceive the resolution of unity into parts, unless it represents a real magnitude.

Cases in which the multiplier or divisor are not abstract numbers.

93. There will occur cases in which the multiplier or divisor will no longer be abstract numbers, where products and quotients will be obtained whose units are no longer identical with those of the multiplicand and dividend respectively: but under such circumstances, a meaning can very rarely be given to the operations of multiplication and division, and even then rather by the aid of a reference to the results which are obtained, than to the primitive and ordinary meaning of these terms themselves. In considering the multiplication and division of fractions, we shall be compelled to have recourse to this extended and in some respects conventional meaning of these operations.

Theory of fractions.

94. We have referred, very briefly and imperfectly, (in Arts. 71 and 92), to the origin and meaning of numerical fractions: in the subsequent articles, we propose to discuss their theory at considerable length, forming as it does, one of the most important departments of Arithmetic.

Their origin and meaning.

Assuming that the units of all numbers represent real magnitudes, we may conceive them to be capable of indefinite subdivision, forming an indefinite series of *subordinate* units related to their primary unit by means of their numerical divisor, to which the name *denominator* is given: thus if the unit, which 1 represents, be divided into three equal parts, $\frac{1}{3}$ will represent one of them, $\frac{2}{3}$ will represent two of them, $\frac{3}{3}$ will represent three of them, or will be equivalent to the primary unit, $\frac{4}{3}$ will represent four of the subordinate units denoted by $\frac{1}{3}$, $\frac{10}{3}$ ten of them and so on, whatever be the *multiple* of the subordinate unit which is required to be expressed, the *number* by which it is multiplied being called the *numerator* of the fraction: more generally if b represent the *denominator*, which *denominates* or determines the subordinate unit $\frac{1}{b}$, $\frac{2}{b}$ will represent two such units, $\frac{3}{b}$ three such units, and $\frac{a}{b}$, a times such units, where a is the numerator of the fraction, which *numbers* or determines the multiple of the subordinate units *denominated* by b.

95. The fraction $\frac{a}{b}$ is said to be *proper* or *improper*, according as its numerator a is less or greater than its denominator b: in the latter case, the numerator a may contain b, p times exactly, or may contain b, p times with a remainder c: the first of these hypotheses gives $\frac{a}{b} = \frac{pb}{b} = p$, (Art. 72.) a whole number expressing the primary units only; whilst the second gives

Proper and improper fractions.

Reduction of improper fractions to whole or mixed numbers and conversely.

$$\frac{a}{b} = \frac{pb + c}{b} = \frac{pb}{b} + \frac{c}{b} = p + \frac{c}{b},$$

or p primary units and c subordinate units denominated by c, (Art. 94.) and is therefore properly called a *mixed* number, involving units of different kinds: it thus appears, that improper fractions, whenever they occur, may be reduced to whole or mixed numbers or conversely.

Thus $\frac{12}{3} = 4$, and conversely $4 = \frac{12}{3}$, whatever the units of the number 4 may denote: $\frac{17}{5} = 3 + \frac{2}{5}$, a mixed number, and conversely $3 + \frac{2}{5}$ (or $3\frac{2}{5}$, as it is commonly written) is equal to the fraction $\frac{17}{5}$.

Examples.

Similarly $\frac{93}{17} = 5 + \frac{8}{17} = 5\frac{8}{17}$:

$$\frac{1519}{111} = 7 + \frac{76}{111} = 7\frac{76}{111}:$$

and conversely $13\frac{12}{13} = \frac{13 \times 13 + 12}{13} = \frac{181}{13}$:

$$407\frac{7}{61} = \frac{407 \times 61 + 7}{61} = \frac{24827}{61}.$$

Rule.

96. Generally an *improper fraction* becomes the *mixed number, whose integral* part is the integral quotient which arises from dividing the numerator by the denominator, and whose fractional part is the fraction whose numerator is the remainder, and whose denominator is the original denominator of the improper fraction;* and conversely a *mixed number* becomes the *improper fraction, whose numerator is the product of the integral part of the mixed number and of the denominator of the fraction, increased by its numerator, and whose denominator is the denominator of the fractional part.*

The numerator and denominator of a fraction may be multiplied or divided by the same number without altering its value.

97. If we suppose the subordinate unit $\frac{1}{b}$ to be again divided by c or to be resolved into c equal parts, it will be equivalent to the division of the primary unit 1 by b times c or bc, and each of them will be represented by $\frac{1}{bc}$, (Art. 94.): if c of these secondary subordinate units represented by $\frac{1}{bc}$ be taken, the result will be represented by $\frac{c}{bc}$, which is evidently equivalent to $\frac{1}{b}$; since c secondary subordinate units such as $\frac{1}{bc}$, compose one primary subordinate unit $\frac{1}{b}$: and if we take ac times the secondary subordinate unit $\frac{1}{bc}$, forming the fraction $\frac{ac}{bc}$ (Art. 94.), it will evidently be equivalent to a times the primary subordinate unit $\frac{1}{b}$, and will consequently form the fraction $\frac{a}{b}$: it follows therefore generally that $\frac{ac}{bc} = \frac{a}{b}$, from whence we derive the following very important propositions:

Proposition.

(1) If the numerator and denominator of a fraction be multiplied by the same number, its value is not altered.

Its converse.

(2) If the numerator and denominator of a fraction be divided by any factor which is common to both, its value is not altered.

---

* An *integral* number is a multiple of the primary unit, whatever it may be: a *fractional* number is a multiple of the subordinate unit denominated by the denominator: in this sense, the term *number* may be correctly applied to fractions.

The whole theory of the reduction, addition, and subtraction of fractions will be found to depend upon these propositions.

98. If a common divisor of the numerator and denominator of a fraction exists, it may be obliterated (Art. 97.), and an equivalent fraction obtained which is in more simple terms (Art. 75.): but inasmuch as the products of numbers present no easily discoverable traces of their component factors, those factors which may be common to the numerator and denominator of a fraction are rarely recognizable by inspection or by the knowledge possessed by ordinary men*, whether from memory or otherwise, of the composition of numbers. Under such circumstances it is necessary to have recourse to the following arithmetical rule, by which the greatest common divisor or the *greatest common measure*, as it is called, of any two numbers, may be found in all cases. *Obliteration of common factors of the numerator and denominator.*

Divide the greater of the two numbers by the less and the last divisor by the last remainder, repeating the process until there is no remainder: the last divisor is the greatest common measure required. *Rule for finding the greatest common measure of two numbers.*

99. The form of the operation, expressed in symbols, may be exhibited as follows: *Form of the operation.*

$$
\begin{array}{r}
b)\,a\,(\,p \\
p\,b \\
\hline
\quad c)\,b\,(\,q \\
q\,c \\
\hline
\qquad d)\,c\,(\,r \\
r\,d \\
\hline
\cdot\ \cdot
\end{array}
$$

The interpretation of this form of the process is very easy: b is contained in a, p times, with a remainder c; c is contained in b, q times, with a remainder d; d is contained in c, r times and there is no remainder. *Its interpretation.*

---

* The unusual and almost instinctive insight which was possessed by some very remarkable boys, such as Zerah Colburn, George Bidder, and others, into the composition of numbers is one of the most curious and unaccountable facts which presents itself in the history of the human mind: in ordinary cases this direct and immediate power of resolving numbers into their factors is extremely limited.

We have supposed the process to terminate after three divisions: the demonstration which follows would be equally applicable, if it had proceeded to a greater number of them: for this purpose, it is convenient for us to premise the two following Lemmas.

Lemma. 100. LEMMA I. If one number measures another, it will measure any multiple of that number.

If $a = cx$, then $ma = mcx$: or if x is contained c times in a, it is contained mc times in ma.

Lemma. 101. LEMMA II. If a number measure each of two others, it will measure their sum and difference.

For if $a = cx$ and $b = dx$, we have

$$a + b = cx + dx = (c + d)x \quad \text{(Art. 46.)};$$
$$\text{and } a - b = cx - dx = (c - d)x \quad \text{(Art. 47.)}:$$

and since c and d are whole numbers, $c + d$ and $c - d$ are whole numbers; and therefore x, which measures a and b, measures $a + b$ and $a - b$.

Proof that *d* is a measure of *a* and *b*. 102. In the first place, we shall prove that d is a measure of a and b.

Since d measures c by the units in r, it measures qc (Art. 100.): it measures $qc + d$ or b, since it measures qc and d (Art. 101.): it measures b, and therefore pb: it measures pb and c, and therefore $pb + c$ or a: it appears, therefore, that d is a measure both of a and b.

Every measure of *a* and *b* is a measure of *d*. 103. In the second place, we shall prove that every measure of a and b is a measure of d.

For if a number measures a and b, it measures a and pb, (Art. 100.) and therefore their difference (Art. 101.) $a - pb$ or c: it measures b and c, and therefore b and qc, and consequently $b - qc$ or d.

Proof that *d* is the greatest measure of *a* and *b*. 104. Since every number which measures a and b, measures d, the greatest number which measures a and b measures d: therefore d, which measures a and b, is their greatest common measure; for no number greater than d can measure d.

Example. 105. The following is an example of the application of the rule, which we have just demonstrated, to reduce the fraction $\dfrac{2553}{2997}$ to its most simple equivalent form:

$$2553 \overline{)\, 2997\, (\, 1}$$
$$2553$$
$$\overline{}$$
$$444 \overline{)\, 2553\, (\, 5}$$
$$2220$$
$$\overline{}$$
$$333 \overline{)\, 444\, (\, 1}$$
$$333$$
$$\overline{}$$
$$111 \overline{)\, 333\, (\, 3}$$
$$333$$
$$\overline{}$$
$$\cdots$$

Consequently 111 is the greatest common measure of the numbers 2553 and 2997, and the fraction $\dfrac{2553}{2997} = \dfrac{23 \times 111}{27 \times 111} = \dfrac{23}{27}$ *.

106.   In connection with the preceding rule for finding the greatest common measure of two numbers, it may be convenient in this place to notice its extension for the purpose of finding the greatest common measure of three or more numbers: thus, if a, b, c, d, &c. be a series of such numbers whose greatest common measure is required, find x, the greatest common measure of a and b: y the greatest common measure of x and c: z the greatest common measure of y and d: and so on, whatever be the number of these successive numbers: then z, or the last of the common measures thus found, is the greatest common measure required. Greatest common measure of three or more numbers.
Rule.

For every common measure of a and b is a measure of x (Art. 103.): and therefore y, the greatest common measure of x and c, is the greatest common measure of a, b, and c. In a similar manner it may be shewn that z is the greatest common measure of a, b, c, and d. Proof.

107.   If a and b have no common measure except unity, they are said to be *prime* to each other, and the fraction $\dfrac{a}{b}$ is in If a be prime to b, there is no other fraction equal to $\dfrac{a}{b}$, whose terms are not equimultiples of a and b.

* Other examples are
$$\frac{63}{405} = \frac{7 \times 9}{45 \times 9} = \frac{7}{45}: \qquad \frac{1919}{2128} = \frac{101 \times 19}{112 \times 19} = \frac{101}{112}:$$
$$\frac{857142}{999999} = \frac{6 \times 142857}{7 \times 142857} = \frac{6}{7}: \qquad \frac{2019}{3873} = \frac{673 \times 3}{1291 \times 3} = \frac{673}{1291}$$

its lowest terms: for in that case there is no *other* fraction equal to $\frac{a}{b}$, whose terms are not equimultiples of a and b.

This proposition is very nearly self-evident, but is capable of being proved in the following manner: for this purpose it is convenient to premise the two following Lemmas.

If two improper fractions be equal to one another, the integral and fractional parts of the mixed numbers equal to them, are also equal to one another.

108. LEMMA I. If two improper fractions be equal to one another, the integral and proper fractional parts of the mixed numbers into which they are severally resolvible, are also equal to one another.

For if $\frac{a}{b} = \frac{a'}{b'}$*, where a is greater than b, and therefore a' greater than b', then if $a = pb + c$ (Art. 95.) and $a' = p'b' + c'$, we get $\frac{a}{b} = p + \frac{c}{b}$ and $\frac{a'}{b'} = p' + \frac{c'}{b'}$: and since $\frac{a}{b} = \frac{a'}{b'}$, we have also $p + \frac{c}{b} = p' + \frac{c'}{b'}$, and therefore $p = p'$ and $\frac{c}{b} = \frac{c'}{b'}$: for it is obvious, since $\frac{c}{b}$ and $\frac{c'}{b'}$ are both of them less than the primary unit, that p and p' cannot differ from each other by 1 or by any multiple of 1.

If two fractions be equal to one another, their reciprocals are also equal to one another.

109. LEMMA II. If two fractions be equal to one another, their reciprocals are also equal to one another.

For if $\frac{a}{b} = \frac{a'}{b'}$, and if we multiply both of them by bb', their equimultiples will be equal to one another: the first product $\frac{a \times b \times b'}{b} = ab'$, and the second $\frac{a' \times bb'}{b'} = a'b$ (Art. 72.): if the equal numbers ab' and $a'b$ be divided by the same number aa', the first becomes $\frac{ab'}{aa'} = \frac{b'}{a'}$, and the second $\frac{a'b}{aa'} = \frac{b}{a}$: it follows therefore that $\frac{b}{a} = \frac{b'}{a'}$, which is the proposition to be proved.

---

* We use the accented letters a' and b' instead of other symbols, such as c and d, inasmuch as these accents sufficiently distinguish them from a and b, and further indicate the connection which both the proposition and the process of demonstration employed establishes between them: the same observation applies to the other accented letters which are employed in this and the following Articles, and may be extended generally to most of the cases in which they will be found to be employed both in this work and others of a similar nature.

110. Supposing $\dfrac{a}{b} = \dfrac{a'}{b'}$, the processes for finding the greatest common measures of these fractions will stand as follows:

$$
\begin{array}{ll}
b)\ a\ (p & \qquad b')\ a'\ (p' \\
\quad pb & \qquad\quad p'b' \\
\overline{} & \qquad\overline{} \\
\quad c)\ b\ (q & \qquad\quad c')\ b'\ (q' \\
\qquad qc & \qquad\qquad q'c' \\
\quad\overline{} & \qquad\quad\overline{} \\
\qquad d)\ c\ (r & \qquad\qquad d')\ c'\ (r' \\
\qquad\quad rd & \qquad\qquad\quad r'd' \\
\qquad\overline{} & \qquad\qquad\overline{} \\
\qquad\quad .\ . & \qquad\qquad\quad .\ .
\end{array}
$$

From the first Lemma (Art. 108.) it will follow that $p = p'$, and also $\dfrac{c}{b} = \dfrac{c'}{b'}$: from the second Lemma (Art. 109.) it will follow that $\dfrac{b}{c} = \dfrac{b'}{c'}$: and since $b = qc + d$, and $b' = q'c' + d'$, it also appears that $q = q'$, $\dfrac{d}{c} = \dfrac{d'}{c'}$, and therefore $\dfrac{c}{d} = \dfrac{c'}{d'}$, or $r = r'$. It follows from hence likewise that the divisions terminate after the same number of operations in both cases.

Since a is prime to b, it follows that the last divisor $d = 1$: for if not, a and b would have a common measure different from unity, which is contrary to the hypothesis. (Art. 98.)

Again, since $r' = r = c$, we get $c' = r'd' = cd'$:
$$\text{also } b' = q'c' + d' = qcd' + d', \text{ (since } q' = q)$$
$$= (qc + 1)d' = bd', \text{ since } b = qc + d = qc + 1:$$
$$\text{and } a' = p'b' + c' = pb' + c' \text{ (since } p = p')$$
$$= pbd' + cd' \text{ (since } b' = bd' \text{ and } c' = cd') = (pb + c)d' = ad',$$
$$\text{since } a = pb + c.$$

It follows therefore that $\dfrac{a}{b} = \dfrac{a'}{b'} = \dfrac{ad'}{bd'}$: or in other words, a' and b' are either equal to a and b respectively (if $d' = 1$) or are equimultiples of them.

111. The proposition just demonstrated, though extremely simple and obvious, is the foundation of several important propositions in the theory of numbers, and is one to which frequent reference will require to be made in our subsequent investiga-

tions connected with the reduction of ordinary into decimal fractions: we shall therefore proceed at once to demonstrate them in connection with the proposition upon which they depend.

If a number
is prime to
each of two
others, it
is prime
to their
product.

112. If a number c be *prime* (Art. 107.) to each of two others a and b, it is prime to their product ab.

For if not, let c and ab have a common measure x: and let us suppose $ab = xp$, and therefore (dividing both of them by bx, Art. 109.) $\dfrac{a}{x} = \dfrac{p}{b}$: but since a is *prime* to x (for by hypothesis a is prime to c and x is a factor of c), it follows that the fraction $\dfrac{a}{x}$ is in its lowest terms, and therefore b is either equal to x or to a multiple of x (Art. 110.): in neither case, therefore, can b be prime to c, which is contrary to the hypothesis: it follows therefore that ab and c can have no common measure.

If a number
is prime to
another, it
is prime to
any power
of it.

113. If c be prime to a, it is prime to any power (Art. 39.) of a, whether a^2, a^3, or more generally a^n.

For by the same process of reasoning as in the proof of the proposition in the last Article, it would appear, that if c be prime to a and a $(b = a)$, it is prime to $a \times a$ or a^2: and therefore if prime to a and a^2 $(b = a^2)$, it is prime to $a \times a^2$ or a^3: and in a similar manner it may be shewn to be prime to a^4, a^5, or to any integral power of a whatsoever.

If one
number
is prime
to another,
any power
of one will
be prime to
any power
of the other.

114. If c be prime to a, then any power of c will be prime to any power of a.

For if c be prime to a, then c is also prime to any power of a, such as a^2, a^3, or a^n: and if a^2, a^3, or a^n be prime to c, also a^2, a^3, or a^n will be prime to c^2, c^3, or any power of c, such as c^m.

If a frac-
tion be in
its lowest
terms, the
fractions
whose
terms are
any powers
of its
numerator
and de-
nominator
are also in
their lowest
terms.

115. If the fraction $\dfrac{a}{b}$ be in its lowest terms, the fractions $\dfrac{a}{b^2}$, $\dfrac{a^2}{b^2}$, $\dfrac{a^2}{b^3}$, $\dfrac{a^3}{b^3}$, $\dfrac{a^n}{b^m}$, will also be in their lowest terms.

This is an immediate corollary from the proposition proved in the last Article.

116. In the reduction of fractions to their most simple common denominators, and in the solution of many other problems, it will be found necessary to find the *least common multiple* of

two or more numbers: we shall begin by the investigation of the rule for finding the least common multiple of two numbers, and subsequently shew in what manner it may be extended to any number of them.

Let m be the least common multiple of two numbers a and b, whose greatest common measure is x: since m is a multiple both of a and b, we may assume $m = pa = qb$, where p and q are whole numbers: also since $pa = qb$, we get (dividing them both by pb, Art. 109.) $\dfrac{a}{b} = \dfrac{q}{p}$: and since m is by hypothesis the *least* possible multiple of a and b, it follows that p and q are the least possible numbers which answer the preceding condition, and that therefore the fraction $\dfrac{q}{p}$ is the fraction $\dfrac{a}{b}$ in its lowest terms: for if not, let any other fraction $\dfrac{q'}{p'}$ be the fraction $\dfrac{a}{b}$ in its lowest terms: then since $\dfrac{q'}{p'} = \dfrac{a}{b}$, we get (multiplying both by $p'b$) $q'b = p'a$, or, there are common multiples of a and b, which are less than pa and qb, which is impossible: it follows therefore, that $\dfrac{q}{p}$ is the fraction $\dfrac{a}{b}$ in its lowest terms, and therefore we have $q = \dfrac{a}{x}$, and consequently $m = qb = \dfrac{ab}{x} = pqx$: a result, from which we conclude, *that the least common multiple of two numbers is their product, divided by their greatest common measure*; or in other words, that it is *the continued product of the greatest common measure of two numbers and of the quotients which arise from dividing them by it.*

(margin) Proof of the rule for finding the least common multiple of two numbers.

117. Every other multiple of two numbers a and b, is a multiple of their least common multiple m. For let M be any other multiple of a and b, different from m, and let us suppose $M = Pa = Qb$: we thus get $\dfrac{a}{b} = \dfrac{Q}{P} = \dfrac{q}{p}$, (Art. 116): and since $\dfrac{q}{p}$ is in its lowest terms, it follows that either $Q = q$ and $P = p$, in which case $M = m$, or that $Q = nq$ and $P = np$, where n is a whole number (Art. 110): we thus get $M = Qb = nqb = nm$, since $m = qb$.

(margin) Every other multiple of two numbers is a multiple of their least common multiple.

118. If the least common multiple of three numbers a, b, c be required, we must find m the least common multiple of

(margin) The least common multiple of three or more numbers.

a and b, and then m' the least common multiple of m and c, is the least common multiple required.

For every common multiple of a and b is a multiple of m, (Art. 117.) and therefore the least common multiple of m and c is the least common multiple of a, b and c. In a similar manner, we may find the least common multiple of four or more numbers.

Another mode of expressing the least common multiple of two or more numbers.

119. If $a = pxy$, $b = qx$, $c = qy$, where p, q and r are prime to each other, then $pqrxyz$ will be the least common multiple of a, b and c.

For $m = \dfrac{ab}{x} = pqxy$ is the least common multiple of a and b:

and $m' = \dfrac{mc}{y} = pqrxyz$ is the least common multiple of m and c, and therefore of a, b and c. (Art. 118.)

It is easy to extend the same reasoning to four or more numbers, between two or more of which common measures exist.

It follows therefore that the least common multiple of two or more numbers will be *the continued product of the common measures which exist between two or more of them and the quotients as prime to each other, which arise from dividing them by all common factors.*

General arithmetical rule for finding the least common multiple.

120. The following easy arithmetical rule for finding the least common multiple of two or more numbers is immediately derivable from the proposition given in the last article.

Write down in the same line all the numbers whose least common multiple is required: find common measures of any two or more of these numbers, which are prime to all others: divide successively all the numbers by these common divisors, and bring down the quotients, or the entire numbers when not divisible, to a succession of lines, continuing the process until the last line contains numbers which are all of them prime to each other: the continued product of all the divisors and of all the numbers in the last line, is the least common multiple required.

The divisors employed must be

121. If divisors, not prime to all the numbers which they do not measure, be employed, cases *may* occur in which the final product obtained by the preceding process, would not be

the least common multiple required: thus if $a = pxy$, $b = qxy$, $c = rx$, then if we make xy, which is a measure of a and b, the first divisor, the process will stand as follows,

$$xy) \, a, \; b, \; c$$
$$\overline{ \, p, \; q, \; c}$$

where p, q and c are prime to each other, but $pqcxy$ is not the least common multiple required. If however we make x and y, the factors of xy, successive divisors, the correct result will be obtained as follows,

$$x) \quad a, \quad b, \quad c$$
$$\overline{y) \, py, \; qy, \; r}$$
$$\overline{ \, p, \quad q, \quad r}$$

and $pqrxy$ is the least common multiple required. (Art. 119.)

122. The following are examples.

Examples.

(1) Let it be required to find the least common multiple of 6, 15, 27, 35.

$$3) \, 6, \; 15, \; 27, \; 35$$
$$\overline{5) \, 2, \quad 5, \quad 9, \; 35}$$
$$\overline{ \, 2 \, . \, 1 \, . \, 9 \, . \, 7}$$

The least common multiple required is
$$3 \times 5 \times 2 \times 9 \times 7 = 1890.$$

In this case 3 is the greatest common measure of 6, 15, 27, and is prime to 35: 5 is the greatest common measure of 5 and 35, and is prime to 2 and 9: the numbers 2, 9 and 7 in the last line are prime to each other.

(2) To find the least common multiple of 12, 14 and 36.

$$2) \, 12, \; 14, \; 36$$
$$\overline{6) \, 6, \quad 7, \; 18}$$
$$\overline{ \, 1 \, . \, 7 \, . \, 3}$$

and $2 \times 6 \times 7 \times 3 = 252$ is the least common multiple required.

If, in this case, we had made 4, which is a common measure of 12 and 36, and *not prime* to 14, the first divisor, the process would have stood as follows:

$$4) \, 12, \; 14, \; 36$$
$$\overline{3) \, 3, \quad 14, \quad 9}$$
$$\overline{ \, 1 \, . \, 14 \, . \, 3}$$

Right margin note:
generally prime to all the numbers which they do not measure.

The numbers 14 and 3 in the last line are prime to each other, but $4 \times 3 \times 14 \times 3 = 504$ is not the least common multiple required.

The same erroneous result would have followed, if we had made 12 the first and only divisor.

It does not follow, however, that the employment of a common divisor, of two or more numbers, *which is not prime to the others*, will in all cases lead to an erroneous result: thus if we make 6 the first divisor, and 2 the second, we get

$$6)\ 12,\ 14,\ 36$$
$$\overline{2)\ 2,\ 14,\ \ 6}$$
$$\overline{\ \ 1\ .\ 7\ .\ 3}$$

where $6 \times 2 \times 7 \times 3 = 252$ the least common multiple required: in this case, the number 14 is not prime to all the other numbers in the second line and consequently its factor, which was a measure of the first divisor, disappears by a second operation.

(3) Let it be required to find the least common multiple of the nine digits.

$$2)\ 1,\ 2,\ 3,\ 4,\ 5,\ 6,\ 7,\ 8,\ 9$$
$$\overline{2)\ 1\ .\ 1\ .\ 3\ .\ 2\ .\ 5\ .\ 3\ .\ 7\ .\ 4\ .\ 9}$$
$$\overline{3)\ 1\ .\ 1\ .\ 3\ .\ 1\ .\ 5\ .\ 3\ .\ 7\ .\ 2\ .\ 9}$$
$$\overline{\ \ 1\ .\ 1\ .\ 1\ .\ 1\ .\ 5\ .\ 1\ .\ 7\ .\ 2\ .\ 3}$$

and $2 \times 2 \times 3 \times 5 \times 7 \times 2 \times 3 = 2520$, the least common multiple required.

The subordinate units of which the numerators of fractions are multiples, are only identical when the denominators are the same. 123. Considering all fractions as *numbers* (Art. 96. Note), and, as such multiples of the subordinate units, denominated by their denominators (Art. 94.), as are expressed by their numerators, it follows, that the component subordinate units of such fractions can only be considered as identical (that is, as expressing the same magnitude) when their denominators are the same: under no other circumstances, therefore, can such fractions (or numbers) be compared with each other with respect to magnitude, or admit of being added together or subtracted from each other.

124. But inasmuch as the values of fractions are not altered (with respect to the value of their primary unit) by having their numerators and denominators multiplied or divided by

the same number (Art. 97.), it will be always possible to reduce them to equivalent fractions having a common denominator
and consequently expressing multiples of *identical* subordinate
units, when the primary unit is the same for them all.   This
may be effected by the following general rule.

Find the least common multiple of the denominators of all the
fractions.

Find the successive quotients which arise from dividing this
least common multiple by the several denominators of all the fractions.

Multiply the several numerators of the fractions by the suc-
cessive quotients which arise from the last process, and the pro-
ducts which arise will form the new numerators of the equivalent
fractions, whose common denominator is the least common multiple
of the primitive denominators.

By the application of this rule, we obtain a series of equivalent fractions, expressing identical subordinate units of the
highest possible order, or with the least possible common denominator.

125.   The following are examples.

(1)   To reduce $\frac{3}{14}$ and $\frac{5}{21}$ to equivalent fractions having
the least common denominator.

Denominators 14, 21.

Least common multiple 42.

Quotients 3, 2.

Old numerators 3, 5.

New numerators 9, 10.

Equivalent fractions $\frac{9}{42}$, $\frac{10}{42}$.

(2) To reduce the fractions,

$$\frac{7}{10}, \quad \frac{11}{15}, \quad \frac{12}{18}, \quad \frac{17}{24}$$

to others, which have the least common denominator.

Denominators 10, 15, 18, 24.

Least common multiple 360.

Quotients 36, 24, 20, 15.

Old numerators 8, 11, 12, 17.

New ditto 252, 264, 240, 255.

Rule for
reducing
two or
more frac-
tions to the
most simple
common
denomina-
tor.

Examples.

$$\text{Equivalent fractions } \frac{252}{360}, \frac{264}{360}, \frac{240}{360}, \frac{255}{360}*.$$

Proof that the fractions produced by this process are the most simple which admit of a common denominator.

126. A very slight attention to the process just exemplified, would shew that the numerator and denominator of every fraction is multiplied and divided by the same number, namely, by the quotient which arises from dividing the least common multiple of all the denominators by its denominator: and, inasmuch as the least common multiple of the denominators is the least number which is divisible by all the denominators, it follows that the fractions which result from this process are in the lowest terms, which admit of a common denominator.

Thus, if the fractions be $\frac{a}{b}, \frac{c}{d}, \frac{e}{f}$, and if m be the least common multiple of b, d, f, so that $m = bx = dy = fz$, then the reduced fractions are

$$\frac{ax}{bx}, \frac{cy}{dy}, \frac{cz}{fz}, \text{ or } \frac{cx}{m}, \frac{cy}{m}, \frac{cz}{m};$$

and since m is the least number which is divisible by b, d and f, it follows that these fractions are in the lowest or most simple terms, which admit of a common denominator.

Comparison of fractions with respect to magnitude.

127. Fractions which are reduced to a common denominator, become numbers which are multiples of identical units, and thus admit of comparison with each other, with respect to magnitude, in the same manner as ordinary numbers: thus the fractions $\frac{3}{5}$ and $\frac{7}{11}$ are reduced to the equivalent fractions $\frac{33}{55}$ and $\frac{35}{55}$, which express respectively 33 times and 35 times the same subordinate unit $\frac{1}{55}$, or one fifty-fifth part of the primary unit, whatever it may be: it is obvious therefore, that

* Other Examples:

The fractions $\frac{7}{10}, \frac{13}{100}, \frac{497}{1000}$ are reduced to $\frac{700}{1000}, \frac{130}{1000}, \frac{497}{1000}$:

the fractions $\frac{1}{2}, \frac{1}{3}, \frac{1}{4}, \frac{1}{5}, \frac{1}{6}, \frac{1}{7}, \frac{1}{8}, \frac{1}{9}$ are reduced to $\frac{1260}{2520}, \frac{840}{2520}, \frac{620}{2520}, \frac{504}{2520}, \frac{420}{2520}, \frac{300}{2520}, \frac{315}{2520}, \frac{280}{2520}$:

the fractions $\frac{3}{4}, \frac{7}{10}, \frac{11}{16}, \frac{18}{25}$ are reduced to $\frac{300}{400}, \frac{280}{400}, \frac{275}{400}, \frac{288}{400}$.

the first of these fractions is less than the second, and that the relation between them, is that of the numbers 33 and 35, whose units are the same, whatever they may be.

128.   Fractions also, when thus reduced, are capable of arithmetical addition and subtraction like ordinary numbers: thus the sum of the fractions $\frac{3}{5}$ and $\frac{7}{11}$, or of $\frac{33}{55}$ and $\frac{35}{55}$, is $\frac{33 + 35}{55} = \frac{68}{55}$, and their difference is $\frac{35 - 33}{55} = \frac{2}{55}$.

Fractions with the same denominators are capable of addition and subtraction.

It is obvious, however, that these operations are impracticable, unless the quantities which are subject to them are numbers of the same donomination: for the same difficulty would present itself in the addition of the fractions $\frac{3}{5}$ and $\frac{7}{11}$ which occurs in the addition of quantities of the same kind but of different denominations, such as £7 and 3 shillings: we can conceive the sum of $\frac{3}{5}$ and $\frac{7}{11}$ (when their primary units are the same) equally with that of £7 and 3 shillings: but it is only when the fractions are reduced to the common denomination $\frac{1}{55}$, and also £7 and 3 shillings to the common denomination of shillings, that the actual operation by which they are incorporated into one term can be performed, when the first sum becomes $\frac{68}{55}$ and the second 143 shillings.   (Art. 91.)

Not otherwise.

129.   The following are examples of the addition and subtraction of fractions.

Examples of addition and subtraction of fractions.

(1)   Add together $\frac{1}{2}$, $\frac{1}{3}$, $\frac{1}{4}$ and $\frac{1}{5}$.

The fractions reduced to the least common denominator are

$$\frac{30}{60}, \quad \frac{20}{60}, \quad \frac{15}{60}, \quad \frac{12}{60}.$$

Their sum $= \frac{30 + 20 + 15 + 12}{60} = \frac{77}{60}$, or 77 times the subordinate unit $\frac{1}{60}$.

(2)   Add together $\frac{3}{10}$, $\frac{4}{100}$, $\frac{7}{1000}$, $\frac{9}{10000}$.

The reduced fractions are

$$\frac{3000}{10000}, \quad \frac{400}{10000}, \quad \frac{70}{10000}, \quad \frac{9}{10000}.$$

$$\text{Their sum} = \frac{3479}{10000}.$$

(3) From the fraction $\frac{17}{21}$ subtract $\frac{11}{14}$.

The reduced fractions, with a common denominator, are $\frac{34}{42}$ and $\frac{33}{42}$: their difference is $\frac{34-33}{42} = \frac{1}{42}$, which is one of the subordinate units, of which the two reduced fractions are severally multiples.

(4) From the sum of the fractions $\frac{8}{11}$ and $\frac{9}{14}$ subtract $1\frac{1}{10}$.

The mixed number $1\frac{1}{10}$ is reduced to the equivalent fraction $\frac{11}{10}$ (Art. 95.): the three fractions $\frac{8}{11}$, $\frac{9}{14}$, and $\frac{11}{10}$ are reduced to the equivalent fractions $\frac{560}{770}$, $\frac{495}{770}$, $\frac{847}{770}$: the sum of the two first is $\frac{1055}{770}$, from which if $\frac{847}{770}$ be subtracted, there remains $\frac{208}{770}$ or $\frac{104}{385}$ *.

Product of a fraction and of an abstract number.

130. A fraction may be multiplied by an abstract number, by multiplying its numerator by it and retaining its denominator.

Thus, twice $\frac{a}{b}$ is denoted by $\frac{2a}{b}$, three times $\frac{a}{b}$ by $\frac{3a}{b}$, and c times $\frac{a}{b}$ by $\frac{ac}{b}$: for $\frac{a}{b}$ means a times the subordinate unit $\frac{1}{b}$, and $\frac{ac}{b}$ denotes ac times the same subordinate unit. (Art. 94.)

* Other examples. The sum of $\frac{1}{8}$, $\frac{1}{12}$, and $\frac{1}{20}$, is $\frac{31}{120}$: the sum of $\frac{1}{6}$, $\frac{1}{4}$, and $2\frac{1}{2}$ is $\frac{35}{12}$: the sum of $6\frac{1}{11}$, $8\frac{9}{17}$, $4\frac{3}{7}$, or of $\frac{67}{11}$, $\frac{145}{17}$, $\frac{31}{7}$, is $\frac{24935}{1309}$.
The difference of $\frac{1}{2}$ and $\frac{1}{3}$ is $\frac{1}{6}$: the difference of $\frac{1}{7}$ and $\frac{1}{9}$ is $\frac{2}{63}$: the difference of $3\frac{1}{15}$ and $2\frac{19}{20}$, or of $\frac{46}{15}$ and $\frac{59}{20}$, is $\frac{7}{60}$. If from the sum of $\frac{4}{10}$ and $\frac{7}{100}$ we take away the sum of $\frac{2}{10}$ and $\frac{4}{100}$, the difference is $\frac{23}{100}$.

131. A fraction may be divided by an abstract number, by multiplying its denominator by it.

Quotient of a fraction divided by an abstract number.

Thus, to divide the subordinate unit $\frac{1}{b}$ by c is the same thing as to divide the primary unit 1 at once into bc equal parts, each of which is denoted by $\frac{1}{bc}$ (Art. 97.) In a similar manner the quotient which arises from dividing a times the subordinate unit $\frac{1}{b}$ or $\frac{a}{b}$ by c, is a times as great as that which arises from dividing $\frac{1}{b}$ by c, and is therefore denoted by $\frac{a}{bc}$.

132. A fraction may be multiplied by one number and divided by another, by multiplying its numerator by the first number and its denominator by the second.

To multiply a fraction by one number and to divide it by another.

For if a fraction $\frac{a}{b}$ be first multiplied by c and then divided by d, it will become by the first operation $\frac{ac}{b}$ (Art. 130.), and by the second $\frac{ac}{bd}$ (Art. 131.): and conversely, if we should first divide the fraction $\frac{a}{b}$ by d, the quotient would be $\frac{a}{bd}$, and subsequently multiplying this quotient $\frac{a}{bd}$ by c, the result would be $\frac{ac}{bd}$.

133. It follows therefore that when a fraction is to be multiplied and divided by two numbers, it is indifferent in what order the operations are performed, inasmuch as the result is the same in both cases.

The operations may be performed in any order.

134. To find the value of a fraction of a fraction.

To find the value of a fraction of a fraction.

If unity be divided into b equal parts, and if a of them be taken, the result is denoted by $\frac{a}{b}$. (Art. 94.)

If a fraction $\frac{c}{d}$ (considered as a unit) be divided into b equal parts, and if a of them be taken, the result will be denoted by $\frac{ac}{bd}$: for to divide $\frac{c}{d}$ (considered as a unit) into b equal parts, is equivalent to dividing the subordinate unit $\frac{1}{b}$ into d equal parts, each of which is denoted by $\frac{1}{bd}$, and then taking c of them, the result of which operations is denoted by $\frac{c}{bd}$: if we now take a times $\frac{c}{bd}$, we obtain $\frac{ac}{bd}$, which is equal therefore to a times the b equal parts into which $\frac{c}{d}$ is divided: this is what is meant when we speak of the fraction $\frac{a}{b}$ of $\frac{c}{d}$.

Thus, $\frac{3}{4}$ of $\frac{5}{7}$, or *three fourths* of $\frac{5}{7}$, is equal to $\frac{3 \times 5}{4 \times 7}$ or $\frac{15}{28}$: $\frac{7}{8}$ of $\frac{9}{11}$, or *seven eighths* of $\frac{9}{11}$, is equal to $\frac{7 \times 9}{8 \times 11}$ or $\frac{63}{88}$: $\frac{1}{2}$ of $\frac{1}{3}$ of $\frac{1}{4}$, or *one half* of *one third* of $\frac{1}{4}$, is equal to $\frac{1}{2}$ of $\frac{1 \times 1}{3 \times 4}$ or $\frac{1}{12}$, which is equal to $\frac{1}{2} \times \frac{1}{12}$ or $\frac{1}{24}$.

In speaking of a fraction of a fraction, we distinctly refer to operations, with abstract numbers, by which the fraction, which is the subject of them, is to be multiplied and divided: we are thus enabled to determine the result which corresponds to the operations indicated.

Product
of two
fractions.

135. To find the product of two fractions $\frac{a}{b}$ and $\frac{c}{d}$.

The fractions $\frac{a}{b}$ and $\frac{c}{d}$, considered absolutely by themselves, are concrete numbers (Art. 92.): and whether they be of the same (when $b = d$) or of different kinds (when b is not equal to d), they are incapable of multiplication into each other in the ordinary sense of the term. (Art. 93.)

Its assumed
meaning.

In order to give a meaning to the term multiplication in this case, we consider the terms a and b of the multiplier $\frac{a}{b}$ as abstract numbers, and we assume that by multiplying this fraction $\frac{a}{b}$ into $\frac{c}{d}$, we are required to multiply the fraction $\frac{c}{d}$ by a, and to divide it by $b*$, which gives the result or product $\frac{ac}{bd}$:

---

* It is indifferent in what order these operations of multiplication by a and division by b succeed each other. (Art. 133.)

in other words, we consider the product of $\frac{a}{b}$ and $\frac{c}{d}$ as identical in meaning with the fraction $\frac{a}{b}$ of $\frac{c}{d}$, as explained in the last Article.

136. Such a sense of the multiplication of a fraction $\frac{c}{d}$ by $\frac{a}{b}$ will be perfectly consistent with its ordinary meaning, whenever $\frac{a}{b}$ becomes an abstract whole number, either by b becoming 1, or by a becoming equal to or a multiple of, b: this is the only condition which the proposition already established respecting the multiplication of fractions by abstract numbers (Art. 130.) requires to be fulfilled: and it may be easily shewn, that no other form of the result of the multiplication of $\frac{c}{d}$ by $\frac{a}{b}$, different from $\frac{ac}{bd}$, is competent to satisfy the condition above-mentioned: for it is this form alone which can become $\frac{c}{d}$ (Art. 97.) when $a = b$, $\frac{ac}{d}$ (Art. 130.) when $b = 1$, or $\frac{mc}{d}$ (Art. 97.), when $a = mb$, m being a whole number.

Having thus shewn that $\frac{ac}{bd}$ will represent the product of $\frac{c}{d}$ by $\frac{a}{b}$, in those cases in which the multiplier $\frac{a}{b}$ assumes such a value, as to give to the term *product*, when thus applied, its ordinary meaning, the interpretation of the phrase *product of two fractions* in all other cases must be derived from that form of the result which alone can correspond to it consistently with the conditions which it must satisfy: it thus appears that the product of $\frac{c}{d}$ by $\frac{a}{b}$, means a times the bth part of the fraction $\frac{c}{d}$. (Art. 134.)

137. The product of two fractions, therefore, can only generally admit of an interpretation when one of the fractions (the multiplier) ceases to have an independent existence and meaning and is merely considered as indicating certain defined operations to be performed upon the other: namely, that the fraction which is their subject, or the multiplicand, shall be multiplied by the numerator and divided by the denominator of the fraction which

is the multiplier: by such a process the product continues to be a multiple of a subordinate unit of that primary unit to which the multiplicand is assumed to correspond.

Cases in which the multiplier has an independent existence.

138. If, however, we should continue to consider the multiplicand and multiplier as fractions which have an independent existence, and therefore as concrete numbers, we may form a product identical in form with that which is obtained upon the preceding hypothesis: but it will only be in certain cases of assigned primary units of the multiplicand and multiplier, that the resulting primary unit of the product will admit of an interpretation: it is not our present object to enter upon the discussion of such cases.

Extended meaning of terms arising from the results connected with them, and not from the terms themselves.

139. We are accustomed to speak of $\frac{a}{b}$ times a fraction $\frac{c}{d}$, simply meaning by such a phrase, the product of these fractions, agreeably to the interpretation which we have given to it (Art. 136.): we must not consider, however, by the use of such a familiar term as *product*, that we make any nearer approach to the derivation of the actual product of two such fractions, independently of the conventions upon which we have determined it: in other words, the product in question is not the necessary result of the operation of multiplication in its ordinary sense, but of a sense of the term which is modified by a reference to the only form of this product, which is consistent with what the result must be when the multiplier becomes a whole number and also when that whole number is further considered to have reference to an operation and not to the expression of magnitude: it is by a reference to such a result alone, that we are enabled to give a meaning to such phrases as *one and a half times, three and three fourth times,* or to the still more startling expressions *one half times, one quarter times,* and so on: if we could obtain no result of a multiplication when the multiplier was $1\frac{1}{2}$, $3\frac{3}{4}$, $\frac{1}{2}$, or $\frac{1}{4}$, we should be unable to assign a meaning to the phrases in question.

It is indeed a very natural tendency of the human mind to attempt to invert the process by which we really pass from words to the things signified, in those cases in which a generalization originating in the use of symbols or in any other cause, has given them a much more extended meaning than when used in their primitive and obvious sense.

140. In common books of arithmetic and algebra, it is generally attempted to *prove* the rule for the multiplication of fractions, and to found the proof upon the primitive meaning of the term multiplication: such attempts must necessarily fail, inasmuch as the term multiplication acquires an extended signification from the assumption of the practicability of the operation, so long as the result which is obtained satisfies certain conditions which have been otherwise established when the multiplier assumes a particular form: it follows, therefore, that the meaning of the term multiplication is modified by the assumed result, and consequently that the result cannot be considered as a necessary deduction from the original and obvious meaning of the term.

Failure of attempts to prove directly the rule for the multiplication of two fractions.

141. The use of symbols, whether digital or general, will lead to many other examples of the use of terms in senses extremely remote from those which they naturally possess, and will be exemplified, as we shall afterwards find in symbolical Algebra, not merely in the varied meanings of the terms which express the fundamental operations of algebra, but in many others: and it will be found, that however great is the licence which we thus assume in the use or abuse of terms, that it will be totally inadequate to meet the almost endless variety of interpretations of symbolical results which the different circumstances of their application will be found to render absolutely necessary.

Great extension of the meaning of terms arising from the interpretation of symbolical and other results.

142. In determining the form of the result of the division of one fraction by another, it is merely necessary to consider the inverse relation of the operations of division and multiplication to each other: a relation which is established from the primitive meaning and application of these terms, and which must continue to be preserved, whatever be the variety of meaning which they may be destined to acquire in the various circumstances of their application: thus, if the quotient of the division of the fraction $\frac{c}{d}$ by $\frac{a}{b}$ be required, it is merely necessary to determine the fraction which multiplied by the divisor $\frac{a}{b}$ will produce the dividend $\frac{c}{d}$: this is obviously $\frac{bc}{ad}$: for the product of $\frac{bc}{ad}$ and $\frac{a}{b}$ is $\frac{abc}{abd}$, which is equal to $\frac{c}{d}$. (Art. 97.)

The quotient of the division of one fraction by another.

Rules for the multiplication and division of fractions.

143. It may be convenient to state in words the rules for the multiplication and division of fractions.

The numerator of the product of two fractions, is the product of their numerators: its denominator is the product of their denominators. The numerator of the quotient of one fraction divided by another, is the product of the numerator of the dividend and of the denominator of the divisor; and its denominator is the product of the denominator of the dividend, and of the numerator of the divisor.

To multiply a number or fraction by $\frac{1}{a}$ is the same thing as to divide it by a and conversely.

144. To multiply a fraction or number by $\frac{1}{a}$ is the same thing as to divide it by a: and to divide a fraction or number by $\frac{1}{a}$ is the same thing as to multiply it by a.

These propositions, which are frequently referred to, are immediate corollaries from the rules in the last Article: for the product of $\frac{c}{d}$ and $\frac{1}{a} = \frac{c}{d} \times \frac{1}{a}$,

$$= \frac{1 \times c}{a \times d} = \frac{c}{ad} = \frac{c}{d} \div a \quad \text{(Art. 131.)}$$

$$= \frac{\left(\frac{c}{d}\right)}{a} = \frac{\frac{c}{d}}{a},$$

considering the fraction $\frac{c}{d}$ included between brackets, or placed above the larger line, as the dividend, and a as the divisor.

The quotient of $\frac{c}{d}$ divided by $\frac{1}{a} = \frac{c}{d} \div \frac{1}{a}$

$$= \frac{a \times c}{1 \times d} = \frac{ac}{d} = \frac{c}{d} \times a \quad \text{(Art. 130.)}$$

$$= \frac{\left(\frac{c}{d}\right)}{\left(\frac{1}{a}\right)} = \frac{\frac{c}{d}}{\frac{1}{a}}.$$

It is very useful to attend to all these varieties of equivalent forms, which are of frequent occurrence, and which are connected with reductions and transformations, which, when once understood, are made with great facility.

Examples.

145. The following are examples of the multiplication and division of fractions.

(1) The product of $\frac{3}{4}$ and $\frac{6}{7}$ is $\frac{3 \times 6}{4 \times 7} = \frac{18}{28} = \frac{9}{14}$.

(2) The product of $\frac{19}{21}$ and $\frac{35}{57}$ is $\frac{19 \times 35}{21 \times 57} = \frac{665}{1197} = \frac{5}{9}$, reducing the product to its most simple terms.

(3) The product of $7\frac{1}{9}$ and $8\frac{11}{12}$, or of $\frac{64}{9}$ and $\frac{107}{12}$

$$\text{is } \frac{64 \times 107}{9 \times 12} = \frac{6848}{108} = \frac{1712}{27}.$$

(4) The product of $\frac{1}{2}$, $\frac{2}{3}$, $\frac{3}{4}$ and $\frac{4}{5}$ is $\frac{1 \times 2 \times 3 \times 4}{2 \times 3 \times 4 \times 5} = \frac{1}{5}$, striking out the common factors of the numerator and denominator.

(5) The product $\frac{3}{10^3}$ and $\frac{5}{10^5}$ (Art. 39),

$$\text{is } \frac{3 \times 5}{10^3 \times 10^5} = \frac{15}{10^8} \quad \text{(Art. 41.)}$$

(6) The product of $\frac{1}{10^m}$ and $\frac{1}{10^n}$ is $\frac{1 \times 1}{10^m \times 10^n} = \frac{1}{10^{m+n}}$. (Art. 44.)

(7) The product of $4\frac{1}{8}$ by $\frac{1}{2}$ of $\frac{3}{5}$, or of $\frac{33}{8}$ and $\frac{1 \times 3}{2 \times 5}$,

or if $\frac{33}{8}$ and $\frac{3}{10}$ is $\frac{33 \times 3}{8 \times 10} = \frac{99}{80}$.

(8) The product of 14, $\frac{5}{6}$, $\frac{4}{5}$ of 9 and 64, or of $\frac{14}{1}$, $\frac{5}{6}$,

$\frac{4 \times 9}{5}$, $\frac{64}{1}$ is $\frac{14 \times 5 \times 4 \times 9 \times 64}{6 \times 5} = 14 \times 2 \times 3 \times 64 = 5376$.

(9) The quotient of 3 divided by $\frac{3}{2}$ is $\frac{3 \times 2}{3} = 2$.

(10) The quotient of $\frac{4}{5}$ divided by $\frac{7}{11}$ is $\frac{4 \times 11}{5 \times 7} = \frac{44}{35}$.

(11) The quotient of $\frac{1}{2}$ of $\frac{2}{3}$ divided by $\frac{2}{3}$ of $\frac{3}{4}$, or of $\frac{1 \times 2}{2 \times 3}$ divided by $\frac{2 \times 3}{3 \times 4}$, or of $\frac{1}{3}$ divided by $\frac{1}{2}$ is $= \frac{2}{3}$.

(12) The quotient of $\frac{5}{10}$ divided by $\frac{7}{10}$ is $\frac{5 \times 10}{7 \times 10} = \frac{5}{7}$

(13) The quotient of $\dfrac{11}{100}$ divided by $\dfrac{13}{10000}$ is $\dfrac{11 \times 10000}{100 \times 13}$

$$= \frac{11 \times 100}{13} = \frac{1100}{13}.$$

(14) The quotient of $\dfrac{1}{10^{m+n}}$ divided by $\dfrac{1}{10^m}$ is $\dfrac{1 \times 10^m}{10^{m+n}} = \dfrac{1}{10^n}$,

(Art. 77.)

(15) The quotient of $\dfrac{1}{10^m}$ divided by $\dfrac{1}{10^{m+n}}$ is $\dfrac{1 \times 10^{m+n}}{10^m} = 10^n$,

(Art. 77.)

(16) The quotient of $\dfrac{4}{5}$ of $\dfrac{5}{7}$ of $\dfrac{7}{9}$, divided by $\dfrac{2}{3}$ of $\dfrac{3}{4}$ of $\dfrac{4}{5}$,

or of $\dfrac{4 \times 5 \times 7}{5 \times 7 \times 9}$ divided by $\dfrac{2 \times 3 \times 4}{3 \times 4 \times 5}$, or of $\dfrac{4}{9}$ divided by $\dfrac{2}{5}$,

is $\dfrac{4 \times 5}{9 \times 2} = \dfrac{20}{18} = \dfrac{10}{9}$.

Decimal scale of superior units.

146. In considering arithmetical notation in its most general form, we may assume the existence of a scale of units indefinitely continued, both ascending and descending, where each succeeding unit is one tenth part of that which precedes it: upon such an hypothesis nine digits and zero will be competent to express any magnitude, which is capable of being expressed by the units of such a scale, and what is not less important, we shall be enabled to pass at once from the expression of numbers, by ordinary numerical language, to their corresponding expression, by means of nine digits and zero, and conversely: thus fifty seven thousand, four hundred and twenty eight, immediately becomes 57428, by merely writing in succession the digits which represent the numbers *five*, *seven*, *four*, *two*, and *eight*, being the multiples of the units of the scale expressing severally ten thousand, one thousand, one hundred, ten, one or the primary unit: in a similar manner, eighty thousand and nineteen becomes, in this system of arithmetical notation, 80019, there being no units or multiples of them in the expression of this number which correspond to *one thousand* and *one hundred* in the general scale of units: it is this immediate transition from ordinary numerical language to the equivalent expressions by means of arithmetical symbols and the exact correspondence between them, which constitutes the great superiority of the Arabic system of numeration

Immediate translation of numeral language into arithmetical symbols and conversely.

above that which was known to the Greeks and Romans and the other nations of antiquity.

147. If the continued *decimal* subdivision of primary units of weights and measures and of specific magnitudes generally, had been sanctioned by usage, and if the inferior or subordinate units which thence arose, had been expressible in ordinary language, the transition from such numerical language to their corresponding expression in arithmetical symbols, would have been equally simple and immediate, as in the case of multiples of the primary unit: but as in the latter case, the digital multiples of the superior units in the scale are placed to the left of the primary unit, the higher the more remote, so likewise in the former case, the digital multiples of the inferior units are placed to the right of the primary unit, the lower the more remote: and in order to mark the position of the primary unit and the separation of the scales of the superior and inferior units, it is usual to place a *dot* to the right of the primary unit and to the left of the inferior units, which is termed the *decimal point*. Thus, if the units in this descending scale were named *primes, seconds, thirds, fourths,* &c. with reference to the primary unit, whatever it might denote, we should express the sum of three *primes,* four *seconds,* seven *thirds,* and nine *fourths,* by .3479: and if the magnitude which was required to be expressed numerically comprehended both superior and inferior units, such as three thousand, four hundred and six, four *seconds,* eight *thirds,* and five *fifths,* it would be represented by

$$3406, 04805,$$

the zeros taking the places of those units in the scale, whether superior or inferior, which are not comprehended in the number which is required to be expressed by means of arithmetical symbols.

Decimal scale of inferior units. Notation of inferior decimal units.

148. Though the numeral language of no nation* (which must express generally the customary subdivisions of primary

Conveniences which attend the adoption of a decimal scale of subordinate units.

---

* The French system of weights and measures was accompanied by a corresponding numeral language, admirably adapted to its purpose, and which has partially survived the general abandonment of their system of decimal subdivisions. The Greeks from the period of Ptolemy adopted the sexagesimal division of primary units, which survives in our subdivisions of a degree and of time: as their system of arithmetical notation was not adapted to a scale of units, and as their arithmetical processes were consequently limited in their extent, and extremely

units, whatever they may be) is adapted to the decimal scale of inferior units, yet the great convenience of a uniform scale of notation, comprehending equally all magnitudes, and leading to uniform and simple arithmetical processes, has lead to the general adoption and use of the inferior as well as the superior decimal scale of units, notwithstanding the necessity which it imposes of departing from the customary subdivisions of specific magnitudes, and the consequent separation which it requires of arithmetical notation and ordinary language: it is true, indeed, as we shall afterwards shew, that there are many very simple subdivisions of a primary unit, and therefore many magnitudes, which are not expressible by any finite succession of such inferior units: but in all such cases, we are enabled to approximate as near as we choose to the expression of the magnitude in question, though the actual and finite numerical expression of the magnitude itself may be unattainable*.

Decimal and integral or whole numbers. 149. We shall now proceed to examine the theory of arithmetical operations with numbers adapted to this extended decimal scale.

It is usual to designate numbers which comprehend units of the descending scale as *decimals,* to distinguish them from such as are multiples of the primary unit or *integrals:* it will be found, however, that there will be no essential distinction in the theory of arithmetical operations upon them, the units of which they are composed being only distinguished from each other by their position in the scale.

tremely difficult in their application, particularly in the treatment of fractions, the sexagesimal was nearly as well adapted as the decimal scale to their system of arithmetic, and possessed some advantages in the great number of divisors of the radix of its scale. Astronomers have continued to retain the use of the sexagesimal division of the degree and of time, partly in consequence of the influence of habit and of names, and still more from a sense of the great inconveniences which would accompany a change, as rendering comparatively useless the great mass of tables and instruments which have been constructed or divided in conformity with this scale.

* If a series of weights, the primary units being 1 lb. avoirdupois or any other customary standard weight, were constructed according to this scale, upwards and downwards, nine for each unit in the scale, it is obvious that it would enable us to weigh any mass, whose weight is a multiple of any unit in the scale, however remote from the primary unit or decimal point, and also to approximate indefinitely to it, in case it should be incommensurable with any unit in the scale whatsoever.

150.   Numbers, whether decimal or integral, may be multiplied or divided by powers of the radix 10, by merely altering the position of the decimal point or of the place of the primary units, without any change in the significant digits which express them, or in their order of succession.

In order to prove this important proposition, it will be convenient to premise the two following Lemmas:

151.   LEMMA I.   The order of a digit of any order will be *raised* n places, if it be multiplied by 10^n.

If a be a *superior* digit of the mth order, denoting a multiple a of the superior unit 10^m, (Art. 146.) or be a multiple of the primary units equal to $a \times 10^m$, then

$$a \times 10^m \times 10^n = a \times 10^{m+n} \quad \text{(Art. 41.)}:$$

or, in other words, the order of the digit is increased by n, or a becomes a multiple of the superior unit 10^{m+n}.

If a be an *inferior* digit of the mth order, equivalent to $\dfrac{a}{10^m}$, or be a multiple a of the subordinate unit $\dfrac{1}{10^m}$, then

$$\frac{a}{10^m} \times 10^n = a \times 10^{n-m},$$

when n is greater than m (Art. 77.), or $= a$, when $n = m$, or $= \dfrac{a}{10^{m-n}}$, when m is greater than n: or, in other words, the *inferior* digit a of the mth order will become a *superior* digit of the order $n - m$, or will become a digit of the primary units simply, or will continue an *inferior* digit of the order $m - n$, according as m is less, equal to, or greater than n: and in all these cases its order is raised by n places.

152.   LEMMA II.   The order of a digit of any order will be *depressed* n places, if it be divided by 10^n.

Let a be a *superior* digit of the order m, then
$$\frac{a \times 10^m}{10^n} = a \times 10^{m-n}, \quad \text{or} = a, \quad \text{or} = \frac{a}{10^{n-m}},$$

according as m is greater, equal to, or less than, n: in all these cases its order is depressed by n places.

Let a be an *inferior* digit of the order m, then
$$\frac{a}{10^m} \div 10^n = \frac{a}{10^m \times 10^n} \quad \text{(Art. 131.)} = \frac{a}{10^{m+n}} \quad \text{(Art. 41.)}:$$

or a becomes an *inferior* digit of the order $m + n$, and its order is therefore depressed by n places.

(side notes) Numbers generally may be multiplied or divided by powers of 10 by a mere alteration of their position on the scale of units. The order of a digit will be raised n places if multiplied by 10^n.

The order of a digit is depressed n places by being divided by 10^n.

Product of a number, whether decimal or not, by 10^n.

153. If we multiply a number and therefore its successive digits, expressing multiples of different orders of units, whether superior or inferior, by 10^n, we raise the order of each of them by n places, (Lemma I. Art. 151.), and we therefore remove the place of primary units, or the decimal point, n places to the left, without altering the digits themselves or their order of succession.

Examples.

Thus,

$$31.245 \times 10^2 = 3124.5$$
$$31.245 \times 10^3 = 31245$$
$$31.245 \times 10^4 = 312450$$
$$.00045 \times 10^3 = .45$$
$$.00045 \times 10^4 = 4.5$$
$$.00045 \times 10^5 = 45$$
$$.00045 \times 10^8 = 45000.$$

A decimal number becomes integral by being multiplied by a power of 10, whose index is the number of decimal places.

154. A decimal number becomes integral, if it be multiplied by a power of 10, whose index is equal to the number of decimal places: for under such circumstances, the decimal place is removed to the right by a number of places equal to the index, and therefore just beyond the limit of the decimal places.

Thus,

$$.0004 \times 10^4 = 4$$
$$74.269 \times 10^3 = 74269$$
$$.0000001 \times 10^7 = 1.$$

Integralized decimal.

This transition from a decimal to the corresponding integral number, which arises from the obliteration of the decimal point, is very frequently required, and it may be convenient to term the whole number which thence arises, the *integralized decimal.*

Quotient of a number whether decimal or not, divided by 10^n.

155. If we divide a number and therefore its successive digits, expressing multiples of orders of units, whether inferior or superior, by 10^n, we depress the order of each of them by r places, (Lemma II. Art. 152.), and we therefore remove the place of primary units, or the decimal point, n places to the right, without altering the digits themselves or their order of succession.

Examples.

Thus,

$$\frac{31.245}{10^2} = .31245$$

$$\frac{31.245}{10^3} = .031245$$

$$\frac{31.245}{10^4} = .0031245$$

$$\frac{45000}{10^2} = 450$$

$$\frac{45000}{10^3} = 45$$

$$\frac{45000}{10^4} = 4.5$$

$$\frac{45000}{10^5} = .45$$

156. A decimal number may be converted into an equivalent fraction, whose numerator is the *integralized* decimal, (Art. 154.), and whose denominator is a power of 10, whose index is the number of decimal places.

Conversion of a decimal into an equivalent fraction whose denominator is a power of 10.

For if the decimal number in question be multiplied by such a power of 10, (whose index is the number of decimal places), the decimal will be integralized, (Art. 154.): and if the integralized decimal be subsequently divided by the same power of 10, which was before employed as a multiplier, the fraction which arises will express the value of the original decimal, inasmuch as it has been multiplied and divided by the same number, (Art. 97.).

Thus,

$$31.245 = \frac{31.245 \times 10^3}{10^3} = \frac{31245}{10^3}$$

$$.045 \qquad = \frac{45}{10^3}$$

$$.00045 \quad = \frac{45}{10^5}$$

$$4.167894 = \frac{4167894}{10^6}.$$

157. Conversely, a fraction whose denominator is a power of 10, may be converted into an equivalent decimal, by omitting the denominator, and striking off in its numerator a number of decimal places equal to the index of 10 in the denominator.

Conversion of a fraction whose denominator is a power of 10 into an equivalent decimal.

This is the converse of the proposition in the last article: it is merely dividing the numerator by a power of 10 equal to the denominator, in conformity with the rule in Art. 155.

Thus,

$$\frac{714}{10^2} = 7.14$$

$$\frac{340}{10^4} = .0340 \text{ or } .034$$

$$\frac{1234}{10^8} = .00001284.$$

Conversion of fractions into equivalent decimals. 158. If the denominator of a fraction be not a power of 10, it may, in many cases, be converted into an equivalent fraction, whose denominator is a power of 10, and therefore into an equivalent decimal of a finite number of places.

Fractions which are convertible into finite decimals. Let the fraction in question, in its lowest terms, be $\frac{a}{b}$: then $\frac{a}{b} = \frac{a \times 10^n}{b \times 10^n}$ (Art. 97.); and if the denominator b be a divisor of 10^n, the fraction will be reduced to the form $\frac{ap}{10^n}$, where $p = \frac{10^n}{b}$, and consequently to a decimal of n places.

Proof. Every number which is prime to a and to 10, is prime to $a \times 10^n$, (Art. 111, 112.): and therefore if b, or any factor of b, be prime to 10, (b is assumed to be prime to a), it is prime also to $a \times 10^n$: but inasmuch as 2 and 5 are the only numbers less than 10 which are *not* prime to 10, it follows that in no case can the fraction $\frac{a}{b}$ be reduced to the form $\frac{ap}{10^n}$ and therefore to a finite decimal of n places (Art. 157.), unless the factors of b be the numbers 2 and 5 only. If however the denominator b be resolvible into factors which are powers of 2 and 5, one or both, and if it be, therefore, of the form $2^r \times 5^s$, then if n be taken equal to the greater of the two numbers r and s, we shall find $\frac{a}{b} = \frac{a \times 10^n}{b \times 10^n} = \frac{a \times 2^n \times 5^n}{2^r \times 5^s \times 10^n} = \frac{a \times 5^{r-s}}{10^r}$, if $n = r$ and if r be greater than s, or $= \frac{a \times 2^{s-r}}{10^s}$, if $n = s$ and if s be greater than r; the first of which is a decimal of r, and the second of s, places. Such fractions *alone* produce equivalent decimals of a finite number of places.

Examples. Thus $\frac{3}{4} = \frac{3}{2^2} = \frac{3 \times 10^2}{2^2 \times 10^2} = \frac{3 \times 2^2 \times 5^2}{2^2 \times 10^2} = \frac{3 \times 5^2}{10^2} = \frac{75}{10^2} = .75:$

$$\frac{7}{125} = \frac{7}{5^3} = \frac{7 \times 10^3}{5^3 \times 10^3} = \frac{7 \times 2^3 \times 5^3}{5^3 \times 10^3} = \frac{7 \times 2^3}{10^3} = \frac{56}{10^3} = .056.$$

$$\frac{1}{400} = \frac{1}{2^4 \times 5^2} = \frac{10^4}{2^4 \times 5^2 \times 10^4} = \frac{2^4 \times 5^4}{2^4 \times 5^2 \times 10^4} = \frac{5^2}{10^4} = \frac{25}{10000} = .0025.$$

159. Fractions, in their lowest terms, whose denominators are not of the form $2^r \times 5^s$, can always be converted into decimals which *never* terminate and whose digits sooner or later recur by periods. Fractions which are convertible into indefinite decimals only.

Let $\frac{a}{b}$ be such a fraction in its lowest terms, whose denominator is prime to 10 and therefore to its powers (Art. 112.), or which contains factors which are so: it will follow therefore that $a \times 10^n$ divided by b, will never give a complete quotient, whatever be the value of n (Art. 158.); and since a is a whole number, it is obvious that $a \times 10^n$ will be expressed by the digits of the number a followed by n zeros*: but $\frac{a}{b} = \frac{a \times 10^n}{b \times 10^n}$, whatever n may be, and we can therefore proceed to divide $a \times 10^n$ by b, and continue the process as long as we choose: if the order of the digits of the dividend be raised n places, and if the remainder from the division be r, the quotient will be a decimal number of n places (Art. 158.), and the remainder will be expressed by $\frac{r}{b \times 10^n}$. It is obvious that by the continuation of this process, the remainder $\frac{r}{b \times 10^n}$, since r is less than b, may be made as small as we choose, and that consequently the decimal quotient may be made to approximate, as near as we please, to the true value of the fraction $\frac{a}{b}$: but, however long this process may be continued, this remainder can never disappear, and consequently no finite decimal quotient can be obtained which is accurately equal to the fraction $\frac{a}{b}$, unless its denominator possess the peculiar composition which we have noticed in Art. 158.

160. Again, since the remainder r is always less than b, and since the process of division, as soon as the dividend begins to comprehend the zeros which arise from multiplying it by powers of 10, can, under no circumstances, produce The indefinite decimals which arise from fractions recur by periods.

---

* Thus $37 \times 10^2 = 3700$: $14 \times 10^5 = 1400000$.

more than $b-1$ remainders different from zero and from b, it follows necessarily, that the same remainders must recur at least within $b-1$ operations, and that they consequently must produce a similar recurrence, in the same order, of the dividends to be divided and of the corresponding digits in the quotient: it is for this reason that the indefinite divisors which arise from such fractions, must sooner or later become *periodic* or *recurring*, and that the number of places included in each period must always be less than the denominator of the fraction in its lowest terms.

Examples. 161. The following are examples :

(1) To convert $\frac{1}{3}$ into a recurring decimal

$$3 \,)\, 1.00000$$
$$\overline{.3333\ldots}$$

The decimal places commence with the first introduction of the new added zeros in the dividend, (Art. 159.).

(2) To convert $\frac{1}{7}$ into a recurring decimal.

$$1 \,)\, 1.00000$$
$$\overline{.142857142857\ldots}$$

The recurring period 142857 comprehends in this case 6 places, which is less by 1 than the divisor: if we take the successive multiples of $\frac{1}{7}$, namely $\frac{2}{7}, \frac{3}{7}, \frac{4}{7}, \frac{5}{7}, \frac{6}{7} \ldots$ the recurring periods will consist of the same digits: and if we further suppose those digits placed round a circle, the successive periods will be formed of those digits in the same circular* order as follows:

$$\frac{2}{7} = .285714285714\ldots$$

$$\frac{3}{7} = .428571428571\ldots$$

$$\frac{4}{7} = .571428571428\ldots$$

* This will be at once seen if the digits are arranged thus,

$$\begin{matrix} & 1 & \\ 7 & & 4 \\ 5 & & 2 \\ & 8 & \end{matrix}$$

$$\frac{5}{7} = .714285714285\ldots$$

$$\frac{6}{7} = .857142857142\ldots$$

$$\frac{7}{7} = 1.$$

$$\frac{8}{7} = 1.142857142857\ldots$$

(3) $\qquad \frac{1}{9} = .1111\ldots$

(4) $\qquad \frac{1}{99} = .0101\ldots$

(5) $\qquad \frac{1}{999} = .001001\ldots$

(6) $\qquad \frac{1}{9999} = .00010001\ldots$

(7) $\qquad \frac{8}{9} = .8888\ldots$

(8) $\qquad \frac{98}{99} = .9898\ldots$

(9) $\qquad \frac{47}{9999} = .00470047\ldots$

If the denominator of the fraction be $10^n - 1$, or be expressed by n times the digit 9 in succession, each period of the recurring decimal will consist of n places, and the significant digits in each of them will be those of the numerator, unless the numerator be greater than the denominator, in which case they will be those of the remainder which arises from its division by the denominator: we shall have occasion to notice this fact more particularly in the next article.

Fractions the digits of whose denominators are 9's.

(10) $\qquad \frac{16}{17} = .9411764705882352\ldots$

The recurring period consists of 16 places.

Fractions, in their lowest terms, whose denominators are 19, 23, 29, 47, 59, 61, 97, 109, 113, 131, 149, 167, 181, 193, will produce recurring decimals, the number of places in each of whose periods reaches the extreme limit, namely, one less than the denominator d.

(11) $\dfrac{1}{41} = .0243902439\ldots$

(12) $\dfrac{1}{67} = .014925373134328358208955223880597\ldots$*.

The recurring period consists of 33 places.

(13) $\dfrac{11}{21} = .523809523809\ldots$

(14) $\dfrac{1}{49} = .020408163265306122448979591836734693877551.$

The recurring period consists of 42 places.

To determine the fraction which is equal to a given recurring decimal. When the decimal comprises recurring periods only beginning from the decimal point.

162. The converse problem of determining the fraction which will produce a given recurring decimal will admit of very easy solution: for if $\dfrac{p}{10^n - 1}$, (Art. 161. Ex. 9.) be a proper fraction, it will produce a recurring decimal, the significant digits of each of whose periods of n places express the number p: it will follow therefore, that the equivalent fractions corresponding to such recurring decimals, will be formed by placing the integral number, which each complete period expresses, in the numerator, and $10^n - 1$, or a number of 9's equal to the number of places in such periods in the denominator: such fractions may be subsequently reduced, when practicable, to their lowest terms.

Thus, $.3737\ldots = \dfrac{37}{99}.$

$.027027\ldots = \dfrac{27}{999} = \dfrac{1}{37}.$

$.010989010989 = \dfrac{10989}{999999} = \dfrac{1}{91}.$

When the repetition does not commence from the decimal point.

163. Inasmuch as the multiplication and division of decimals by 10^m will remove the decimal point m places to the left or to the right, and consequently may place the commencement

* There are many curious propositions connected with these conversions of fractions into recurring decimals, whose demonstration requires a knowledge of some important propositions in the theory of numbers: thus if the denominator d be a prime number, the number of places in each period must be $d-1$, or a submultiple of it. The property of numbers upon which this proposition depends, is demonstrated in Art. 530, Chap. x. of this volume. See also a Memoir by John Bernoulli, the younger, in the Berlin Memoirs for 1771.

of the repeating period m places before or after the decimal point, it will follow that the value of the circulating decimal, which results, will be expressed by $\dfrac{10^m p}{10^n - 1}$ in one case, and by $\dfrac{p}{10^m \times (10^n - 1)}$ in the other.

Thus, $.003\dot{3}\ldots = \dfrac{3}{10^2 \times 9} = \dfrac{1}{300}$;

the first repeating period being removed 2 places to the right of the decimal point.

$$.00002439\dot{2}43\dot{9}\ldots = \dfrac{2439}{10^4 \times 9999} = \dfrac{271}{11110000},$$

the first repeating period being removed 4 places to the right of the decimal point.

$$12.512\dot{5}\ldots = \dfrac{10^2 \times 125}{999} = \dfrac{12500}{999},$$

the first repeating period being removed 2 places to the left of the decimal point.

164. In some cases the repeating period will commence at a certain point, and the preceding part of the recurring decimal, whether integral or not, will not partake of the repetition: in this case, we must add the number or equivalent fraction which expresses this non-repeating portion, to the fraction which expresses the value of the repeating portion of the decimal. *When the decimal is partly repeating and partly not.*

Thus, $13.07692\dot{3}07692\dot{3}\ldots = 13 + \dfrac{76923}{999999} = 13 + \dfrac{1}{13} = \dfrac{170}{13}$.

$$.636\dot{4}6\dot{4}\ldots = \dfrac{63}{100} + \dfrac{64}{100 \times 99} = \dfrac{6301}{9900}.$$

$$13.9423076\dot{9}23076\dot{9}\ldots = \dfrac{1394}{100} + \dfrac{230769}{100 \times 999999} = \dfrac{725}{52}.$$

In the first of these examples 13, in the second .63, and in the third 13.94, forms no part of the recurring period.

165. In the three last Articles we have determined the fraction whose conversion will generate any assigned repeating decimal: and it is obvious, from the process which we have adopted, that there exists no such repeating decimal, which does not admit of being generated by an assignable fraction. We are also further authorized to conclude, that a decimal indefinitely continued, whose terms follow no assignable law of *All repeating decimals, whether regular or not, are generated by finite fractions.*

succession or which never recur, will be incapable of being generated by a fraction whose terms are any finite numbers whatsoever: for if it were so, the digits of the equivalent decimal must be repeated within a number of places, as an extreme limit (Art. 160.), which is less than the denominator of the fraction: such indefinite decimals, whenever they occur, may be considered as *incommensurable*, inasmuch as they express no assignable multiple of a *subordinate unit*, however small it may be.

Non-repeating decimals indefinitely continued express incommensurable magnitudes.

166. The fraction which generates an assigned repeating decimal, may be also considered as its *sum*, or as the result of the aggregation of all its terms or periods *indefinitely* continued. When such terms or periods, as in the case of repeating decimals, diminish rapidly, it is very easy to shew that a *finite* number of them may be determined, which will differ from the entire *sum*, as defined above, less than any *fractional number* (Art. 96, Note.) which can or may be assigned: thus if the repeating decimal be *regular* or consist of repeating periods only, commencing from the decimal point, (Art. 162.), and if p be the integral number, which corresponds to each period of n places, then the decimal may be replaced by the indefinite series

The fraction which generates a repeating decimal may be considered as its sum.

$$\frac{p}{10^n} + \frac{p}{10^{2n}} + \frac{p}{10^{3n}} + \dots in\ infinitum \dots *(1).$$

If we express the fraction which generates this series (1), which is $\dfrac{p}{10^n - 1}$ by s, we shall also express the fraction which generates the series which arises from dividing each of its terms by 10^{rn}, or

$$\frac{p}{10^{rn+n}} + \frac{p}{10^{rn+2n}} + \frac{p}{10^{rn+3n}} + \&c. \dots (2)$$

by $\dfrac{s}{10^{rn}}$ (Art. 163.): if we now subtract the second series (2) from the first (1), we shall get the value of the sum of its r first terms, or

$$\frac{p}{10^n} + \frac{p}{10^{2n}} + \dots \frac{p}{10^{rn}}$$

---

* Thus the decimal .333... is equivalent to the series

$$\frac{3}{10} + \frac{3}{10^2} + \frac{3}{10^3} + \dots in\ infin.$$

and the decimal .125125125 is equivalent to

$$\frac{125}{10^3} + \frac{125}{10^6} + \frac{125}{10^9} + \&c. \dots in\ infin.$$

which is $s - \dfrac{s}{10^{rn}}$: and it is obvious that a value of r may always be assigned which will make $\dfrac{s}{10^{rn}}$ less than any fractional number or than any subordinate unit which can be assigned: it follows therefore, that the result of the aggregation of a finite number of the terms of the series (1), and therefore of the decimal which it expresses, may be made to differ both from s and from the result of the aggregation of all the terms of the series, by a fractional number which is less than any that can be assigned: we therefore conclude that s or $\dfrac{p}{10^n - 1}$ correctly expresses its sum.

167. We speak of quantities as being arithmetically equal, which differ from each other by arithmetical quantities which are less than any which can be assigned: in comparing magnitudes of the same nature, we consider them either as equal or as different, and we are incapable of conceiving a difference which is less than any which is assignable: it is for this reason that we consider the absence of any such assignable, and therefore conceivable, difference as the test of arithmetical equality: or in other words, we assume all quantities in arithmetic to be equal, whose differences are less than any which are assignable*. *(margin: Test of arithmetical equality.)*

168. It is in this sense also that we consider the results of operations, expressed decimally, whether repeating or not, (as in the case of *incommensurable* quantities, Art. 165.) as continually approximating to the true results and as ultimately equal to them: for under such circumstances, if we assume any number of terms as representing the result which is required, the sum of the remaining terms will be necessarily less than the next ascending unit, and probably less than half of it: in other words, if r such terms be taken after the decimal point, the sum of all the remaining terms must be less than $\dfrac{1}{10^r}$, and is probably less than $\dfrac{1}{2 \times 10^r}$†: it follows therefore, that the pro- *(margin: The results of operations expressed decimally are capable of indefinite approximation.)*

---

* Equality both in Geometry and Arithmetic is determined by definition, though such definitions are not arbitrary, but such as most accurately express our conceptions of their subjects, which have an existence in our minds antecedently to the definitions themselves.

† Since $\dfrac{1}{3} = .333\ldots$ and therefore $1 = 3 \times \dfrac{1}{3} = .999\ldots$ it follows that $\dfrac{1}{10^r}$ will be equal to a series of 9's, with r zeros interposed between them and the decimal point

bable error, or defect from the true result required, becomes less and less the further the operation is continued, and may be made less than any arithmetical quantity which can be assigned.

All magnitudes, whether commensurable or incommensurable, expressible by nine digits and zero.

169. It thus appears that decimals, either definite or indefinite, are competent to express the values, not merely of *commensurable* magnitudes, which are multiples of some assignable subordinate unit, but also of such as are *incommensurable*, (Art. 165.): for there are no magnitudes existing between limits of values which are expressible numerically, to which an indefinite approximation may not be made: thus, if $\frac{1}{a}$ and $\frac{1}{b}$ be two such limits, expressible by means of decimal notation, we can also express by it

$$\frac{1}{a} + \frac{1}{10^r}, \ \frac{1}{a} + \frac{2}{10^r}, \ \ldots \ldots \ \frac{1}{a} + \frac{n}{10^r}, \ \frac{1}{b},$$

where we may suppose $\frac{1}{a} + \frac{n}{10^r}$ to be less than $\frac{1}{b}$, and $\frac{1}{a} + \frac{n+1}{10^r}$ to be greater than $\frac{1}{b}$, or that the series is continued until we find two successive terms which are respectively less and greater than $\frac{1}{b}$: it will follow therefore, that the incommensurable magnitude in question will differ from some one of those which are expressed by the terms of this series by a quantity less than $\frac{1}{10^r}$: and by taking r as great as we please, we can make $\frac{1}{10^r}$ less than any unit which can be assigned; or in other words, we can approximate indefinitely to the numerical expression of incommensurable magnitudes: it is in this sense that we suppose it possible to express

point: if therefore the first r decimal places be aggregated together, their sum will differ from the sum of the digits of the result of the same operation indefinitely continued by an arithmetical quantity less than $\frac{1}{10^r}$ or the next ascending unit: for it is obvious, that the sum of the terms of the remaining portion of the indefinite result will be less than the sum of an indefinite series of 9's, placed in the same successive places: and also since, if a number of digits be taken at random, the chances are, that the greatest number of them will be not greater than 5, it follows also that, if each of the digits of this remaining portion of the result be replaced by 5, it is probable that the error committed by neglecting them will be less than the sum of such a series of 5's, which is equal to $\frac{4}{9 \times 10^r}$ and is therefore less than $\frac{1}{2 \times 10^r}$.

every gradation of magnitude, whether continuous or not, by means of nine digits and zero.

170. The operations of addition and subtraction in Arithmetic, require that digits of the same order, or *like* digits, whether superior or inferior, should be placed underneath each other, preparatory to their being added together or subtracted from each other; for without such a previous arrangement, it would be difficult to avoid, in performing these operations, confounding digits of different orders with each other: and inasmuch as the decimal point determines the position of the primary units, it likewise determines the position of digits of all orders.

Operations of addition and subtraction.

Position of like digits.

171. The identity of the units of the digits placed underneath each other being thus ascertained, the operation of addition or subtraction is carried on from right to left, beginning with the extreme digit, so as to allow of the conversion of the digits of one order into those of the order next superior or inferior: in addition, we transfer multiples of ten to the next superior order: in subtraction, we borrow, when necessary, a unit from the next superior order, and convert it into ten units of the order next inferior to it: it is this mutual transfer of units from one order to another, which renders it necessary to carry on the process from right to left: if we should proceed from left to right, the digits of the sum or remainder could not be absolutely or finally determined, as the process proceeded, without reference to those which succeeded them.

Operations carried on from right to left.

172. The following are examples:

Examples.

(1)　To add together 769.1234, .00024 and 24000.

$$769.1234$$
$$.00024$$
$$24000.$$
$$\overline{24769.12364}$$

In this example no transfers are required, and the result would be obtained with equal readiness, whether we proceeded from right to left or from left to right.

(2)　To add together 74.8495, .06947 and 365.000748.

$$74.8495$$
$$.06947$$
$$365.000748$$
$$\overline{439.919718}$$

In this example, 5 transfers or conversions of 10 into a unit of the next superior order are required : if the process was carried on from left to right, it must stand as follows :

$$74.8495$$
$$.06947$$
$$365.000748$$
$$\overline{339.808618}$$

Add digits carried   1   1111

$$\overline{439.919718}$$

(3)   To subtract 4.32015 from 5.46427.

$$5.46427$$
$$4.32015$$
$$\overline{1.14412}$$

In this example no digits are borrowed.

(4)   To subtract 71.96405 from 100.24162.

$$100.24162$$
$$71.96405$$
$$\overline{28.27757}$$

If the process had been carried on from left to right, it would have stood as follows :

$$100.24162$$
$$71.96405$$
$$\overline{139.38767}$$

Subtract digits borrowed   111.11 1

$$\overline{28.27757}$$

Zeros are suppressed when not required for the determination of the position of significant digits.

173. The use of *zeros* in arithmetical notation is merely subsidiary to the determination of the positions of the significant digits, and whenever such positions are sufficiently determined by succession, by their known orders, or in any other manner, it is usual to suppress them, in conformity with the great principle which ought to characterize all processes in Arithmetic and Algebra, *of writing no sign or symbol whatever which is not required for the performance of the operation, or for the distinct and unambiguous exhibition of its result.* Thus i it was required to add together a series of numbers 1234

2345, 3456, 4567, whose final digits are known to belong to successive descending orders, it is usual to write them as follows:

$$1234$$
$$2345$$
$$3456$$
$$4567$$
$$\overline{1507627}$$

and if the order of the first or last of these digits is known, the position of the primary units or the decimal point is determined: thus if the final digit 7 be of the 10th inferior order, the required sum is .0001507627: if the final digit be of the 4th superior order, the required sum is 15076270000, and similarly in other cases: if the final digits of the numbers 1234, 2345, 3456, 4567, were known to belong to successive *ascending* orders, they would be written as follows:

$$1234$$
$$2345$$
$$3456$$
$$4567$$
$$\overline{4937284}$$

and the position of the place of units or of the decimal point would be at once determined, as before, from our knowledge of the order of the first or last or of any other assigned digit in the sum*.

174. In examining the theory of the arithmetical operation of multiplication, our first object will be the determination of the

Given the orders of the final digits of the multiplicand and multiplier to find the order of the final digit of their product.

* It may be very easily shewn how much superfluous writing is saved by the suppression of the zeros in the conduct of such operations: thus, if the last digit in 1234 was of the fourth ascending order, and if the several numbers written at full length were 12340000, 234500000, 3456000000, 45670000000, the process for their addition would stand as follows:

$$12340000$$
$$234500000$$
$$3456000000$$
$$45670000000$$
$$\overline{49372840000}$$

where all the zeros, excepting those in the first and last line, are superfluous, and consequently such as a properly framed arithmetical rule would necessarily exclude.

orders of the digits of the product, when the orders of the digits of the multiplicand and multiplier are given.

Thus if a and b be the multiplicand and multiplier, and if their final digits be of the mth and nth *superior* orders, the final digit of their product ab will be of the $(m+n)$th *superior* order. (Art. 151.)

If the final digits of a and b be of the mth and nth *inferior* orders, the final digit of ab will be of the $(m+n)$th inferior order. (Art. 152.)

If the final digit of a be of the mth *superior* order, and that of b be of the nth *inferior* order, the final digit of ab will be of the $(m-n)$th *superior* order, if m be greater than n, or of the $(n-m)$th inferior order, if n be greater than m. (Art. 151 and 152.)

The following are examples:

Examples.

(1) $.7000 \times 80000 = 560000000$, where 6 is of the 7th *superior* order.

(2) $.007 \times .0008 = .0000056$, where 6 is of the 7th *inferior* order.

(3) $70000 \times .008 = 560$, where 6 is of the first *superior* order.

(4) $70000 \times .0008 = 56$, where 6 is of the order *zero*, or in the place of primary units.

(5) $70000 \times .00008 = 56$, when 6 is of the first *inferior* order.

(6) $70000 \times .0000008 = .056$, where 6 is of the 3d inferior order.

It thus appears that the order (or position with respect to the place of units or the decimal point) of the final digit, whether it be zero or a significant digit, of a product, is at once known, from the order of the final digits of the component factors.

Process of multiplication carried on from right to left of the multiplicand.

175. If the operation of multiplication be carried on from right to left, the order of the final digits (including zero) of the successive partial products will ascend regularly by unity and we shall thus be enabled to write down their sum from right to left, by transferring the multiples of ten to the nex

superior places * : and if we proceed with the successive digits of the multiplier from right to left, the orders of the final digits of the successive products which arise, will ascend regularly by unity, and their entire sum, or the complete product of the multiplicand and multiplier, will be found by placing *like* digits underneath each other and adding them in the ordinary manner: thus the product of 23.45 and 642.9 will be found as follows:

$$
\begin{array}{r}
23.45 \\
642.9 \\
\hline
21105 \\
4690 \\
9380 \\
14070 \\
\hline
15076.005
\end{array}
$$

The final digit 5, of the first partial product, is of the third inferior order (Art. 174.): there are, therefore, three decimal places in the product.

176. It is usual to take the digits of the multiplier from right to left, or in the same order in which we multiply the digits of the multiplicand: it would be equally convenient however, to take them from left to right, in which case the order of the final digits of the partial products would *descend* successively by unity: thus the example, given in the last Article, if treated in this manner, would stand as follows:

$$
\begin{array}{r}
23.45 \\
642.9 \\
\hline
14070 \\
9380 \\
4690 \\
21105 \\
\hline
15076.005
\end{array}
$$

The digits of the multiplier may be taken from left to right.

177. This second form of the process of multiplication possesses some advantages above the one which is commonly

This second form of the operation of multiplication leads immediately to the inverse operation of division.

---

* If we multiplied the successive digits of the multiplicand from left to right, we should not be able to write down in one line the digits of the partial products, (corresponding to one digit of the multiplier) as the process proceeded, in consequence of the changes which they may undergo from the transfer of multiples of 10 and their conversion into simple digits of a superior order.

followed, inasmuch as it leads more directly and obviously to the form of the process for the inverse operation of division, by presenting the several partial products, which are successively subtracted from the dividend, in the same order in the two operations: thus, let it be required to divide 15076.005 by 23.45:

$$23.45) \, 15076.005 \, (642.9$$

$$
\begin{array}{r}
14070 \\
\hline
10060 \\
9380 \\
\hline
6800 \\
4690 \\
\hline
21105 \\
21105 \\
\hline
\cdots\cdots
\end{array}
$$

It is obvious that the sum of the partial products 14070, 9480, 4690, and 21105, considered with reference to their proper orders, is equal to 15076.005, which is therefore the sum of the same series of addends which forms the product of 23.45 and 642.9.

Theory of the operation of division.

178. The process of division proceeds necessarily from left to right, determining successively the digits of the quotient in the same order, and subtracting the partial products from the dividend as they are formed, so as to leave a series of remainders, from which the highest multiples of the divisor by digits of descending orders in the quotient, which are contained in them, are successively subtracted: if the result of these operations leaves no remainder, the quotient obtained is *complete* (Art. 88.): if not, it may be continued until a complete period of the circulating decimal of the quotient is formed, (Art. 160.) which must take place after a finite number of operations: such a quotient, as we have already shewn (Art. 166.), may be made to approximate as near as we choose to its true value.

Rule for determining the order of the digits of the quotient.

179. The order of the final or of any other digit of the quotient, may be determined by attending to the following rule.

If the last digit of the dividend, included in any assigned operation, be of the superior order m, *and the last digit of the divisor be of the superior order* n, *the corresponding digit of the quotient will be of the superior order* m − n, *or of the inferior order* n − m, *according as* m *is greater or less than* n.

If the last digit of the included dividend be of the inferior order m, *and the last digit of the divisor be of the inferior order* n, *the corresponding digit of the quotient will be of the inferior order* m − n, *or of the superior order* n − m, *according as* m *is greater or less than* n.

If the last digits of the included dividend and divisor be of the same order, whether inferior or superior, the corresponding digit of the quotient will be of order zero, or in the place of primary units.

If the last digit of the included dividend be of the superior order m, *and the last digit of the divisor be of the inferior order* n, *the corresponding digit of the quotient will be of the superior order* m + n.

If the last digit of the included dividend be of the inferior order m, *and the last digit of the divisor be of the superior order* n, *the corresponding digit of the quotient will be of the inferior order* m + n.

The proof of all these cases will follow immediately from considering the order of the final digit of the product of the last digit of the divisor and of the corresponding digit of the quotient, given by the preceding rule, as determined by the rule given in Art. 174.

180.   An arithmetical rule, if it be properly framed, should *Methods of abbreviating arithmetical processes.* give the precise result required, without the introduction of superfluous terms and in the most simple and expeditious manner: thus in the multiplication and division of numbers consisting of many places, we may require in the product or quotient no digits below a certain order and we may adopt any process of abbreviation, which will give us the required digits either with perfect or with sufficient accuracy for our purpose.   In a similar manner irreducible fractions may be required to be expressed approximately in lower terms, and rules can be given, not merely for determining such approximating or converging fractions, but also for estimating the course and degree of their approximation; and even incommensurable quantities, which are not expressible by arithmetical notation, may be subjected to similar approximations.   We shall now proceed to explain some of the methods which have been adopted for this purpose.

181.   The conversion of multiples of 10 inferior digits into *Abbreviated multiplication.* simple digits of superior orders, which is the great principle of

our arithmetical notation, and the consequent dependence of the superior digits of the product upon combinations of digits of the multiplier and multiplicand, whose order is inferior to those in the required product, makes it impracticable to determine its digits *absolutely*, without the complete formation and addition of all the addends, and, consequently, without the completion of the entire process of multiplication of all the digits of the multiplicand by all the digits of the multiplier: if, however, an approximate result is considered sufficient for the purposes required, we may form the addends by multiplying together those digits only, the final digits in whose products are within the prescribed orders: for this purpose it is convenient to take the digits of the multiplier from left to right (Art. 176.): thus, if it was required to multiply 347.12567 by 14.0069, neglecting all digits below the 4th inferior order, the process would stand as follows:

$$347.12567$$
$$14.0069$$

34712567		
13885024	omitting 7 in the multiplicand.	
20826	do. 2567	do.
3123	do. 12567	do.

$$4862.1540$$

The correct result, to the fourth place of decimals, is 4862.1545.

Abbreviated or ordinate division.

182. When the dividend and divisor consist of many places, or are even indefinite decimals, we may obtain, in most cases, with perfect accuracy, any required number of digits in the quotient, by taking a limited number of digits of the true, as the approximate, divisor, and correcting the successive remainders by subtracting from them the sums of those products of the successive digits of the quotient and of the neglected digits of the divisor whose final digits are severally of the same order with the final digits of the remainders: by this means we shall obtain a series of *corrected* remainders which either coincide with, or approximate to, the initial digits of the real remainders if complete, and which consequently will enable us to determine, *tentatively* at least, the successive digits of the real quotient: thus, let it be required to find the quotient of 4862.154547123 divided by 347.12567:

$\overline{347.12567}$) 4862.154547123 (14.0069000000

   34 = 1 × 34, making 34 the partial divisor.

  $\overline{146}$ 1st remainder.   [6 in 146.

   7 = 1 × 7, for this product is of the same order with

  $\overline{139}$ 1st corrected remainder.
  136 = 4 × 34.

   $\overline{32}$ 2d remainder.
   29 = 4 × 7 + 1 × 1.

    $\overline{3}$ 2d corrected remainder, less than 34.
   31 3d remainder.
    6 = 0 × 7 + 4 × 1 + 1 × 2.

    $\overline{25}$ 3d corrected remainder, less than 34.
    255 4th remainder.
     13 = 0 × 7 + 0 × 1 + 4 × 2 + 1 × 5.

    $\overline{242}$ 4th corrected remainder.
    204 = 6 × 34, taken in defect.

     $\overline{384}$ 5th remainder.
     68 = 6 × 7 + 0 × 1 + 0 × 2 + 4 × 5 + 1 × 6.

     $\overline{316}$ 5th corrected remainder.
     306 = 9 × 34.

      $\overline{105}$ 6th remainder.
      100 = 9 × 7 + 6 × 1 + 4 × 6 + 1 × 7.

       $\overline{54}$ 7th remainder.
       49 = 9 × 1 + 6 × 2 + 4 × 7.

       $\overline{57}$ 8th remainder.
       48 = 9 × 2 + 6 × 5.

        $\overline{91}$ 9th remainder.
        81 = 9 × 5 + 6 × 6.

        $\overline{102}$ 10th remainder.
        96 = 9 × 6 + 6 × 7.

         $\overline{63}$ 11th remainder.
         63 = 9 × 7.
         $\overline{\cdot\ \cdot}$

 The operation is in this instance complete, and an examination of it will shew that we have subtracted from the dividend in their proper places the products of all the digits of the divisor and quotient: and inasmuch as there is no remainder, the quotient which is obtained is complete: the last six subtractions give no additional digits to the quotient, and are merely required to exhaust the remaining part of the dividend 10547123.

183. If we should multiply the divisor and quotient, both of them from left to right, considering the partial divisor which we have employed as a single digit, and placing underneath each other in their proper places the products of the successive digits of the quotient, and also of 34 and of the successive digits of the divisor, we shall be enabled to obtain the product as follows:

$$\overline{3}47.12567$$
$$14.0069$$

$$1 \times 34 = \dots\dots\dots\dots\ 34$$
$$1 \times 7 \ = \dots\dots\dots\dots\ 7$$
$$4 \times 34 = \dots\dots\dots\dots\ 136$$
$$4 \times 7 + 1 \times 1 = \dots\dots\dots\ 29$$
$$4 \times 1 + 1 \times 2 = \dots\dots\dots\ 6$$
$$4 \times 2 + 1 \times 5 = \dots\dots\dots\ 13$$
$$6 \times 34 = \dots\dots\dots\dots\ 204$$
$$6 \times 7 + 4 \times 5 + 1 \times 6 = \dots\dots\ 68$$
$$9 \times 34 = \dots\dots\dots\dots\ 306$$
$$9 \times 7 + 6 \times 1 + 4 \times 6 + 1 \times 7 = \dots\ 100$$
$$9 \times 1 + 6 \times 2 + 4 \times 7 = \dots\dots\ 49$$
$$9 \times 2 + 6 \times 5 = \dots\dots\dots\ 48$$
$$9 \times 5 + 6 \times 6 = \dots\dots\dots\ 81$$
$$9 \times 6 + 6 \times 7 = \dots\dots\dots\ 96$$
$$9 \times 7 = \dots\dots\dots\dots\ 63$$

$$4862.154547123$$

In the reverse operation, the quotient is complete as soon as its last digit 9 is determined, but the product is not complete without the formation and addition of all the addends: this will explain the reason why this process may be a real abbreviation for one operation and not for the other.

184. Inasmuch as the successive corrected remainders, as furnished by this process, may be erroneous in excess, in consequence of the omission of the subtraction of all the inferior digits of each complete subtrahend in the operation at full length, there will frequently be an uncertainty in the corresponding digits of the quotient: it is for this reason, when the correction is likely to be considerable (which is very easily seen from inspection of the digits which come into combination with each other for this purpose), that we take, under such circumstances, the digit in the quotient less than its extreme value, as it would be determined in the ordinary process of division: if, however, we should take a digit which is too great, the error will always be detected in the next step of the process, unless the next digit be 0:* and if we should take a digit which is too small, the occurrence of 9 or of a succession of 9's in the quotient with continually increasing remainders, will sooner or later direct attention to its origin: as an example, let it be required to divide 10 by the repeating decimal 3.3343334...

$$3.334333\overset{.}{4}) \; 10.000\ldots \; (3.00$$

$$\underline{9}$$

10   remainder.

$9 = 3 \times 3.$

$\underline{}$

10   corrected remainder.

$9 = 3 \times 3.$

$\underline{}$

10   remainder.

$12 = 3 \times 4$ correction too large.

$\underline{}$

It thus appears that the last remainder 10 is less than its correction: it follows, therefore, that the digit 3 in the quotient, *preceding the zeros*, is too great.

---

* A rule might easily be framed to guide us in most cases (not in all) to the selection of the digit in the quotient, whether it should be taken in defect or not; but it is hardly necessary to propound it, inasmuch as it would encumber a process which, when not complete and therefore not admitting of verification from the result, is generally directed to the determination of an approximate result only.

Again, resuming the process:

$$3.33\dot{4}33\dot{4})\ 10.000\ (2.99909\ldots$$

$$\begin{array}{l} 6 \\ \hline \end{array}$$

40   remainder.
$$6 = 2 \times 3.$$

34   corrected remainder.
27

70   remainder.
$$33 = 2 \times 3 + 9 \times 3.$$

37   corrected remainder.
27

100   remainder.
$$62 = 2 \times 4 + 9 \times 3 + 9 \times 3.$$

38   corrected remainder.
27

110   remainder.
$$96 = 2 \times 3 + 9 \times 4 + 9 \times 3 + 9 \times 3.$$

140   remainder.
$$96 = 2 \times 3 + 9 \times 3 + 9 \times 4 + 9 \times 3.$$

44   corrected remainder.
27

170

If, in this and similar cases, we had taken a complete period 3.334, of the recurring decimal, for the *partial divisor*, no ambiguity could have occurred in the determination of the digits of the quotient.*

Abbreviated division when the original divisor is to be increased by the quotient obtained.

185.   The same method is applicable to the solution of many other arithmetical problems of considerable importance in different applications of mathematics: thus, if it was required to find the quotient arising from the division of one number divided by another, increased by the unknown quo-

* In the selection of the partial divisor, it is generally convenient to include a large digit, if succeeded by zero or a small digit: thus, if 79164321 be the divisor, it is more convenient to take 79 than 7 for the partial divisor: by this means the corrections of the successive remainders will be smaller numbers, and there will be less danger of introducing erroneous digits into the quotient.

tient which results, we may solve the problem in all cases
where the initial digit of the quotient sought for is of a lower
order than the final digit of the divisor*: thus let it be required
to divide 11 by 12, increased by the quotient of the division.

Example.

$12.8'5'5'6'5'4'$) $11.000\ldots$ ($.855654$

$96 = 8 \times 12$: add $.8$ to the divisor.

$\overline{140}$ = first remainder.
$64 = 8 \times 8.$

$\overline{76}$ = corrected remainder.
$60 = 5 \times 12$, taken in defect: add $.05$ to the divisor.

$\overline{160}$ = 2d remainder.
$80 = 5 \times 8 + 8 \times 5.$

$\overline{80}$ = corrected remainder.
$60 = 5 \times 12$, taken in defect: add $.005$ to the divisor.

$\overline{200}$ = 3d remainder.
$105 = 5 \times 8 + 5 \times 5 + 8 \times 5.$

$\overline{95}$ = corrected remainder.   [divisor.
$72 = 6 \times 12$, taken in defect: add $.0006$ to the

$\overline{230}$ = 4th remainder.
$146 = 6 \times 8 + 5 \times 5 + 5 \times 5 + 6 \times 8.$

$\overline{84}$ = corrected remainder.   [divisor.
$60 = 5 \times 12$, taken in defect: add $.00005$ to the

$\overline{240}$ = 5th remainder.
$165 = 5 \times 8 + 6 \times 5 + 5 \times 5 + 6 \times 5 + 5 \times 8.$

$\overline{75}$ = corrected remainder.   [the divisor.
$48 = 4 \times 12$, taken in defect: add $.000004$ to

$\overline{270}$ = 6th remainder.
$\ldots$

The accentuated digits are those of the quotient, which are
successively added to the divisor, in their proper places, as they
are formed: the value $.855654$, which is obtained, is the approximate solution of the equation $x = \dfrac{11}{12 + x}$ or $x^2 + 12x = 11.$

* If we call x the unknown quotient, D the dividend and d the divisor, then
$x = \dfrac{D}{d + x}$: it is obvious therefore that $x(x + d) = D$, or $x^2 + dx = D$, which is, as
will be afterwards shown, one of the four algebraical forms of quadratic equations.

We shall have occasion to pursue this subject further in the following Chapter on the extraction of roots.

Importance of the theory of continued fractions.

186. The conversion of ordinary into continued fractions, and their subsequent reconversion into a series of fractions converging in value to the primitive fractions from which they are derived, forms, or rather ought to form, one of the most important departments of arithmetic, not merely as furnishing approximations to them in their most simple terms and the means of estimating their closeness, but also on account of their use in the solution of a great variety of interesting problems: it is for this reason, that we shall subjoin to the present chapter, a short theory of their formation and of some of their most useful properties; an enquiry which will involve no algebraical or arithmetical operations or principles which have not already been sufficiently explained or established.

Conversion of an ordinary into a continued fraction.

187. Let $\dfrac{B}{A}$ be any *proper* fraction*, whose terms are either finite or indefinite numbers, and let us apply to its terms A and B the process which we have employed, (Art. 99.) for finding the greatest common measure of two numbers, as follows:

$$B)\,A\,(a$$
$$\overline{C)\,B\,(b}$$
$$\overline{D)\,C\,(c}$$
$$\overline{E)\,D\,(d}\ +$$
$$\cdots$$

---

* If $\dfrac{B}{A}$ be not a proper fraction, it may be reduced to an equivalent mixed number, (Art. 95.), and the process which follows may be applied to the fractional part; otherwise, the continued fraction which arises will correspond to $\dfrac{A}{B}$ or the reciprocal of $\dfrac{B}{A}$.

† Thus, if the fraction be $\dfrac{130}{421}$, we get

$$130)\,421\,(3$$
$$390$$
$$\overline{\quad 31)\,130\,(4}$$
$$124$$
$$\overline{\quad\quad 6)\,31\,(5}$$
$$30$$
$$\overline{\quad\quad\quad 1)\,6\,(6}$$

where the quotients are the numbers 3, 4, 5 and 6, and there is no remainder.

This process may be continued, if required, as long as a remainder exists: if the terms of the fraction $\frac{B}{A}$ be finite numbers, it must necessarily terminate, sooner or later, the last divisor being 1, in all cases where there exists no common measure of A and B, (Art. 104.).

It will immediately follow from the nature of division, (Art. 95.) that

$$A = aB + C \quad \text{and therefore} \quad \frac{A}{B} = a + \frac{C}{B},$$

$$B = bC + D \quad \ldots\ldots\ldots\ldots \quad \frac{B}{C} = b + \frac{D}{C},$$

$$C = cD + E \quad \ldots\ldots\ldots\ldots \quad \frac{C}{D} = c + \frac{E}{D} *$$

$$\ldots\ldots\ldots\ldots \qquad \ldots\ldots\ldots$$

Again, taking the reciprocals of the improper fractions $\frac{A}{B}$, $\frac{B}{C}$, $\frac{C}{D}$, &c. and of the mixed numbers (Art. 95.) corresponding to them, we get (Art. 109.)

$$\frac{B}{A} = \cfrac{1}{a + \cfrac{C}{B}},$$

$$\frac{C}{B} = \cfrac{1}{b + \cfrac{D}{C}},$$

$$\frac{D}{C} = \cfrac{1}{c + \cfrac{E}{D}} \dagger$$

$$\ldots\ldots\ldots\ldots$$

---

* Thus for the fraction $\frac{130}{421}$, we get

$$421 = 3 \times 130 + 31, \quad \text{and therefore} \quad \frac{421}{130} = 3 + \frac{31}{130},$$

$$130 = 4 \times 31 + 6 \ldots\ldots\ldots\ldots\ldots \quad \frac{130}{31} = 4 + \frac{6}{31},$$

$$31 = 5 \times 6 + 1 \ldots\ldots\ldots\ldots\ldots \quad \frac{31}{6} = 5 + \frac{1}{6},$$

$$6 = 6 \times 1 \ldots\ldots\ldots\ldots\ldots\ldots \quad \frac{6}{1} = 6.$$

† Thus, if $\frac{B}{A} = \frac{130}{431}$, we find $\frac{130}{431} = \cfrac{1}{3 + \cfrac{31}{130}}$, $\quad \frac{31}{130} = \cfrac{1}{4 + \cfrac{6}{31}}$, $\quad \frac{6}{31} = \cfrac{1}{5 + \cfrac{1}{6}}$:

If in the value $\dfrac{1}{a+\dfrac{C}{B}}$ of $\dfrac{B}{A}$, we replace $\dfrac{C}{B}$ by its value $\dfrac{1}{b+\dfrac{D}{C}}$,

we shall get

$$\frac{B}{A}=\frac{1}{a+\dfrac{1}{b+\dfrac{D}{C}}};$$

and if in this second value of $\dfrac{B}{A}$, we further replace $\dfrac{D}{C}$ by its

value $\dfrac{1}{c+\dfrac{E}{D}}$, we shall get

$$\frac{B}{A}=\frac{1}{a+\dfrac{1}{b+\dfrac{1}{c+\dfrac{E}{D}}}}.$$

It is now obvious in what manner this process may be continued, as long as the quotients exist, the successive quotients forming the successive terms of the continued fraction.

The same continued fraction will result whether the fraction $\dfrac{B}{A}$ be in its lowest terms or not, inasmuch as the successive quotients will be the same in both cases. (Art. 110.)

and if in $\dfrac{1}{3+\dfrac{31}{130}}$, we replace $\dfrac{31}{130}$ by $\dfrac{1}{4+\dfrac{6}{31}}$, we get

$$\frac{130}{431}=\frac{1}{3+\dfrac{1}{4}+\dfrac{6}{31}};$$

and if we further replace in this second value of $\dfrac{130}{431}$, $\dfrac{6}{31}$ by its value $\dfrac{1}{5+\dfrac{1}{6}}$,

we shall get

$$\frac{130}{431}=\frac{1}{3+\dfrac{1}{4}+\dfrac{1}{5}+\dfrac{1}{6}},$$

which is a complete continued fraction, formed by the several quotients 3, 4, 5 and 6.

188. (1) Let the fraction be $\dfrac{79}{135}$,

$$79\,)\,135\,(\,1$$
$$\underline{79}$$
$$56\,)\,79\,(\,1$$
$$\underline{56}$$
$$23\,)\,56\,(\,2$$
$$\underline{46}$$
$$10\,)\,23\,(\,2$$
$$\underline{20}$$
$$3\,)\,10\,(\,3$$
$$\underline{9}$$
$$1\,)\,3\,(\,3$$

The quotients are 1, 1, 2, 2, 3 and 3, and the corresponding continued fraction is

$$\cfrac{1}{1+\cfrac{1}{1+\cfrac{1}{2+\cfrac{1}{2+\cfrac{1}{3+\cfrac{1}{3}}}}}}.$$

(2) Let the fraction be $\dfrac{601}{6040}$.

The quotients will be found to be 10, 20 and 30: and therefore

$$\frac{601}{6040}=\cfrac{1}{10+\cfrac{1}{20+\cfrac{1}{30}}}.$$

(3) Let the fraction be $\dfrac{5225670}{7489051}$.

The quotients will be found to be the numbers 1, 2, 3, 4, 5, 6, 7, 8, 9 and 10; and therefore

$$\frac{5225670}{7489051}=\cfrac{1}{1+\cfrac{1}{2+\cfrac{1}{3+\cfrac{1}{4+\cfrac{1}{5+\cfrac{1}{6+\cfrac{1}{7+\cfrac{1}{8+\cfrac{1}{9+\cfrac{1}{10}}}}}}}}}}.$$

The partial fractions which are formed by omitting all the quotients after the first, second, third, fourth, &c. are alternately greater and less than the primitive fraction.

189. If a, b, c, d, &c. be the several quotients of a continued fraction, then the several fractions

(1) $\dfrac{1}{a}$,

(2) $\dfrac{1}{a + \dfrac{1}{b}}$,

(3) $\dfrac{1}{a + \dfrac{1}{b + \dfrac{1}{c}}}$,

(4) $\dfrac{1}{a + \dfrac{1}{b + \dfrac{1}{c + \dfrac{1}{d}}}}$,

which are formed by taking one, two, three, four, and so on of these quotients, and omitting all those which follow them, will be alternately greater and less than the primitive fraction; those which comprehend an odd number of quotients being greater, and those which comprehend an even number of them being less.

Proof.

(a) For it is obvious that the first partial fraction $\dfrac{1}{a}$ is greater than the primitive fraction $\dfrac{B}{A} = \dfrac{1}{\left(\dfrac{A}{B}\right)}$ (Art. 144.), since a is less than $\dfrac{A}{B}$ or than the complete quotient of the division of A by B.

(b) The second fraction (2)

$$\dfrac{1}{a + \dfrac{1}{b}}$$

is less than $\dfrac{B}{A}$, since $a + \dfrac{1}{b}$ is greater than $\dfrac{A}{B}$: for $\dfrac{1}{b}$ is greater, for the reasons just given, than the continued fraction

$$\dfrac{1}{b + \dfrac{1}{c + \dfrac{1}{d} + \&c.}}$$

and therefore $a + \dfrac{1}{b}$ is greater than the complete quotient of the division of A by B, and consequently,

$$\frac{1}{a + \dfrac{1}{b}}$$

is less than $\qquad$ $\dfrac{1}{\left(\dfrac{A}{B}\right)}$ or than $\dfrac{B}{A}$.

(c) The third fraction (3)

$$\frac{1}{a + \dfrac{1}{b + \dfrac{1}{c}}}$$

is greater than $\dfrac{B}{A}$, since

$$\frac{1}{b + \dfrac{1}{c}}$$

is less, as has been just demonstrated (b), than the continued fraction which must be added to a, in order to make up the entire quotient of the division of A by B.

(d) The fourth fraction (4)

$$\frac{1}{a + \dfrac{1}{b + \dfrac{1}{c + \dfrac{1}{d}}}}$$

is less than $\dfrac{B}{A}$, since

$$\frac{1}{b + \dfrac{1}{c + \dfrac{1}{d}}}$$

is greater, as has been just demonstrated (c), than the continued fraction which must be added to a, in order to make up the entire quotient of A divided by B.

The same process of reasoning (c) and (d) will be sufficient to shew that if any one partial fraction in the series is greater than $\dfrac{B}{A}$, the next in order will be less, and so on for ever: it follows therefore, that since one partial fraction with an odd number of quotients is greater than $\dfrac{B}{A}$, that all other similar fractions which have an odd number of quotients are greater than $\dfrac{B}{A}$: and also, that all the intermediate fractions, alternating with them, which have an even number of quotients, are less than $\dfrac{B}{A}$

Conversion
of a series
of partial
into ordi-
nary frac-
tions.

190. The partial continued fractions, which were the subject of the last Article, may be successively reconverted into ordinary fractions by a very simple rule : it is under this reconverted form that those properties of such fractions present themselves, which give them their peculiar usefulness in a great variety of very important applications.

In order to investigate this rule, let us represent the successive reconverted fractions by

$$\frac{p}{q}, \ \frac{p'}{q'}, \ \frac{p''}{q''}, \ \frac{p'''}{q'''}, \ \frac{p^{\mathrm{iv}}}{q^{\mathrm{iv}}}, \ \&c.,$$

distinguishing the successive numerators and denominators by means of accents or by Roman numerals, when their number exceeds four, (Art. 108, Note)* : we thus get

(1) $\frac{p}{q} = \frac{1}{a}$, or $p = 1$ and $q = a$: we shall continue to represent the numerator and denominator of this fraction by p and q, in order to give greater symmetry to the results which follow and to make the law of their formation more manifest.

(2) $\frac{p'}{q'} = \dfrac{1}{a + \dfrac{1}{b}}$, which is derived from $\frac{1}{a}$ by putting $a + \frac{1}{b}$ in the place of a : if we multiply its numerator and denominator by b, it becomes $\dfrac{b}{ab + 1}$, which is the reconverted value of

$$\frac{1}{a} + \frac{1}{b} \ \text{ or of } \ \frac{p'}{q'}.$$

(3) $\qquad \dfrac{p''}{q''} = \dfrac{1}{a + \dfrac{1}{b + \dfrac{1}{c}}} = \dfrac{\left(b + \dfrac{1}{c} \right)}{a \left(b + \dfrac{1}{c} \right) + 1} ;$

for $\qquad \dfrac{1}{a} + \dfrac{1}{b + \dfrac{1}{c}}$ is formed from $\dfrac{1}{a} + \dfrac{1}{b}$,

by putting $b + \frac{1}{c}$ in the place of b ; or from its equivalent

---

* Roman instead of common numerals are used for the purpose of distinguishing them from ordinary indices.

fraction $\dfrac{b}{ab+1}$ (2), by putting $b+\dfrac{1}{c}$ in the place of b: if we remove the brackets from $\left(b+\dfrac{1}{c}\right)$ (Art. 24.), and replace 1 by p (1), a by q (1), b by p' (2), and $ab+1$ by q' (2), we shall get

$$\frac{p''}{q''}=\frac{b+\dfrac{1}{c}}{ab+1+\dfrac{a}{c}}=\frac{p'+\dfrac{p}{c}}{q'+\dfrac{q}{c}}=\frac{p'c+p}{q'c+q},$$

multiplying the numerator and denominator by the quotient c.

$$(4)\qquad \frac{p'''}{q'''}=\cfrac{1}{a+\cfrac{1}{b+\cfrac{1}{c+\cfrac{1}{d}}}}=\frac{p'\left(c+\dfrac{1}{d}\right)+p}{q'\left(c+\dfrac{1}{d}\right)+q}\qquad(3):$$

for it is obviously formed from $\dfrac{1}{a+\cfrac{1}{b+\cfrac{1}{c}}}$ by putting $\dfrac{1}{c+\dfrac{1}{d}}$ in the

place of c, or by putting $c+\dfrac{1}{d}$ in its equivalent $\dfrac{p''}{q''}$ or $\dfrac{p'c+p}{q'c+q}$ (3), in the place of c: if we now remove the brackets from $\left(c+\dfrac{1}{d}\right)$, we easily get

$$\frac{p'''}{q'''}=\frac{p'c+p+\dfrac{p'}{d}}{q'c+q+\dfrac{q'}{d}}\cdot\frac{p''+\dfrac{p'}{d}}{q''+\dfrac{q'}{d}},$$

replacing $p'c+p$ by p'' and $q'c+q$ by q'' (3): if we further multiply the numerator and denominator by the quotient d, we get

$$\frac{p'''}{q'''}=\frac{p''d+p'}{q''d+q'}.$$

The same process of reasoning would shew that

$$\frac{p^{\mathrm{iv}}}{q^{\mathrm{iv}}}=\frac{p'''e+p''}{q'''e+q''},$$

$$\frac{p^{\mathrm{v}}}{q^{\mathrm{v}}}=\frac{p^{\mathrm{iv}}f+p'''}{q^{\mathrm{iv}}f+q'''},$$

and so on successively until we arrive at the last of the quotients: it being merely necessary in passing from one fraction to the following, to *advance* the order of the numerators denoted by p, of the denominators denoted by q, and of the final quotients of each fraction, by unity.

Rule.

191. The law of formation which is expressed algebraically in the preceding formula, if expressed in words, will form the following rule.

The numerator of any fraction, after the second, will be formed by adding the product of the last quotient and of the ultimate numerator to the penultimate numerator.

The denominator of any fraction, after the second, will be formed by adding the product of the last quotient and of the ultimate denominator to the penultimate denominator.

Formation of the two first fractions.

It is only for the third and following fractions that this law becomes applicable: *the first is the reciprocal of the first quotient; the numerator of the second is the second quotient, and its denominator is the product of the two first quotients increased by* 1.

The last of the reconverted fractions will be the primitive fraction in its lowest terms.

192. The last of the successive fractions formed by the rule in the last Article will be the primitive fraction in its lowest terms: for it is necessarily equal to the entire continued fraction, and the quotients from which it is formed are the same (Art. 108.) whether the primitive fraction be in its lowest terms or not.

The difference of two successive fractions in the series (the less being taken from the greater) is equal to the reciprocal of the product of their denominators.

193. The series of fractions $\frac{p}{q}$, $\frac{p''}{q''}$, $\frac{p^{iv}}{q^{iv}}$, ... are greater than the primitive fraction, and the intermediate series $\frac{p'}{q'}$, $\frac{p'''}{q'''}$, $\frac{p^{v}}{q^{v}}$, &c. are less (Art. 189.): and it may be shewn that the difference between any fraction of the first series and the inferior fraction of the second series which *immediately* precedes or follows it, will be a fraction whose numerator is 1 and its denominator the product of the denominators.

Thus (1),

$$\frac{p}{q} - \frac{p'}{q'} = \frac{pq' - qp'}{qq'} \quad \text{(Art. 128.):}$$

and its numerator $pq' - qp' = ab + 1 - ab = 1$, replacing p, q, p', and q' by their values as given in Art. 190, (1), (2).

Secondly (2),

$$\frac{p''}{q''} - \frac{p'}{q'} = \frac{p''q' - p'q''}{q'q''} :$$

and since $p'' = p'c + p$, Art. 190, (3), and $q'' = q'c + q$, Art. 190, (3), we get

$$p''q' = p'q'c + q'p,$$
$$p'q'' = p'q'c + qp',$$

and therefore, subtracting the second from the first,

$$p''q' - p'q'' = q'p - qp' = 1.$$

Thirdly (3),

$$\frac{p''}{q''} - \frac{p'''}{q'''} = \frac{p''q''' - p'''q''}{q''q'''} :$$

and since $p''' = p''d + p'$ and $q''' = q''d + q'$, Art. 190, (4), we get

$$p''q''' = p''q''d + p''q',$$
$$p'''q'' = p''q''d + p'q'' ;$$

and therefore

$$p''q''' - p'''q'' = p''q' - p'q'' = 1.$$

By successive repetitions of this process, we may shew that

$$1 = p^{iv}q''' \quad p'''q^{iv} = p^{iv}q^{v} - p^{v}q^{iv} = p^{vi}q^{v} - p^{v}q^{vi} = \ldots$$

and so on, until the quotients terminate.

It consequently follows that

$$\frac{p}{q} - \frac{p'}{q'} = \frac{1}{qq'},$$

$$\frac{p''}{q''} - \frac{p'}{q'} = \frac{1}{q'q''},$$

$$\frac{p''}{q''} - \frac{p'''}{q'''} = \frac{1}{q''q'''},$$

$$\frac{p^{iv}}{q^{iv}} - \frac{p'''}{q'''} = \frac{1}{q'''q^{iv}},$$

$$\frac{p^{iv}}{q^{iv}} - \frac{p^{v}}{q^{v}} = \frac{1}{q^{iv}q^{v}},$$

and so on to the end of the series of fractions.

194. It appears, therefore, that the difference of any two consecutive fractions (the less being taken from the greater) is equal to the reciprocal of the product of their denominators: and inasmuch as these denominators, as we advance in the series, increase perpetually (and also very rapidly when the quotients

The series of fractions formed by the rule in Art. 191 converge perpetually to the value of the primitive fraction.

are large numbers) as is manifest from the law of their formation (Art. 191.),* it will necessarily follow that these successive fractions will approximate perpetually in value to each other, and therefore also to the value of the primitive fraction, which is always intermediate between them: it is from this property of such fractions that they derive the name of *converging fractions*.

Examples of the formation of converging fractions.

195. The following are examples of the formation of converging fractions.

(1) To find a series of fractions converging to the fraction $\frac{532}{1193}$.

From the rule in Art. 187, we get

$$\frac{532}{1193} = \cfrac{1}{2 + \cfrac{1}{4 + \cfrac{1}{8 + \cfrac{1}{16}}}}.$$

The quotients are therefore 2, 4, 8, 16.

The converging fractions formed by the rule in Art. 191, are

$$\frac{1}{2}, \quad \frac{4}{9}, \quad \frac{33}{74}, \quad \frac{532}{1193},$$

the last of which is the primitive fraction.†

(2) To find a series of fractions converging to 3.1415926 or to the equivalent fraction

$$\frac{31415926}{10000000}.$$

---

* For $q'' = q'c + q$, $q''' = q''d + q'$, $q = q'''e + q''$, and so on, where the quotients c, d, e, &c. are necessarily either 1 or whole numbers.

† The first of them $\frac{p}{q} = \frac{1}{a} = \frac{1}{2}$.

The second $\frac{p'}{q'} = \frac{b}{ab+1} = \frac{4}{2 \times 4 + 1} = \frac{4}{9}$.

The third $\frac{p''}{q''} = \frac{p'c+p}{q'c+q} = \frac{4 \times 8 + 1}{9 \times 8 + 2} = \frac{33}{74}$.

The fourth $\frac{p'''}{q'''} = \frac{p''d+p'}{q''d+q'} = \frac{33 \times 16 + 4}{74 \times 16 + 9} = \frac{532}{1193}$.

In this case also

$$\frac{p}{q} - \frac{p'}{q'} = \frac{1}{18}, \quad \frac{p''}{q''} - \frac{p'}{q'} = \frac{1}{666}, \quad \frac{p''}{q''} - \frac{p'''}{q'''} = \frac{1}{88282}:$$

it hence appears how nearly the fraction $\frac{33}{74}$ converges to $\frac{532}{1193}$.

The quotients of the equivalent continued fraction are

3, 7, 15, 1, 243, 1, 1, 9, 1, 1, 4.

The converging fractions *inverted*, (for the fraction is improper, Art. 187, Note,) are

$$\frac{3}{1}, \quad \frac{22}{7}, \quad \frac{333}{106}, \quad \frac{355}{113}, \quad \frac{86598}{27565}, \quad \frac{86953}{27678}, \quad \frac{173551}{55243}, \quad \frac{1648912}{524865},$$

$$\frac{1822463}{580108}, \quad \frac{3471375}{1104970}, \quad \frac{15707963}{5000000}.$$

The final fraction $\frac{15707963}{5000000}$ is the primitive fraction in its lowest terms. (Art. 192.)

If the diameter of a circle be expressed by 1, its circumference has been found to be approximately expressed by 3.1415926, though its real value is *incommensurable* (Art. 165.) with the diameter: it will follow, therefore, that the converging fractions given above, are approximate values of the circumference of a circle, the primary unit being the diameter.

Those converging fractions which precede large quotients furnish near approximations to the primitive fraction: for such fractions differ much less from those converging fractions which immediately follow, than from those which immediately precede them: this observation applies to the fractions $\frac{22}{7}$ and $\frac{355}{112}$, which severally precede the quotients 15 and 243*.

(3) To find a series of fractions converging to $\frac{224.7}{365.25}$ or $\frac{14.98}{2435}$, which is equivalent to it.

The quotients of the equivalent continued fraction are

1, 1, 1, 1, 2, 30, 1, 15.

---

* For if three consecutive denominators of such fractions be denoted by q, q', q'', the last of them $q'' = q'x + q$, will be much greater than q, if the quotient x be a large number: the difference of the two first fractions is $\frac{1}{qq'}$, and the difference of the two last is $\frac{1}{q'q''}$, and the second is therefore much smaller than the first.

The first approximation $\frac{22}{7}$ was given by Archimedes: the second $\frac{355}{113}$ by Metius: they are both of them too great, but the second is accurate within one three millionth part of the diameter.

The converging fractions are

$$\frac{1}{1}, \frac{1}{2}, \frac{2}{3}, \frac{3}{5}, \frac{8}{13}, \frac{243}{395}, \frac{251}{408}, \frac{1498}{2435},$$

the last of which is the primitive fraction in its lowest terms. The numbers 224.7 and 365.25 express, in days, very nearly the periods of a complete revolution of the planet Venus and of the Earth in their orbits round the Sun, and since the fraction $\frac{8}{13}$ precedes the large quotient 30, it will furnish a very near approximation to the primitive fraction: it will be consequently found, that 13 complete periods of the planet Venus will be very nearly equal (within one day) to 8 complete periods of the Earth, or to 8 sidereal years, an astronomical fact of no inconsiderable importance *.

* The fractions $\frac{8}{13}$ and $\frac{243}{395}$ involve almost the entire theory of the recurrence of those rare but very important phœnomena, the transits of Venus over the disk of the Sun, the two last of which took place on the 5th of June 1761 and on the 3d of June 1769, at an interval of 8 years, and the two next of which will take place on the 8th of December 1874 and on the 6th of December 1882, at intervals of $113\frac{1}{2}$ years ($121\frac{1}{2}-8$) and $121\frac{1}{2}$ years (the half of 243) from the first of the former: the two last transits will take place at a different node from the two first, which will explain the occurrence of half a period of Venus, and of half a period of the Earth, in addition to 184 and 197 complete periods of one planet, and of 113 and 121 complete periods of the other: the first approximation is not sufficiently near to allow two successive transits to take place at intervals of 8 years each.

The complete period of the planet Mercury is 87.97 days nearly, and the four first fractions converging to the fraction $\frac{87.97}{365.25}$ will be found to be

$$\frac{1}{4}, \frac{6}{25}, \frac{7}{29} \text{ and } \frac{13}{54}:$$

the transits of this planet over the disk of the Sun may be expected at intervals of 7 and 13 years, at the same node, and at intervals of $3\frac{1}{3}$ years at a different node: there were transits on the 7th of May 1799, the 8th of November 1802, the 11th of November 1815, and the 4th of November 1822.

The complete periods of the great planets Jupiter and Saturn are nearly 4333 and 10759 days respectively: the three first fractions converging to $\frac{4333}{10759}$ are

$$\frac{1}{2}, \frac{2}{5}, \frac{29}{72},$$

and the second is therefore, with reference to the large numbers 4333 and 10759, a near approximation; we are thus led to observe that 5 periods of Jupiter are nearly equal to 2 periods of Saturn, an important fact in physical astronomy, and connected with the explanation of the cause of what is termed the *great inequality* of Jupiter and Saturn : a similar effect, though comparatively very minute in

(4)   To find a series of fractions converging towards
.2422638...

The first six quotients of the corresponding continued fraction are

$$4, \; 7, \; 1, \; 4, \; 1, \; 7.$$

The successive converging fractions are

$$\frac{1}{4}, \; \frac{7}{29}, \; \frac{8}{33}, \; \frac{39}{161}, \; \frac{47}{194}, \; \frac{418}{1519} \; *.$$

196.   The formation of converging fractions is applicable to the solution of the following problem, which will be found to be one of the most important which occurs in the theory of numbers.

Given two numbers a and b which are prime to each other, Problem. to find two others x and y, which will satisfy the equation

$$a x - b y \mp 1 = 0.$$

For this purpose it is merely necessary to form the whole series converging to $\frac{a}{b}$, when y and x will be found to be the numerator and denominator of the converging fraction which precedes $\frac{a}{b}$: it having been shewn (Art. 189.) that if $\frac{y}{x}$ occupy an odd place in the series of converging fractions, that

$$b y - a x = 1, \quad \text{or} \quad a x - b y + 1 = 0;$$

and if $\frac{y}{x}$ occupy an even place, that

$$a x - b y = 1, \quad \text{or} \quad a x - b y - 1 = 0.$$

quantity, results from the relation of the numbers 8 and 13 to the periods of Venus and the Earth.

These observations might be very easily extended, but what we have said is sufficient to shew the bearing of a very simple arithmetical process, upon some of the most interesting and difficult enquiries in astronomy.

* The length of the tropical year, upon which the recurrence of the seasons depends, is 365.2422638 days....(less than the complete or sidereal period) and its excess above 365 days, may be expressed by $\frac{1}{4}$, $\frac{7}{29}$, $\frac{8}{33}$, $\frac{39}{161}$, $\frac{47}{194}$, the primary unit being one day : if the first of these fractions be taken, it will give one day in four years, which is provided for by the *leap year* or the Julian correction of the calendar: this is too great: if we take the fraction $\frac{47}{194}$ (which is also too great, though very nearly accurate), it will give 47 days in 194 years, or 94 days in 388 years, or very nearly 94 + 3, or 97 days in 388 + 12, or 400 years : this is the Gregorian correction of the Julian Calendar, and is effected by the omission of the intercalary day in three centurial years out of four. Thus, of the years 1800, 1900, 2000, and 2100, which would be leap years according to the Julian Calendar, the year 2000 alone is a leap year according to the Gregorian Calendar.

Examples.

197. (1) Let a be 9 and b, 13 : then the converging fractions are

$$\frac{1}{1}, \quad \frac{2}{3}, \quad \frac{9}{13},$$

and therefore

$$9 \times 3 - 13 \times 2 - 1 = 0.$$

(2) Let a be 77 and b, 344 : then the converging fractions are

$$\frac{1}{4}, \quad \frac{2}{9}, \quad \frac{15}{67}, \quad \frac{77}{344},$$

consequently

$$77 \times 67 - 344 \times 15 + 1 = 0.$$

We shall resume the consideration of this problem, when we come to the Chapter on the solution of indeterminate problems.

Every finite fraction leads to a finite continued fraction.

198. The process by which the quotients of a continued fraction are deduced from the primitive fraction, shews that they must always terminate, inasmuch as every successive remainder is less than that which precedes it: and conversely likewise it will follow, that every finite continued fraction will lead to a finite equivalent fraction in its ordinary form. If therefore we should meet with an interminable continued fraction in whatever manner formed, we should conclude that it does not originate in any fraction with finite terms or in any *commensurable* number: and conversely likewise that the continued fraction which is equivalent to any *incommensurable number*, (if such a phrase may be used) must be necessarily interminable*.

Different modes of resolving fractions into a series of rapidly converging terms.

199. There are various other modes of resolving fractions into a series of rapidly converging terms, which either terminate or not, and one of these constitutes the method, which we have already explained at considerable length, of converting a fraction into an equivalent decimal. Thus, let $\frac{a}{b}$ be a fraction, and let us multiply a and its remainders successively by the series of numbers q, q', q'', q''', &c. and divide the successive results by b, when we shall find

$$\frac{aq}{b} = p + \frac{c}{b}, \text{ and therefore } \frac{a}{b} = \frac{p}{q} + \frac{c}{bq},$$

* The square root of a number not a complete square, such as 4, 9, 16, &c. is *incommensurable*, and will be expressible (as we shall shew in the next Chapter) by a continued indefinite fraction with quotients recurring in periods. We shall discuss the subject of incommensurable quantities or numbers at some length in the Chapter on Ratios and Proportions.

$$\frac{cq'}{b} = p' + \frac{d}{b} \text{ and therefore } \frac{c}{b} = \frac{p'}{q'} + \frac{d}{bq'},$$

$$\frac{dq''}{b} = p'' + \frac{e}{b} \quad \cdots \cdots \cdots \quad \frac{d}{b} = \frac{p''}{q''} + \frac{e}{bq''},$$

and consequently

$$\frac{a}{b} = \frac{p}{q} + \frac{1}{q} \cdot \frac{c}{b} \text{ (and replacing } \frac{c}{b} \text{ by its value),}$$

$$= \frac{p}{q} + \frac{1}{q} \left(\frac{p'}{q'} + \frac{d}{bq'} \right),$$

$$= \frac{p}{q} + \frac{p'}{qq'} + \frac{1}{qq'} \cdot \frac{d}{b} \text{ (and replacing } \frac{d}{b} \text{ by its value),}$$

$$= \frac{p}{q} + \frac{p'}{qq'} + \frac{1}{qq'} \left(\frac{p''}{q''} + \frac{e}{bq''} \right),$$

$$= \frac{p}{q} + \frac{p'}{qq'} + \frac{p''}{qq'q''} + \&c.$$

200. If we make $q = q' = q'' \ldots = 10$, we get

$$\frac{a}{b} = \frac{p}{10} + \frac{p'}{10^2} + \frac{p''}{10^3} + \ldots$$

General theory of decimals.

where p, p', p'', &c. are the digits of an ordinary decimal*.

201. If we make $q = q' = q'' = \ldots = 12$, we get

$$\frac{a}{b} = \frac{p}{12} + \frac{p'}{12^2} + \frac{p''}{12^3} + \&c \; ;$$

forming a series of ordinary duodecimals, where p, p', $p'' \ldots$ are some one of the digits 0, 1, 2, 3, 4, 5, 6, 7, 8, 9, 10, 11, and where the numbers 10 and 11, considered as digits in the decimal scale, may be denoted by X and Җ †.

Theory of duo-decimals.

---

* Thus the fraction

$$\frac{7}{13} = \frac{5}{10} + \frac{3}{10^2} + \frac{8}{10^3} + \frac{4}{10^4} + \frac{6}{10^5} + \frac{1}{10^6} + \frac{5}{10^7} + \&c. = .5384615\ldots,$$

when expressed by the ordinary decimal notation.

† Thus the fraction

$$\frac{11}{17} = \frac{7}{12} + \frac{9}{12^2} + \frac{2}{12^3} + \frac{1}{12^4} + \frac{4}{12^5} + \frac{11}{12^6} + \frac{3}{12^7} + \&c. = : 79214 \text{ Җ } 36429 \text{ X } 7\ldots,$$

if : be used to denote the duodecimal point.

Of other forms of resolution.

202. If we make $q = q' = q'' = \ldots = 2$, we get

$$\frac{a}{b} = \frac{p}{2} + \frac{p'}{2^2} + \frac{p''}{2^3} + \frac{p'''}{2^4} + \&c. \ldots$$

where p, p', p'', p''' ... are either 1 or zero*.

If we make $q = 2$, $q' = 3$, $q'' = 4$, $q''' = 5$, and so on, following the series of natural numbers, we shall get

$$\frac{a}{b} = \frac{p}{2} + \frac{p'}{2 \cdot 3} + \frac{p''}{2 \cdot 3 \cdot 4} + \frac{p'''}{2 \cdot 3 \cdot 4 \cdot 5} + \&c. \dagger$$

If we assume successively such values of q, q', q'', &c. as will make $p = p' = p'' = \ldots = 1$, we shall get

$$\frac{a}{b} = \frac{1}{q} + \frac{1}{qq'} + \frac{1}{qq'q''} + \&c. \ldots \ddagger$$

Certain series which necessarily represent incommensurable numbers.

203. In the last case, the remainders from each division go on diminishing, and the factors q, q', q'', &c. of the denominators increasing §, and consequently the resulting series must sooner or later terminate: in other words, no finite fraction can produce an interminable series of such a form: conversely likewise we may conclude, that no interminable series of such a form can originate in a finite fraction, which, consequently, must in all cases be considered as the representative of an *incommensurable* number.

Example.

Of this kind is the series

$$1 + 1 + \frac{1}{1 \cdot 2} + \frac{1}{1 \cdot 2 \cdot 3} + \frac{1}{1 \cdot 2 \cdot 3 \cdot 4} + \&c. \ldots \textit{in infin.}$$

* Thus, $\frac{7}{11} = \frac{1}{2} + \frac{0}{2^2} + \frac{1}{2^3} + \frac{0}{2^4} + \frac{0}{2^5} + \frac{0}{2^6} + \frac{1}{2^7} + \frac{0}{2^8} + \ldots = |\ 10100010\ldots,$

if the binary point be denoted by the line $|$.

$\dagger$ Thus,

$$\frac{142}{73} = 1 + \frac{1}{2} + \frac{2}{2 \times 3} + \frac{2}{2 \times 3 \times 4} + \frac{3}{2 \times 3 \times 4 \times 5} + \frac{2}{2 \times 3 \times 4 \times 5 \times 6} + \frac{2}{2 \times 3 \times 4 \times 5 \times 6 \times 7}, + \&c.$$

$\ddagger$ Thus, $\frac{13}{33} = \frac{1}{3} + \frac{1}{3 \times 6} + \frac{1}{3 \times 6 \times 11},$

$$\frac{101}{147} = \frac{1}{2} + \frac{1}{2 \times 3} + \frac{1}{2 \times 3 \times 9} + \frac{1}{2 \times 3 \times 9 \times 10} + \frac{1}{2 \times 3 \times 9 \times 10 \times 49}.$$

§ For, if q be the multiplier and $\frac{qa}{b} = 1 + \frac{a'}{b}$, then if a' be not less than a, a less value of q may be taken.

whose law of formation is manifest, which is the representative of an *incommensurable* number of very great importance in analysis *.

204. Another very simple mode of resolving fractions into a terminable series of terms, whose numerators are 1, originates in dividing the denominator of the fraction by the numerator and the successive remainders: thus if the fraction (supposed proper) be $\frac{b}{a}$, we proceed as follows:

$$b) a (q$$
$$\overline{}\ c) a (q'$$
$$\overline{}\ d) a (q''$$
$$\overline{}\ e) a (q'''$$
$$\overline{}\ f.\ .$$

We thus get

$$a = bq + c, \quad b = \frac{a}{q} - \frac{c}{q} \text{ and } \frac{b}{a} = \frac{1}{q} - \frac{c}{qa},$$

$$a = cq' + d, \quad c = \frac{a}{q'} - \frac{d}{q'} \text{ and } \frac{c}{a} = \frac{1}{q'} - \frac{d}{q'a},$$

$$a = dq'' + e, \quad d = \frac{a}{q''} - \frac{e}{q''} \text{ and } \frac{d}{a} = \frac{1}{q''} - \frac{e}{q''a};$$

consequently,

$$\frac{b}{a} = \frac{1}{q} - \frac{1}{q}.\frac{c}{a} \text{ (and replacing } \frac{c}{a} \text{ by its value)}$$

$$= \frac{1}{q} - \frac{1}{q}.\left(\frac{1}{q'} - \frac{d}{q'a}\right)$$

$$= \frac{1}{q} - \frac{1}{qq'} + \frac{d}{qq'a} \text{ (and replacing } \frac{d}{a} \text{ by its value)}$$

$$= \frac{1}{q} - \frac{1}{qq'} + \frac{1}{qq'}.\left(\frac{1}{q''} - \frac{e}{q''a}\right)$$

$$= \frac{1}{q} - \frac{1}{qq'} + \frac{1}{qq'q''} - \frac{1}{qq'q''}.\frac{e}{a},$$

and so on, until the quotients terminate.

---

* It is the base of Napierian logarithms, which enters very extensively into symbolical expressions, and is usually denoted by the symbol *e*.

Example. Thus let it be required to resolve in this manner, the fraction $\dfrac{769}{1114}$:

$$769\,)\,1114\,(\,1$$
$$769$$
$$345\,)\,1114\,(\,3$$
$$1035$$
$$79\,)\,1114\,(\,14$$
$$79$$
$$324$$
$$316$$
$$8\,)\,1114\,(\,139$$
$$1112$$
$$2\,)\,1114\,(\,557$$
$$1114$$

Therefore,

$$\frac{769}{1114} = 1 - \frac{1}{3} + \frac{1}{3 \times 14} - \frac{1}{3 \times 14 \times 139} + \frac{1}{3 \times 14 \times 139 \times 557}.$$

Resolution of the units of concrete magnitudes into equivalent fractions.

205. The expression of concrete magnitudes in terms of units of different denominations, which neither follow the decimal nor any regular scale of subdivision, will furnish immensurable examples of the resolution of fractions similar to those which we have been considering in Art. 199. Thus if $a, b, c \ldots$ be the successive divisors of the primary unit, the several subordinate units will be expressed, with reference to it, by the several fractions $\dfrac{1}{a}, \dfrac{1}{ab}, \dfrac{1}{abc}$ &c.: if the primary unit be £1. sterling, its subordinate units, which are a shilling, a penny and a farthing, will be expressed by $\dfrac{1}{20}, \dfrac{1}{12 \times 20}, \dfrac{1}{4 \times 12 \times 20}$: if the primary unit be 1 lb Troy, its subordinate units which are an ounce, a penny weight and a grain, will be expressed by $\dfrac{1}{12}, \dfrac{1}{20 \times 12}$ and $\dfrac{1}{24 \times 20 \times 12}$: if the primary unit be 1 yard in length, its subordinate units, a foot, an inch and its successive duodecimal parts, will be expressed by $\dfrac{1}{3}, \dfrac{1}{12 \times 3}, \dfrac{1}{12^2 \times 3}$, $\dfrac{1}{12^3 \times 3}$ &c.: if the primary unit be 1 week of time, its subor-

dinate units, which are a day, an hour, a minute, a second and its successive sexagesimal parts, will be expressed by $\frac{1}{7}$, $\frac{1}{24 \times 7}$, $\frac{1}{60 \times 24 \times 7}$, $\frac{1}{60^2 \times 24 \times 7}$ and so on: and in every case, it is merely necessary to know the successive divisors which connect the successive subordinate units with each other, in order to form the corresponding series of equivalent fractions, whose common primary unit is the primary unit of the series.

206. The expression of a composite concrete number by means of fractions of the primary unit, is immediate, whenever the divisors which connect it with the several subordinate units are known: thus £244. 17s. 8¼d. becomes, in terms of the primary unit or £1. sterling, $244 + \frac{17}{20} + \frac{8}{12 \times 20} + \frac{1}{4 \times 12 \times 20}$.

Resolution of a composite concrete number into equivalent fractions.

In a similar manner 1 ton 11 hundred weight 3 quarters 15 pounds and 10 ounces avoirdupoise, becomes

$$1 + \frac{11}{20} + \frac{3}{4 \times 20} + \frac{15}{28 \times 4 \times 20} + \frac{10}{16 \times 28 \times 4 \times 20},$$

the connecting divisors being 20, 4, 28 and 16: and in a similar manner 3 hours 17 minutes and 35 seconds become

$$3 + \frac{17}{60} + \frac{35}{60^2};$$

all the subdivisions proceeding regularly according to the sexagesimal scale.

207. Fractions, whether proper or improper, of any primary concrete unit, may be converted into the equivalent composite numbers by resolving them into a series of subordinate fractions with their appropriate divisors: thus the fraction $\frac{17}{32}$ of the primary unit £1. sterling is equal to

$$\frac{10}{20} + \frac{7}{12 \times 20} + \frac{2}{4 \times 12 \times 20},$$

Resolution of fractions of a primary concrete unit into an equivalent composite number.

and therefore equivalent to 10s. 7½d.: in a similar manner, the fraction $\frac{13}{27}$ of a week is resolved into the series of equivalent fractions

$$\frac{3}{7} + \frac{8}{24 \times 7} + \frac{53}{60 \times 24 \times 7} + \frac{20}{60^2 \times 24 \times 7},$$

and is equal therefore to 3 days, 8 hours, 53 minutes and 20 seconds.

208. A composite concrete number is immediately expressible, as we have seen, in terms of a series of equivalent fractions; and such fractions are reducible to a simple fraction of any primary unit, whose denominator is the continued product of the successive divisors, which may or may not admit of further reduction: thus, 1 oz. 3 drams 2 scruples and 14 grains (apothecaries weight) becomes, the primary unit being 1 ounce,

$$1 + \frac{3}{8} + \frac{2}{3 \times 8} + \frac{14}{20 \times 3 \times 8},$$

which is convertible into

$$\frac{480}{480} + \frac{180}{480} + \frac{46}{480} + \frac{14}{480} + \frac{714}{480} = \frac{119}{80}$$

of one ounce, when reduced to its lowest terms.

209. The expression of the values of composite concrete numbers, or of their correspondent series of fractions, by means of the ordinary decimal notation and the reconversion of such expressions into composite concrete numbers, constitute two of the most common and most useful operations of commercial arithmetic: thus if it be required to express £3. 17s. 8¼d. by means of the ordinary decimal notation, the primary unit being £1., we proceed as follows:

4) 1

.25, the decimal expression for one farthing, the primary unit being one penny: it follows therefore that 8¼d. is equivalent to 8.25d.

12) 8.25

.6875, the decimal expression for 8¼d. if the primary unit be 1 shilling: it follows therefore that 17s. 8¼d. is equivalent to 17.6875s.

20) 17.6875

.884375, the decimal expression for 17s. 8¼d. the primary unit being £1. sterling: it follows therefore that £3. 17s. 8¼d. is equivalent to £3.884375.

210. The regular and ordinary arithmetical process for this conversion of £3. 17s. 8¼d. into an equivalent decimal of £1. would stand as follows:

$$4 \overline{)\ 1}$$
$$12 \overline{)\ 8.25}$$
$$20 \overline{)\ 17.6875}$$
$$\overline{3.884375}$$

The rule which is followed in this and all similar cases, is to place in succession underneath each other the numbers which compose the composite concrete number, beginning with the lowest, and to divide them and the several resulting decimals placed after them by the successive divisors which connect the successive units of different denominations with each other: the result in the last line is the equivalent decimal required.

Thus let it be required to express 17 yards, 1 foot and 6 inches by an equivalent decimal of 1 mile.

$$12 \overline{)\ 6}$$
$$3 \overline{)\ 1.5}$$
$$1760 \overline{)\ 17.5}$$
$$\overline{.00994318,}$$

the equivalent decimal required.

Let it be required to reduce 11 gallons 3 quarts and 1 pint of wine to an equivalent decimal of a hogshead.

$$2 \overline{)\ 1}$$
$$4 \overline{)\ 3.5}$$
$$63 \overline{)\ 11.895}$$
$$\overline{.188492063492063\ldots}$$

which is the equivalent decimal required.

211. The decimal of a concrete unit may be converted into an equivalent composite concrete number, by simply reversing the steps of the preceding process; namely, multiplying those parts of such expressions *only* which *follow* the decimal point, by the divisors which successively connect the superior with the inferior units: thus the decimal 3.884375 of £1. may be re-converted into an equivalent composite number as follows:

$$3.884375$$
$$20$$
$$\overline{17.687500}$$
$$12$$
$$\overline{8.\quad 2500}$$
$$4$$
$$\overline{1.\quad 00.}$$

The successive integers which present themselves to the right of the decimal point form the successive parts of the composite number required, which is £3. 17s. 8¼d.

Again, let it be required to convert .42857 of a month into an equivalent composite concrete number.

$$.42857$$
$$4 \qquad \text{weeks in 1 month.}$$
$$\overline{1.71428}$$
$$7 \qquad \text{days in 1 week.}$$
$$\overline{4.99996}$$
$$24 \qquad \text{hours in 1 day.}$$
$$\overline{399984}$$
$$199992$$
$$\overline{23.99904}$$
$$60 \qquad \text{minutes in 1 hour.}$$
$$\overline{59.94240}$$
$$60 \qquad \text{seconds in 1 minute.}$$
$$\overline{56.54400}$$

Consequently 1 week 4 days 23 hours 59 minutes 56 seconds, and the decimal .544 of a second, or the fraction $\frac{68}{125}$ of a second, is equivalent to .42857 of a month: if the name of trines, quatrines and quines, were applied to the subsequent sexagesimal sub-divisions of time, the decimal .544 would be convertible into 32 trines, 38 quatrines and 24 quines.

Conversion of a decimal into a series of equivalent fractions of the same primary unit.

212. The same process which converts a decimal of any assigned primary unit into an equivalent composite number, effects its conversion into a series of equivalent fractions of the same primary unit, where the successive multipliers become the

factors of the denominators,' and the successive integers become their numerators :· thus the last example gives the decimal .42857 of a month equal to the series of fractions

$$\frac{1}{4} + \frac{4}{4 \times 7} + \frac{23}{24 \times 4 \times 7} + \frac{59}{60 \times 20 \times 4 \times 7} + \frac{56}{60^2 \times 24 \times 4 \times 7}$$

$$\frac{32}{60^3 \times 24 \times 4 \times 7} + \frac{38}{60^4 \times 24 \times 4 \times 7} + \frac{24}{60^5 \times 24 \times 4 \times 7} .$$

213. These conversions of composite concrete numbers into equivalent decimals, and the reconversion of decimals of an assigned primary unit into equivalent composite numbers, bring all the relations of concrete magnitudes, which the customs and laws of nations have established, however arbitrary and irregular, immediately under the dominion of the same uniform notation, by nine digits and zero, and consequently under the same regular and uniform system of arithmetical operations. It will by no means follow, however, that the practical processes which thence arise, are the easiest or the most rapid which can be formed, or that they may not be superseded in the real transactions of life by other methods, which, though less general and systematic, are much better adapted to the ordinary habits and acquirements of those who are required to use them. In the preceding chapter, however, we have considered arithmetic rather as a speculative than a merely practical science, with a view to the complete theoretical establishment of its rules, and to shew the dependence of the forms of its fundamental operations upon the principles of arithmetical notation.

Reduction of all arithmetical operations to one system.

CHAPTER III

ON THE THEORY OF THE EXTRACTION OF THE ROOTS OF
NUMBERS AND THE PROPERTIES OF SURDS.

Meaning of the square root of a number.

214. THE square root of a number is that number, whether expressed by a finite series of digits or not, which multiplied into itself will produce the primitive number: thus the square root of 4 is 2, since $2 \times 2 = 4$: the square root of 1069.29 is 32.7, since $32.7 \times 32.7 = 1069.29$: the square root of 10 is interminable, but its first seven digits are 3.162277, the product of which approximate root or number into itself differs from the primitive number 10 by .000004175271 only.

Formation of the square of $a+b$.

215. The rule for the extraction of the square root of numbers is derived from the rule for the formation of their squares: thus if the symbols a and b represent two numbers, the square of their sum, or

$$(a + b)^2 = a^2 + 2ab + b^2, \quad (\text{Art. 62.}):$$

Orders of its digits.

and if we further suppose a to represent a number whose final digit is of the rth *superior* order and b to represent a digit of the $(r-1)^{\text{th}}$ or next inferior order, then the final digits of a^2, $2ab$ and b^2 will be of the $2r^{\text{th}}$, $(2r-1)^{\text{th}}$ and $(2r-2)^{\text{th}}$ *superior* orders respectively *: and also if the final digit of a be of the rth *inferior* order and if the digit b be of the $(r+1)^{\text{th}}$ or next inferior order, then the final digits of a^2, $2ab$ and b^2 will be of the $2r^{\text{th}}$, $(2r+1)^{\text{th}}$ and $(2r+2)^{\text{th}}$ *inferior* orders respectively. In both cases therefore, the orders of the final digits of the three terms a^2, $2ab$ and b^2, of which the square of $a+b$

---

* This follows at once from Art. 174: in the view which we have given of arithmetical notation by nine digits and zero, we have assumed the existence of successive orders of units determined by their position with respect to the place of primary units or of the decimal point: and whenever the relative *orders* of the final digits of any numbers are in any way determined, we can place them underneath each other, add them together, subtract them from each other or from any other number, without any immediate reference to the absolute orders of the digits themselves: it is this principle which is the source of so much abbreviation in the exhibition and conduct of arithmetical operations.

is composed, will be successive and descending; and the distance of the last digit from the decimal point, whether to the right or to the left, will be *double* the number which expresses the order of the last digit of the root.

216. Again $(a + b)^2 = a^2 + 2ab + b^2 = a^2 + (2a + b) b$, since $(2a + b) b = 2ab + b^2$; and inasmuch as the final digit of a and the digit b are of successive orders, the digital expression for $2a + b$ will be found by writing b immediately after the digit or digits of $2a$.

Second symbolical form of the square of $a + b$.

Thus, if $a = \quad 3$ and $b = 2, \quad 2a + b = \quad 62$:

if $a = \quad 32$ and $b = 4, \quad 2a + b = \quad 644$,

if $a = 324$ and $b = 6, \quad 2a + b = 6486$,

and similarly in all other cases.

217. After this preparation, it will be very easy to exhibit the formation of the square of a number in that form in which it immediately leads to the inverse operation of extracting the square root.

Arithmetical process for forming the square of a number preparatory to the inverse process.

Thus let it be required to form the square of 3246.

$$3246$$
$$3246$$

$a \quad = 3.$	9	$= a^2,$
$2a = 6, \quad b = 2, \quad 2a + b = 62 \times 2$	124	$= (2a + b) b,$
$a' \quad = 32.$	1024	$= (32)^2,$
$2a' = 64, \quad b' = 4, \quad 2a' + b' = 644 \times 4$	2576	$= (2a' + b') b',$
$a'' \quad = 324.$	104976	$= (324)^2,$
$2a'' = 648, \quad b'' = 6, \quad 2a'' + b'' = 6486 \times 6$	38916	$= (2a'' + b'') b'',$
	10536516	$= (3246)^2.$

The preceding process furnishes successively the squares of the number expressed by the first, two first, three first, &c. digits, and so on until all the digits are exhausted: it is analogous to the method of multiplication proposed in Art. 183, upon which the inverse process of ordinate division, given in Arts. 182 and 184 was founded.

218. The arithmetical rule for performing the operation, whose scheme has been exhibited in the last Article, is as follows: *Rule.*

Write down the square of the first digit (a^2). *After double* ($2a$) *the first digit, place the second digit* (b) *and multiply the resulting number* ($2a+b$) *by the second digit* (b), *placing it underneath the first square and advancing its last digit two places to the right : the sum which arises from their addition, adding like digits to like digits, will be the square of the number expressed by the two first digits.*

After double ($2a'$) *the number* (a') *formed by the two first digits, write down the third* (b'), *and multiply the number* ($2a'+b'$), *which thence arises, by the third digit* (b'), *and place their product beneath the square of the number expressed by the two first digits* (a'^2), *advancing its last digit two places to the right : their sum, adding like digits to like digits, will be the square of the number* (a'') *expressed by the three first digits.*

The same process must be repeated until all the digits of the root are exhausted, when the final result will be the square of the entire number.

Principle of the inverse process for extracting the square root.

219. The inverse process for extracting the square root teaches us to subtract from the given number (whose root is required) the complete square of the number expressed by the digits of the root: if there be no remainder, we conclude that the given number is the complete square of the root which has been assigned: if not, we conclude that no such root, with a finite number of places, exists: let us take as an example of this inverse process the number 10536516, which has been shewn (Art. 217.) to be the square of 3246.

$a =$	3	10536516 (3246	
$a =$	3	9	
$2a + b$	62	153	Resolvend.
b	2	124	Subtrahend $= 2ab + b^2$.
$2a' + b'$	644	2965	Resolvend.
b'	4	2576	Subtrahend $= 2a'b' + b'^2$.
$2a'' + b''$	6486	38916	Resolvend.
b''	6	38916	Subtrahend $= 2a''b'' + b''^2$.
		. . . . .	

220. The description and explanation of the different steps of this process will furnish the rule which may be followed in all cases.

Divide the square, or number whose square root is required, *into periods of two places, by placing a dot over the place of units and over every second place both to the left and to the right.*

For if the order of the highest digit in the root be r, the order of the highest digit of the square will be $2r$ or $2r+1$, or the number of places, including that of primary units, will be $2r+1$ or $2r+2$*: in the first case, the first period will consist of one place only, and, in the second, of two: and again, if the order of the lowest inferior digit in the root be r, the order of the lowest inferior digit of the square will be $2r$†: or in other words, the number of decimal places in the square will always be even and double of the number of decimal places in the root.

Find the greatest number whose square is less than the first *period: write this in the first place of the root and also on the left of the square, repeating it again immediately beneath it: their sum placed below* (2a) *(in the third line) is the first divisor: their product* (a²) *is placed below the first period, and subtracted from it; and the remainder with the digits of the second period written after it, forms the first* resolvend: *divide the resolvend (omitting its last digit) by the divisor, taking the quotient in defect when necessary: this quotient is the second digit in the root, which is written after the first divisor and also beneath itself as before: the sum of the numbers thus placed beneath each other is the second divisor: their product is subtracted from the resolvend and the remainder, augmented by writing the third period after it, is the second resolvend: we now employ the divisor and resolvend as before, to find the third digit of the root, and so on, until the last resolvend disappears, in which case the complete root is obtained; but if the remainder and therefore the resolvend never disappears, the process is interminable.*

---

* For if a be a superior digit of the rth order and therefore equal to $a \times 10^r$ in terms of primary units, its square will be $a^2 \times 10^{2r}$, and therefore the final digit of a^2 is of the $2r^{th}$ superior order: and since the root a or $a \times 10^r$ is less than 10×10^r, whose square is 10^{2r+2} or the least number of the $(2r+2)$ order, it follows that no digit of $a^2 \times 10^{2r}$ can exceed the $(2r+1)^{th}$ order, or can consist of more than $2r+2$ or of less than $2r+1$ places.

† If a be an inferior digit of the rth order, and therefore equal to $\dfrac{a}{10^r}$ in terms of primary units, it follows that its square is $\dfrac{a^2}{10^{2r}}$, the final digit of which is of the $2r^{th}$ order, or exactly double the number of decimal places in the root.

221. The preceding Rule has been adapted to the scheme of the operation which is given in Art. 219, and which is that which is most convenient and most rapid in practice. Its principle is very obvious: supposing that we have subtracted a^2 from the square, and that we wish to subtract $(a+b)^2$ or $a^2 + 2ab + b^2$ from it, where b is the next digit inferior to the last digit in a, we observe that the order of the last digit of $(a+b)^2$ is lower by 2 than that of the last digit of a^2, and consequently that its significant digits can only embrace two more digits of the original square: we therefore bring down the digits of one additional period only, to form the remainder or resolvend from which the subtrahend $2ab + b^2$ is to be taken, a^2 having been already subtracted by the previous operations: we first determine b *tentatively* by dividing the resolvend, omitting its last digit, by $2a$*; when b is thus found, we form $2a + b$ by writing the digit b after the digits of $2a$, (Art. 216): we multiply $2a + b$ by b and subtract the product from the resolvend: we then form a new resolvend and a new divisor as before, and so on until the operation is concluded.

222. The following are examples:

(1) Extract the square root of 119550.669121.

3	119550.669121 (345.761	
3	9	
64	295	Resolvend.
4	256	Subtrahend.
685	3950	
5	3425	
6907	52566	
7	48349	
69146	421791	
6	414876	
691521	691521	
	691521	
	....	

* There are two places in $2ab + b^2$ below the last digit in a^2: in dividing $2ab + b^2$ by $2a$, we should get *generally* two places in the quotient: by omitting the last digit of the dividend we reduce the quotient to one place only.

(2)   Extract of the square root of 10.

3	$1\dot{0}.000\dot{0}00\ (\ 3.16227$
3	9
61	100
1	61
626	3900
6	3756
6322	14400
2	12644
63242	175600
2	126484
632447	4911600
7	4427129
632454	48447100

The process is interminable.

(3)   The square root of .1 is .316228....
The process is interminable.

(4)   The square root of .00000256 is .0016.

(5)   The square root of $\dfrac{582169}{956484} = \dfrac{763}{978}$.

In this case we extract the square root of the numerator and denominator respectively to form the numerator and denominator of the root of the fraction : for it is obvious that the square root of the fraction $\dfrac{a^2}{b^2}$ is $\dfrac{a}{b}$.

(6)   The square root of $\dfrac{7}{4}$ is 1.32287...and is interminable without repetition.

(7)   The square root of $3\frac{1}{3}$, or of .3.333 ... is 1.8257, and is interminable without repetition.

223.   The sign $\sqrt{}$ is usually placed before a number or al- Sign of the square root. gebraical quantity, to indicate that its square root is to be taken : thus $\sqrt{4}$, $\sqrt{189}$, $\sqrt{(a^2 + 2\,ab + b^2)}$, $\sqrt{\dfrac{a}{b}}$, denote the square roots of 4, 189, $a^2 + 2\,ab + b^2$ and $\dfrac{a}{b}$ respectively.

The square root denoted by the fractional index ½.

224. Another mode of denoting the square root by means of a fractional index $\frac{1}{2}$, is derived from the principles of symbolical algebra, and therefore involves higher and more general views than we are yet authorized to refer to: we shall thus find that

$$(4)^{\frac{1}{2}}, \quad (189)^{\frac{1}{2}}, \quad (a^2+2ab+b^2)^{\frac{1}{2}}, \quad \left(\frac{a}{b}\right)^{\frac{1}{2}}, \quad \text{will denote respectively}$$

the square roots of 4, 189, $a^2+2ab+b^2$ and $\dfrac{a}{b}$.

Cases in which the process for extracting the square root is interminable.

225. Whenever a remainder continues to exist, after all the periods of the number, whose root is required, which involve significant digits, are exhausted, so that the corresponding resolvend and all those which follow it have necessarily two zeros in their lowest places, the digits of the root will be interminable: for the last digit of the subtrahend, being the last digit of the square of one of the nine significant digits, is necessarily different from zero, and therefore when subtracted from a number terminated by zeros, will necessarily leave a remainder: it will follow therefore that such a remainder can never disappear, and consequently by writing after it one or more pairs of zeros, the process may always be continued, so as to furnish for ever significant digits in the root.

The digits of the square roots of finite numbers never form recurring periods.

226. Such interminable roots will never form recurring decimals: for such a root, if it existed, would be convertible into an equivalent fraction, and its square would also be a fraction which would not be reducible to a finite number, whether decimal or not *: it follows therefore, that no finite number, whether decimal or not, can possess an interminable root which is a recurring decimal.

What recurring decimals have roots which are recurring decimals.

227. If the root of a recurring decimal be required, which is convertible into an equivalent fraction whose numerator and denominator are complete squares, it will be found to present itself, if extracted by the ordinary rule, in the form of a recurring decimal †: the roots of all other recurring decimals,

---

* If the root be the fraction $\dfrac{a}{b}$ in its lowest terms, or the recurring decimal which is equal to it, its square will be $\dfrac{a^2}{b^2}$, which is also in its lowest terms, and not convertible therefore into a finite number, whether decimal or not.

† The root of the recurring decimal .444 ... is the recurring decimal .666 ... as will appear upon the application of the common rule.

will not form recurring decimals and will therefore be incommensurable numbers.

228. The square roots of numbers, which are not complete
squares, may be exhibited in the form of continued fractions,
which will be found to possess some remarkable properties.

Thus, let it be required to exhibit in this form the square
root of 19.

Reduction of the square root of a number, not a square, to a continued fraction.

(1) $\quad \sqrt{19} - 4 = \dfrac{3}{\sqrt{19}+4} = \dfrac{1}{\dfrac{\sqrt{19}+4}{3}}:$ and $\sqrt{19} = 4 + \dfrac{1}{\dfrac{\sqrt{19}+4}{3}}.$

For $\left(\sqrt{19}-4\right) \times \left(\sqrt{19}+4\right) = 3^{*}:$ and $\dfrac{3}{\sqrt{19}+4} \times \dfrac{\sqrt{19}+4}{3} = 1,$

or, $\quad \dfrac{3}{\sqrt{19}+4} = \dfrac{1}{\dfrac{\sqrt{19}+4}{3}}.$

(2) $\dfrac{\sqrt{19}+4}{3} - 2 = \dfrac{\sqrt{19}-2}{3} = \dfrac{1}{\dfrac{\sqrt{19}+2}{5}}:$ and $\dfrac{\sqrt{19}+4}{3} = 2 + \dfrac{1}{\dfrac{\sqrt{19}+2}{5}}.$

For $\dfrac{\left(\sqrt{19}-2\right)}{3} \times \dfrac{\left(\sqrt{19}+2\right)}{5} = 1.$

(3) $\dfrac{\sqrt{19}+2}{5} - 1 = \dfrac{\sqrt{19}-3}{5} = \dfrac{1}{\dfrac{\sqrt{19}+3}{2}}:$ and $\dfrac{\sqrt{19}+2}{5} = 1 + \dfrac{1}{\dfrac{\sqrt{19}+3}{2}}$

(4) $\dfrac{\sqrt{19}+3}{2} - 3 = \dfrac{\sqrt{19}-3}{2} = \dfrac{1}{\dfrac{\sqrt{19}+3}{5}}:$ and $\dfrac{\sqrt{19}+3}{2} = 3 + \dfrac{1}{\dfrac{\sqrt{19}+3}{5}}:$

(5) $\dfrac{\sqrt{19}+3}{5} - 1 = \dfrac{\sqrt{19}-2}{5} = \dfrac{1}{\dfrac{\sqrt{19}+2}{3}}:$ and $\dfrac{\sqrt{19}+3}{5} = 1 + \dfrac{1}{\dfrac{\sqrt{19}+2}{3}}.$

(6) $\dfrac{\sqrt{19}+2}{3} - 2 = \dfrac{\sqrt{19}-4}{3} = \dfrac{1}{\dfrac{\sqrt{19}+4}{3}}:$ and $\dfrac{\sqrt{19}+2}{3} = 2 + \dfrac{1}{\dfrac{\sqrt{19}+4}{3}}.$

(7) $\sqrt{19}+4 - 8 = \sqrt{19} - 4 = \dfrac{1}{\dfrac{\sqrt{19}+4}{3}}:$ and $\sqrt{19}+4 = 8 + \dfrac{1}{\dfrac{\sqrt{19}+4}{3}}.$

We have thus arrived at the same complete quotient as
in (1): the same series of quotients, after the first, will therefore
recur and in the same order, for ever, the series being

$$4 \mid 2, 1, 3, 1, 2, 8 \mid 2, 1, 3, 1, 2, 8.$$

* For generally $(a + b)(a - b) = a^2 - b^2$ (Art. 66.); and if we replace a by
$\sqrt{n}$, we shall get

$$(\sqrt{n} + b)(\sqrt{n} - b) = n - b^2.$$

The continued fraction is therefore

$$\sqrt{19} = 4 + \frac{1}{2} + \frac{1}{1} + \frac{1}{3} + \frac{1}{1} + \frac{1}{2} + \frac{1}{8} + \dots$$

The process exhibited in general symbols.

229. We will now exhibit the same process in general symbols, with a view to the deduction of the general rule for conducting it.

Let n be the number, $\sqrt{n}$ its root, (Art. 223.), a the greatest whole number which is less than $\sqrt{n}$; b, b', b'', b'''... the several quotients which follow the first quotient a: then

$$\sqrt{n} = a + \sqrt{n} - a = a + \frac{1}{\frac{\sqrt{n+a}}{r}}, \quad \text{where } r = n - a^2.*$$

$$\frac{\sqrt{n}+a}{r} = b + \frac{\sqrt{n}+a-rb}{r} = b + \frac{1}{\frac{\sqrt{n+a'}}{r'}}, \quad \text{where } a' = r\,b - a,$$
$$\dots\dots \; r' = \frac{n - a'^2}{r}\dagger,$$

$$\frac{\sqrt{n}+a'}{r'} = b' + \frac{\sqrt{n+a'-r'b'}}{r'} = b' + \frac{1}{\frac{\sqrt{n+a''}}{r''}}, \quad \text{where } a'' = r'b' - a',$$
$$\dots\dots \; r'' = \frac{n - a''^2}{r'}\ddagger,$$

and so on, until we arrive at a value r which is equal to 1, which gives the last quotient (Art. 232.) of each period.

Rule for the formation of the quotients.

230. The examination of these results will make the law of their formation sufficiently manifest.

* For $n - a^2 = (\sqrt{n} - a)(\sqrt{n} + a) = r$, and therefore
$$\sqrt{n} - a = \frac{r}{\sqrt{n}+a} = \frac{1}{\frac{\sqrt{n+a}}{r}}.$$

† For $\frac{\sqrt{n}+a}{r} - b = \frac{\sqrt{n}+a-rb}{r} = \frac{\sqrt{n}-(rb-a)}{r} = \frac{\sqrt{n}-a'}{r}$ (if $a' = rb - a$)
$$= \frac{n - a'^2}{r(\sqrt{n}+a')} \text{ (multiplying its numerator and denominator by } \sqrt{n}+a')$$
$$= \frac{r'}{\sqrt{n}+a'}, \quad \text{if } r' = \frac{n - a'^2}{r}.$$

‡ The values of r are necessarily whole numbers, for
$$r'' = \frac{n - a''^2}{r'} = \frac{n - (r'b' - a')^2}{r'} = \frac{n - a'^2 + 2a'b'r' - b'^2 r'^2}{r'} = \frac{rr' + 2a'b'r' - b'^2 r'^2}{r'}$$
$$\text{(for } r' = \frac{n - a'^2}{r} \text{ or } rr' = n - a'^2) = r + 2a'b' - b'^2 r' = r + b'(a' - a''),$$
for $a'' = r'b' - a'$, and therefore $a' - a'' = 2a' - r'b'$.

The several quotients are the greatest whole numbers which are less than the mixed fractions or complete quotients

$$\frac{\sqrt{n}+a}{r}, \quad \frac{\sqrt{n}+a'}{r'}, \quad \frac{\sqrt{n}+a''}{r''}, \quad \&c.$$

The several integral portions of the numerators a', a'', a''', &c. are formed by subtracting the preceding integral portion of the numerator from the product of the preceding denominator and integral quotient, as expressed by the formula $a' = rb - a$.

The several denominators r, r', r'', &c. are formed by dividing the excess of the given number above the square of the integral portion of the numerator just formed by the denominator of the preceding complete quotient, as expressed by the formula

$$r' = \frac{n - a'^2}{r}.$$

231. Thus let it be required to deduce the quotients of Examples. $\sqrt{13}$ by the aid of the preceding rule:

$$\sqrt{13} = 3 + \frac{1}{x}: \quad a = 3: \quad r = \frac{13 - 3^2}{1} = 4: \quad x = \frac{\sqrt{13} + 3}{4}.$$

$$\frac{\sqrt{13} + 3}{4} = 1 + \frac{1}{x'}: \quad a' = 4 \times 1 - 3 = 1: \quad r' = \frac{13 - 1^2}{4} = 3: \quad x' = \frac{\sqrt{13} + 1}{3}.$$

$$\frac{\sqrt{13} + 1}{3} = 1 + \frac{1}{x''}: \quad a'' = 3 \times 1 - 1 = 2: \quad r'' = \frac{13 - 2^2}{3} = 3: \quad x'' = \frac{\sqrt{13} + 2}{3}.$$

$$\frac{\sqrt{13} + 2}{3} = 1 + \frac{1}{x'''}: \quad a''' = 3 \times 1 - 2 = 1: \quad r''' = \frac{13 - 1^2}{3} = 4: \quad x''' = \frac{\sqrt{13} + 1}{4}.$$

$$\frac{\sqrt{13} + 1}{4} = 1 + \frac{1}{x^{iv}}: \quad a^{iv} = 4 \times 1 - 1 = 3: \quad r^{iv} = \frac{13 - 3^2}{4} = 1: \quad x^{iv} = \frac{\sqrt{13} + 3}{1}.$$

$$\frac{\sqrt{13} + 3}{1} = 6 + \frac{1}{x^{v}}.$$

The quotients 1, 1, 1, 1, 6, which succeed the first quotient 3, recur perpetually, in the same order.

It follows, therefore, that

$$\sqrt{13} = 3 + \frac{1}{1} + \frac{1}{1} + \frac{1}{1} + \frac{1}{1} + \frac{1}{6} + \ldots$$

. (2) ..The quotients corresponding to $\sqrt{33}$ are 5, 1, 2, 1, 10, 1, 2, 1, 10, &c.

(3) The quotients corresponding to $\sqrt{48}$ are 6, 1, 12, 1, 12, &c.

(4) The quotients corresponding to $\sqrt{50}$ are 7, 14, 14.

(5) The quotients corresponding to $\sqrt{150}$ are 12, 4, 24, 4, 24, &c.

The quotients after the first are periodical.

232. The quotients, which succeed the first, in the preceding and in all other cases, are periodical, the final quotient in each period being double of the first, or of the greatest whole number which is less than the root: the proof however of this proposition, as well as of some others which are connected with it, of great importance in the theory of numbers*, is not sufficiently elementary to allow of its introduction at this stage of a student's progress in Algebra, and we have therefore reserved it for a Note at the end of this volume.

Formation of cubes.

233. The rule for the extraction of the cube root is founded upon that for the formation of the cube: thus, (Art. 67.),
$$(a + b)^3 = a^3 + 3a^2b + 3ab^2 + b^3,$$
which may be put under the form $a^3 + (3a^2 + 3ab + b^2)b$: and it appears, therefore, that in order to pass from the cube of a

General rule.

number a to the cube of the sum of two numbers a and b, *we must add to the cube of the first, the product of the second into the sum of three times the square of the first, of three times the product of the first and second and of the square of the second.*

Arithmetical rule for the formation of the augment corresponding to an additional digit of the root.

234. In the preceding rule for the formation of the cube, we may suppose $a + b$ to represent a number of two or more digits, where b is the last of them, considered in its proper order: but inasmuch as in the actual process for the formation of the cube, we advance progressively from one digit to two, from two digits to three and so on, it becomes important to propose a proper arithmetical rule for the formation of the compound factor of the product which forms the *augment* in passing from the cube of a to that $a + b$.

---

* Of this kind are the propositions which furnish the solution of the equation
$$x^2 - ay^2 = 1,$$
when x, a and y are whole numbers; and which also enable us to judge of the possibility of the solution of the equation
$$x^2 - ay^3 = b,$$
under similar circumstances.

For this purpose, *we write down the new digit* (b) *after three* Rule. *times the first digit or number* (3a) (*since the order of the first is superior by unity to that of the second Art.* 216.) *and we multiply their sum by the new digit* b: *we add the resulting product* $(3a+b)b$ *to three times the square of the first digit or number* $(3a^2)$, *the final digit of* $(3a+b)b$ *being two places lower than the final digit of* $3a^2$: *the product of the new digit* (b) *and of the resulting sum* $(3a^2+3ab+b^2)$ *forms the* augment *of* a^3, *it being kept in mind that the final digit of* $(a+b)^3$ *is three places in advance* (*reckoning from left to right*) *of the final digit of* a^3.

If we include an additional digit (b') *in the root, calling the portion of the root* (a+b), *whose cube is already formed,* a', *we may form the new augment* $(3a'^2+3a'b'+b'^2)b'$ *in the following manner: since* $3a'^2 = 3(a+b)^2 = 3a^2+6ab+3b^2$, *it exceeds the compound factor of the preceding augment by* $3ab+2b^2$, *or by* $(3a+2b)b$: *we therefore add* b *to* $3a+b$, *which is already formed, we multiply their sum by* b *and we add the result to* $3a^2+3ab+b^2$, *which gives us* $3a'^2$: *we then add* b *to* $3a+2b$ *already formed, and after their sum* $3a+3b$ *or* $3a'$ *we write* b', *making* $3a'+b'$, *which multiplied by* b' *and added to* $3a'^2$, *gives us* $3a'^2+3a'b'+b'^2$, *or the compound factor, which multiplied into* b', *gives the augment connecting* $(a+b)^3$ *with* $(a'+b')^3$.

We repeat the same process for every additional digit of the root until they are all of them exhausted, when the sum of a^3 *and of all its successive augments will be the complete cube of the root required.*

235. Thus let it be required to form the cube of 765.

$$
\begin{array}{llll}
a= & 7 \\
3a= & 21 & 147=3a^2 & 343=a^3 & (765 \\
b= & 6 \\
\cline{1-2}
3a+b= & 216 \times 6 & 1296=(3a+b)b \\
b & 6 & 15996 \times 6= & 95976=(3a^2+3ab+b^2)b \\
\cline{1-2}
3a+2b= & 222 \times 6 & 1332=(3a+2b)b \\
b & 6 & 17328=3a'^2 \\
\cline{1-2}
3a'+b'= & 2285 \times 5 & 11425=(3a'+b')b' \\
& & 1744225 \times 5 & 8721125=(3a'^2+3a'b'+b'^2)b' \\
& & & 447697125
\end{array}
$$

The reverse process of extracting the cube root.

236. The process for extracting the cube root is the reverse of the preceding, requiring us, from the given cube, to find the digits of the root, and to subtract successively from the former the cube of the first digit of the root and also the successive *augments* Art. 234, (which now become *subtrahends,*) corresponding to the successive digits of the root as they are successively determined : these digits are discovered *tentatively,* by dividing the successive remainders which result from the subtraction of the cube of the first digit and of the succeeding subtrahends, the quotients being taken in defect, when necessary, and due regard being paid to the orders of the digits in the divisors and dividends employed : before however, we proceed to the formal statement of the rule to be followed, we will exhibit the process for extracting the cube root of the cube of 765, which was formed in the last Article.

		44̇7697125̇	(765
21	147	343	
216 × 6	1296	104697	first resolvend.
	15996 × 6	95976	first subtrahend.
6			
222 × 6	1332	8721125	second resolvend.
6	17328		
2285 × 5	11425		
	1744225 × 5	8721125	second subtrahend.

Rule.

237. The following is the general rule for performing this operation.

Method of pointing.

Divide the number whose cube root is required into periods, by marking off every third digit to the right and left from the place of units : the number of periods to the right or to the left of the decimal point will determine the number of places in the root to the right or to the left of the decimal point *.

The first digit of the root and the first resolvend.

Find the greatest number whose cube is less than the first period : this is the first digit of the root : subtract its cube from the first

---

* The final digit of the cube of a digit of the nth superior or inferior order will be of the $3n$th superior or inferior order : thus, the order of the final digit 3 of the cube of 7 in the example just given is 6, which is the number of places which succeeds it ; and similarly in other cases.

period, and after the remainder write down the second period: this forms the first resolvend.

To the right of the cube, write three times the first digit of the root and also three times its square, which becomes the first divisor: divide the resolvend (omitting its two last digits *) by the divisor and the quotient (taken in defect if necessary) will form the second digit of the root.

Mode of finding the first divisor and the second digit of the root.

After three times the first digit place the second: multiply the resulting number by the second digit and add the product to the first divisor, advancing its last digit two places to the right †: multiply their sum by the second digit to form the subtrahend.

Mode of forming the subtrahend.

Subtract the subtrahend from the resolvend and after the remainder write the next period of the cube: this forms the new resolvend.

Mode of forming the second resolvend.

To the last number formed in the first column add the second digit, multiply their sum by the second digit, and add their product to the last number placed in the second column, forming the second divisor; divide the second resolvend by it (omitting its two last digits) and the quotient (taken in defect if necessary) is the third digit of the root.

Formation of the second subtrahend and discovery of the third digit of the root

To the last number placed in the first column add the second digit of the root, and after their sum write the third digit: multiply the resulting number by the third digit, adding their product to the second divisor, its final digit being advanced two places to the right: multiply their sum by the third digit of the root, and the resulting product is the second subtrahend.

Formation of the second subtrahend.

We proceed in a similar manner to form the third resolvend, and so on until there is no remainder, or until it is thought proper to terminate the process, which is necessarily interminable if the remainder does not disappear when all the periods of significant digits in the number whose cube root is required, are exhausted.

* For the order of the final digit of $3a^2b$ is higher by two places than the final digit of $(a+b)^3$, which is of the same order with the final digit of the resolvend.

† For the order of the final digit of $3a^2$ is higher by two places than the final digit of $(3a+b)b$ or $3ab+b^2$.

238. The following are examples.

(1) To extract the cube root of 41278.242816.

$$4\overset{.}{1}278.24\overset{.}{2}81\overset{.}{6}\ldots(34.56$$

9		27	1st divisor.	27
94	× 4	376		14278	1st resolvend.
4		3076 × 4 =		12304	1st subtrahend.
98	× 4	392		1974242	2d resolvend.
4		3468	2d divisor.	
1025	× 5	5125		
5		351925 × 5		1759625	2d subtrahend.
1030	× 5	5150		214617816	3d resolvend.
5		357075	3d divisor.	
10356	× 6	62136		
		35769636 × 6.		214617816	3d subtrahend.

(2) To extract the cube root of 12.

$$1\overset{.}{2}.00\overset{.}{0}\ldots(2.289$$

6		12	8
62 × 2		124	
			4000
2		1324 × 2	2648
64 × 2		128	
2		1452	1352000
668 × 8		5344	
8		150544 × 8	1204352
676 × 8		5408	147648000
8		155952	
6849 × 9		61641	
		15656841 × 9	140911569
			6736431

The process is obviously interminable *.

* The rule for extracting the cube root might be framed so as to exclude all
repetitions of digits which do not forward the operation: thus, in the second
column of this example, we find 24 in the second and third line, 44 in the sixth

(3) The cube root of 27054036008 is 3002.
(4) The cube root of .01 is .2154...
(5) The cube root of 102.875 is 4.68565...
(6) The cube root of $\frac{2}{3}$ is .87358...

239. When the earlier digits of the root have been formed and many more are not required, the operation may be abbreviated, by omitting all those digits of the resolvends and subtrahends which are below an assigned order, and consequently likewise all those digits of the partial and complete divisors which form digits in the subtrahends below the prescribed orders: thus, let it be required to extract the cube root of 147, admitting no digit into the resolvend below the 6th inferior order.

Abbreviated form of the operation.

15	75	147...(5.277626
2		
152 × 2	304	125
2		22000
154 × 2	7804 × 2	15608
.2	308	
	8112	6392000
1567 × 7	10969	
7	822169 × 7	5755183
1574 × 7	11018	636817
7	83318	
15817 × 7	110	
	83428 × 7	583996
	7	
	8350	52821
	7	
	8357 × 6	50142
		1679
	835 × 2	1670
		9

and seventh line, 41 in the tenth line repeated twice: this might be easily avoided, if the first three lines were written as follows,

$$12$$
$$1$$
$$\overline{1324}$$

placing the two last digits of 124 *at once* in the third line, and similarly for the other cases: the operation under this form, however, would lose more in the distinct exhibition of the numbers which form the divisors, whether complete or incomplete, than it would gain in brevity.

T

The extraction of roots is equivalent to the solution of an equation of the same order with the root.

240. The extraction of the square root of a number n may be considered as equivalent to the arithmetical solution of the equation

$$x^2 = n,$$

where x, or the square root of n, is an unknown quantity, until the operation is concluded: for it is obvious that x is equal to $\sqrt{n}$ or to the square root of n. In a similar manner the extraction of the cube root of a number n is equivalent to the arithmetical solution of the equation

$$x^3 = n,$$

where x, or the cube root of n, is an unknown quantity, until the operation is concluded.

This unknown root, which we have denoted by x, may be required to satisfy more complex conditions than those which we have hitherto considered: thus, it may be such that the sum of its cube, of (a) times its square, and of (b) times the unknown quantity or number itself, may be equal to a given number n, a series of conditions which would be expressed algebraically by the equation

$$x^3 + ax^2 + bx = n\,^*,$$

a and b being any assigned numbers: it remains to assign an arithmetical rule by which such roots of n or values of x may be determined in this and similar cases.

Investigation of the rule for the extraction of a compound cubic root.

241. Let r be the greatest whole or decimal number, of an assigned order, such that $r^3 + ar^2 + br$ shall be less than n, and which may be found by making x successively $1, 2, 3\ldots$, or $.1, .2, .3$, or $.01, .02, .03, \ldots$ &c., until we arrive at two successive substitutions, one of which gives $r^3 + ar^2 + br$ less and the other greater, than n: if however in consequence of the small value of r or from other causes, any one term of $r^3 + ar^2 + br$, such as br, becomes very much greater than the others, a more or less near approximation will be made to the value of r by dividing n by b.

Let us now suppose $x = r + x'$, and therefore

$$(r + x')^3 + a(r + x')^2 + b(r + x') = n,$$

or, $(r^3 + 3r^2 x' + 3r x'^2 + x'^3) + a(r^2 + 2r x' + x'^2) + br + bx' = n,$

or, $x'^3 + (3r + a)\,x'^2 + (3r^2 + 2ar + b)\,x' = n - R,$

---

* Any equation which involves the cube of an unknown quantity or number x and no higher power of it, when freed from fractions, is called a cubic equation: such equations admit of a great variety of forms.

$$(\text{if } R = r^3 + ar^2 + br),$$

$$\text{or, } x'^3 + a'x'^2 + b'x' = n',$$

$$\text{if } a' = 3r + a, \quad b' = 3r^2 + 2ar + b \quad \text{and} \quad n' = n - R.$$

It remains to exhibit the formation of a', b' R, and n', under such a form as may become the foundation of a simple arithmetical rule.

a	b	$n \ldots (r$
$(r + a) \times r$	$r^2 + ar$	
r	$(r^2 + ar + b) \times r$	$r^3 + ar^2 + br$
r	r^2	n'
$3r + a$ or a'	$3r^2 + 2ar + b$ or b'	

We place at the head of three successive columns a, b and n: we write down $r + a$ in the first column and multiply it by r, placing the product $r^2 + ar$ in the second column underneath b: beneath $r^2 + ar$ we again write the sum of the same product $r^2 + ar$ and b, which multiplied by r, gives $r^3 + ar^2 + br$, or the first subtrahend R: underneath $r + a$ in the first column, we write down r twice and form the sum which is $3r + a$ or a': underneath $r^2 + ar + b$ in the second column, we write r^2 and the sum of the three numbers $r^2 + ar$, $r^2 + ar + b$ and r^2, which are placed underneath each other, gives $3r^2 + 2ar + b$ or b': we also subtract the subtrahend R from n, which gives n': we now repeat the same operations with a', b' and n', and so on, as long as a value of n remains, or until we choose to terminate the operation.

Since the successive values of r will be decimals of descending orders, the term br will sooner or later become much greater than r^3 and ar^2, and consequently under such circumstances, approximate values of r (taken in defect) will be found by dividing n by b, considering n and b as the representatives of any of their successive values n', n'' &c. and b', b'', &c.

242. Thus let it be required to find the value of x in the Example. equation

$$x^3 + 10x^2 + 6x = 120.$$

The root is included between the numbers 2 and 3.

148

```
  10              6                    120 ...(2.8330
   2
 12 × 2          24
   2             30        × 2         60
   2              4                    60000
              ⎧  58
168 × 8       ⎨ 1344
   8          ⎩ 7144      × 8          57152
   8             64                    2848000
              ⎧ 8552
1843 × 3      ⎨ 5529
   3          ⎩ 860729    × 3          2582187
   3              9                    265813000
              ⎧ 866267
18493 × 3     ⎨  55479
              ⎩ 86682179  × 3          262046537
                   9                   3766463
               86737667
```

By referring to the scheme of the operation in the preceding Article, replacing in the first instance a, b, n, r by 10, 6, 120, and 2; in the second by 16, 58, 60 and .8; in the third by 18.4, 85.52, 28.48 and .03, and so on, the course of the process will be made manifest: and if we should successively replace in the equation whose root is required, a, b and n by their successive values, we should get the following series of transformed equations corresponding to them;

$$x^3 + 10x^2 + 6x = 120 \ldots (1),$$
$$x'^3 + 16x'^2 + 58x' = 60 \ldots (2),$$
$$x''^3 + 18.4x''^2 + 85.52x'' = 2.848 \ldots (3),$$
$$x'''^3 + 18.49x'''^2 + 86.6267x''' = .265813 \ldots (4).$$

Rules for the extraction of compound roots generally presuppose a knowledge of the theory of equations.

243. We might easily frame rules for the extraction of compound roots in cases much more complicated than those which are comprehended in the two last Articles: but the enquiry would be somewhat premature, inasmuch as it involves the determination of the numerical limits between which roots

are placed, and consequently a knowledge of some of the most important parts of the theory of equations: we shall therefore defer the further consideration of such compound roots, until we come to that part of our subject *.

244. The extraction of the fourth and higher roots of numbers, will be found to be dependent upon the rules for the formation of the fourth and higher powers of their roots: the arithmetical processes which would be found to result are extremely operose and difficult, and are almost entirely superseded by the use of logarithms, which enable us to determine a considerable number of digits of such roots with very great facility: it is for this reason that we shall not attempt the investigation and illustration of the rules for finding any roots which are higher than the cube.

Rules for the extraction of the fourth and higher roots of numbers.

245. Those roots which are incapable of being exhibited in a finite form, and which are therefore *incommensurable* for the reasons assigned in Article 165, are commonly called *surds,* and are differently denominated according to the denomination of the root to which they correspond: thus, *quadratic, cubic,* and *biquadratic* surds are those which originate in the extraction of the *square, cube,* and *biquadratic* roots respectively: and generally a *surd* of the nth order will be that which originates in the extraction of the nth root.

Meaning of the term surd.

246. Quadratic surds are denoted by prefixing the sign $\sqrt{}$ before the number or *base* whose root is to be extracted: cubic surds are denoted by the sign $\sqrt[3]{}$, biquadratic surds by the sign $\sqrt[4]{}$, surds of the fifth order by $\sqrt[5]{}$, and surds of the nth order by $\sqrt[n]{}$, the number which accompanies the sign (the sign of quadratic surds excepted) denominating the order of the root: thus, $\sqrt{3}$ is a quadratic surd, $\sqrt[3]{14}$ a cubic surd, $\sqrt[4]{27}$ a biquadratic surd, and $\sqrt[n]{124}$ is a surd of the nth order.

Signs by which they are denoted.

In symbolical algebra we shall replace the signs $\sqrt{}$, $\sqrt[3]{}$, $\sqrt[4]{}$, $\sqrt[n]{}$ by the indices $\frac{1}{2}$, $\frac{1}{3}$, $\frac{1}{4}$, $\frac{1}{n}$, denoting $\sqrt{3}$ by $(3)^{\frac{1}{2}}$, $\sqrt[3]{14}$ by $(14)^{\frac{1}{3}}$, $\sqrt[4]{27}$ by $(27)^{\frac{1}{4}}$, and $\sqrt{124}$ by $(127)^{\frac{1}{n}}$: there are, however, no principles which we have hitherto assumed or esta-

Denoted also by indices.

* These methods, which enable us to subject the actual numerical solution of equations, when the limits of their roots are determined, to uniform arithmetical processes, are chiefly though not entirely due to Mr Horner: see a very clear exposition of them in Professor Young's Theory of Equations, Chap. v. and vi.

blished which are competent to explain and justify the use of such indices with such a meaning.

Surds of the same order which are reducible to multiples of the same surd.

247. Surds of the same order are comparable with each other like finite numbers, when their bases have a common measure different from unity and when the roots of the proper order of their other factors are finite or rational numbers: thus, $\sqrt{2}$ and $\sqrt{8}$ are reducible to $\sqrt{2}$ and $2\sqrt{2}$, involving the same quadratic surd $\sqrt{2}$: $\sqrt{45}$ and $\sqrt{80}$ or $\sqrt{9 \times 5}$ and $\sqrt{16 \times 5}$ are reducible to $3\sqrt{5}$ and $4\sqrt{5}$, or are multiples of the same quadratic surd $\sqrt{5}$: $\sqrt[3]{108}$ and $\sqrt[3]{1372}$ are equivalent to $\sqrt[3]{27 \times 4}$ and $\sqrt[3]{343 \times 4}$, and are therefore reducible to $3\sqrt[3]{4}$ and $7\sqrt[3]{4}$, or to multiples of the same cubic surd $\sqrt[3]{4}$: $\sqrt[5]{224}$ and $\sqrt[5]{1701}$ are equivalent to $\sqrt[5]{32 \times 7}$ and $\sqrt[5]{243 \times 7}$, and are therefore reducible to $2\sqrt[5]{7}$ and $3\sqrt[5]{7}$, which are multiples of the same surd $\sqrt[5]{7}$: and generally $\sqrt[n]{a^n c}$ and $\sqrt[n]{b^n c}$ are reducible to $a\sqrt[n]{c}$ and $b\sqrt[n]{c}$, which are multiples of the same surd $\sqrt[n]{c}$, if c be not a complete n^{th} power. Such surds are called *like* surds. If, however, the bases of surds of the same order have no common factors or if their other factor be not a complete power of the same order with the denomination of the surd, they will be incapable of reduction to multiples of a common surd, and will not admit therefore of comparison with each other like ordinary numbers.

The product of two irreducible surds of the same order will be a surd of the same order irreducible with its factors.

248. The product of two *unlike* surds of the same order will be a surd of the same order, whose base is the product of the bases of the factors: thus, if $\sqrt{a}$ and $\sqrt{b}$ be two quadratic surds, their product $\sqrt{a}\sqrt{b}$ will be equal to $\sqrt{ab}$, which will not be reducible, under any circumstances, to the same surd either with $\sqrt{a}$ or $\sqrt{b}$, nor to a rational number, unless $\sqrt{a}$ and $\sqrt{b}$ are *like* surds: for, in the first place, since the square of the product $\sqrt{a}\sqrt{b}$ is ab, which is also the square of $\sqrt{ab}$, it follows that their roots $\sqrt{a}\sqrt{b}$ and $\sqrt{ab}$ are equal to each other: and in the second place, if we suppose $\sqrt{ab} = ra$, where r is a finite number, whether fractional or not, then we get $ab = r^2 a^2$, and therefore $b = r^2 a$ and $\sqrt{b} = r\sqrt{a}$, which shews that $\sqrt{a}$ and $\sqrt{b}$ are reducible under such circumstances to a common surd: it will follow therefore generally that $\sqrt{ab}$ will be a quadratic surd different from either of its factors $\sqrt{a}$ or $\sqrt{b}$. The same reasoning may be extended to the products of cubic, biquadratic, and other surds of higher orders.

Thus, $\sqrt{3} \times \sqrt{5} = \sqrt{15}$: $\sqrt[3]{7} \times \sqrt[3]{10} = \sqrt[3]{70}$: but $\sqrt{18} \times \sqrt{98} = 42$, since $\sqrt{18} = 3\sqrt{2}$ and $\sqrt{98} = 7\sqrt{2}$, and are therefore *like* surds.

249. Quadratic surds cannot differ from each other by a finite number, whether fractional or not: for if we suppose

$$\sqrt{a} = b + \sqrt{c},$$

where $\sqrt{a}$ and $\sqrt{c}$ are quadratic surds and b a finite number, then the squares of these equal quantities will be equal, or

$$a = b^2 + 2b\sqrt{c} + c :$$

and if from each of these equal quantities we take away the same number $b^2 + c$, we get

$$a - b^2 - c = 2b\sqrt{c} :$$

if we further divide these equal quantities by $2b$, the quotients will be equal, or

$$\frac{a - b^2 - c}{2b} = \sqrt{c} :$$

It appears, therefore, that $\sqrt{c}$ is not a surd, but a finite number, whether fractional or not, which is contrary to the hypothesis which we have made: it will follow, therefore, that two quadratic surds cannot differ from each other by a finite number *.

Two quadratic surds cannot differ from each other by a finite number.

250. One quadratic surd cannot be equal to the sum of two others which are irreducible with it: for if possible, let us suppose

$$\sqrt{a} = \sqrt{b} + \sqrt{c},$$

where $\sqrt{b}$ and $\sqrt{c}$ are irreducible with each other and with $\sqrt{a}$: then taking the squares of these equal quantities or numbers, we get

$$a = b + 2\sqrt{bc} + c :$$

and subtracting $b + c$ from both these equal quantities, we get

$$a - b - c = 2\sqrt{bc},$$

and also

$$\frac{a - b - c}{2} = \sqrt{bc}.$$

A quadratic surd cannot be equal to the sum of two other surds which are irreducible with it.

---

* It will follow from this proposition, that no two quadratic surds, when reduced to the form of continued fractions, can possess the same period of recurring quotients: for if so, they would differ from each other by a finite number only, or in their first quotients only.

It appears therefore that $\sqrt{bc}$ is a finite number, and that therefore $\sqrt{b}$ and $\sqrt{c}$ are reducible to common surds, such as $r\sqrt{x}$ and $r'\sqrt{x}$; (Art. 247.) and consequently

$$\sqrt{a} = r\sqrt{x} + r'\sqrt{x}$$
$$= (r + r)\sqrt{x},$$

or $\sqrt{a}$ is reducible to the form $(r + r')\sqrt{x}$, and therefore to a common surd with $\sqrt{b}$ and $\sqrt{c}$, which is contrary to the hypothesis which we have made: we therefore conclude that a quadratic surd cannot be the sum of two others which are irreducible with it.

The properties of quadratic surds are distinct and incommunicable.

251. More generally it might be shewn, though not without the aid of principles of reasoning and methods of investigation which we are not yet authorized to use, that a quadratic surd cannot be formed by the addition, or subtraction of any number of quadratic surds, which are not all of them equally reducible to the same common surd with it: but even without the assistance of this more general conclusion, we have sufficiently shewn that the properties of such surds are altogether *distinct and incommunicable with each other*, and that they are therefore incapable of reduction unless *approximatively*, by means of the arithmetical processes of addition and subtraction to equivalent results, in which all traces of the elements of which such results are composed have disappeared in the course of the operation, as in the case of ordinary and finite numbers.

The properties of cubic and other surds similar to those of quadratic surds.

252. Cubic surds, considered with reference to each other, will possess no properties which are communicable with each other, unless in those cases in which they are reducible to the same cubic surd: and the same remark may be extended to the series of surds which belong to any assigned order whatsoever, as we shall afterwards have occasion to shew.

Surds of one order are always equal to surds of an inferior order, whose denomination is a multiple of the first.

253. Again, in considering surds of different orders, it may be easily shewn that a surd of one order cannot be equal to a surd of any other, unless the order of the second surd be an entire multiple of the first: thus $\sqrt{a}$ cannot be equal to $\sqrt[3]{b}$, for in that case we should have $a = \sqrt[3]{b^2}$, or $\sqrt[3]{b^3}$ a rational number, which cannot take place unless b be a perfect cube, and therefore $\sqrt[3]{b}$ not a surd. But $\sqrt{a}$ may be equal to $\sqrt[4]{b}$, if b^2 be equal to a: in a similar manner $\sqrt{a}$ may be equal to $\sqrt[6]{b}$ if b^3 be equal to a, and also $\sqrt[3]{a}$ may be equal to $\sqrt[6]{b}$, if b^2 be equal to a: and generally $\sqrt[n]{a}$ may be equal to $\sqrt[mn]{b}$, if b^m be equal to a.

254. If we write down a series of the nth roots of the natural numbers, all of them will be surds except those whose
bases are perfect n^{th} powers: and all those surds will be irreducible to a common surd, unless their bases have a common
factor, multiplied by perfect n^{th} powers. In a similar manner,
if we write down the series of successive roots of a number a
from the quadratic downwards, all those descending roots will
be surds unless a be resolvible into two or more equal factors,
in which case there will be as many whole numbers in the series,
as there are different ways in which is a resolvible into equal
factors.

Surds of the same order, whose bases are the natural numbers, or surds of the same base, the denomination of whose orders are the natural numbers.

255. Again all powers of a surd will be surds except those
whose denominations are equal to or multiples of, the denomination
of the root: thus the successive powers of $\sqrt[n]{a}$, will form a series
$\sqrt[n]{a}$, $\sqrt[n]{a^2}$, $\sqrt[n]{a^3}$, $\sqrt[n]{a^{n-1}}\,a$, $a\sqrt[n]{a}$, $a\sqrt[n]{a^2}$, $\ldots\ldots$, the first $n-1$ of
which are surds irreducible with each other, and all the other
terms of the series are whole numbers or multiples of the first
$(n-1)$ terms: and if we could conceive the existence of a root
whose denomination was an incommensurable number, such as
we shall afterwards be called upon to consider, then all its powers,
however far continued, will be surds irreducible with each other.

All powers of surds whose indices are less than the denomination of the root are irreducible surds.

256. The theory of surds, under the form in which we have
just presented it, is necessarily very imperfect, in consequence
of our not being able to avail ourselves of many propositions
in algebra, which are essential to its more complete develope-
ment: those properties of them however which we have noticed
in the preceding articles will be sufficient to point out their
general relation to each other, and also the extent to which they
are capable of being compared with each other by means of
the ordinary processes of arithmetic.

Imperfections in the preceding theory.

CHAPTER IV

ON RATIOS AND PROPORTIONS.

The term ratio.

257. THE term ratio in ordinary language, is used to express the relation which exists between two quantities of the same kind with respect to magnitude: thus we speak of the ratio of two numbers, of two forces, of two periods of time, and of any other concrete quantities of the same kind, the relation of whose magnitude to each other admits of being estimated or conceived.

In what manner represented.

258. A *ratio* (the term is here used absolutely) consists of two terms or members, which are denominated the *antecedent* and the *consequent*, from the order of their position: it may be denoted in arithmetic as well as in geometry, by writing the antecedent before the consequent, with two dots, one above the other, between them: thus the ratio of 3 to 5 is written 3 : 5.

In a similar manner, if *a* and *b* denoted any other two numbers, lines or other magnitudes of the same kind, their ratio, whatever meaning it may possess or receive, would be denoted by *a* : *b*.

Geometrical representation of ratio.

259. Such a mode of representing a ratio, merely exhibits its terms to the eye, in a certain order, as objects of comparison, and consequently conveys to the mind no idea of absolute magnitude: it may be called the geometrical representation of ratio, being the only one which is used in that science.

No geometrical definition of ratio properly so called.

Whatever modes, however, we may adopt in geometry for the representation of ratios, they must all of them be equally arbitrary and independent of each other: for there is, properly speaking, no definition of ratio in geometry, by which the equivalence of different modes of representation may be ascertained as necessary consequences of it: for ratio is said to be (Euclid, Book V. Def. 3.) *the mutual relation of two magnitudes of the same kind to one another, with respect to quantity,* a description of its meaning much too vague and general to be considered as a proper *definition*, inasmuch as it cannot be made the foundation of any propositions respecting it. It is for this reason that ratios in geometry are only considered when placed in connection with each other, as constituting or not constituting a *proportion*.

260. A little examination however of some of the conditions which ratios, taken according to the popular usage of the term, must satisfy, will lead to an arithmetical mode of representing them, by which their absolute magnitude may be ascertained, and which will thus conduct us to an arithmetical definition of ratio, which will be independent of the connection of ratios with each other: for it is perfectly conformable to our common idea of ratios, to consider them in the first place, as necessarily the *same* for the *same* magnitudes, in whatever manner they may be represented; and in the second place, as independent of the specific affections or properties (of the same kind) of the magnitudes themselves. *Popular meaning of the term ratio.*

261. Thus, if two lines admitted of resolution into 3 and 5 parts respectively, which were equal to each other, the lines themselves might be correctly represented by the numbers 3 and 5, and their ratio therefore by 3 : 5. But their common primary unit is itself divisible into 2, 3 or m equal parts, and the numbers of these successive parts which the original lines, under such circumstances would contain, would be severally 6 and 10, 9 and 15, $3m$ and $5m$, which might denote them equally with the original numbers 3 and 5; their ratio therefore, which remains the same, in conformity with the principle referred to, would be equally represented by 6 : 10, 9 : 15, and $3m$: $5m$. *Changes which the terms of the same ratio may undergo.*

Again, this mode of representing lines and their ratio, which possess this particular relation to each other, is equally applicable to any other magnitudes of the same kind which possess the same relation to each other: thus two areas, two solids, two forces, two periods of time, may be so related to each other, as to admit of resolution into 3 and 5 parts or units respectively, which are equal to each other: under such circumstances they must admit likewise of resolution into numbers of parts or subordinate units equal to each other, which are any equimultiples of 3 and 5: such pairs of numbers therefore, will equally represent those magnitudes, and will likewise equally form the terms of the ratio which expresses their relation to each other.

Conclu-
sions
thence
deduced.

262. The preceding observations will conduct us naturally to the following conclusions:

(1) Magnitudes of the same kind, which admit of resolution into any numbers of parts or units, which are equal to each other, may be properly represented by such numbers, or by any equimultiples * of them.

(2) The numbers which represent two magnitudes of the same kind will form the terms of the ratio, which expresses their relation to each other: and this ratio remains unaltered, when its terms are replaced by any equimultiples of them.

(3) Such ratios are dependent upon the numbers only, which form their terms and are the same, whatever be the nature and magnitude of the concrete unit of which those numbers may be respectively composed.

(4) The ratios of two magnitudes of the same kind, which have no common measure with each other, and which are therefore incommensurable with each other, may be approximately represented by such numbers of common units of those magnitudes as approximate to them in value.

A ratio
may be re-
presented
by means of
a fraction.

263. All these conditions will be fully satisfied, if we *agree* to denote a ratio by means of a fraction, of which the antecedent is the numerator, and the consequent the denominator: for the value of this fraction is determined solely by the numbers which form its numerator and denominator, and is entirely independent of the specific value or nature of the units of the same kind, of which they are respectively composed: and it remains unaltered, when its numerator and denominator are multiplied or divided by the same number, that is, when the terms of the ratio corresponding, are replaced by any equimultiples of them.

Arithmeti-
cal defini-
tion of
ratio.

In arithmetic, therefore, and also in arithmetical algebra, a ratio may be *defined*, as the fraction whose numerator is the antecedent, and denominator is the consequent of the ratio.

It will follow, therefore, that both in Arithmetic and Arithmetical Algebra, the theory of ratios will be identified with the theory of fractions.

Includes
geometrical
as well as
other mag-
nitudes.

264. The symbols of arithmetic represent geometrical as well as other quantities, and the lines, areas and solids of geo-

---

* We shall generally give an enlarged signification to the term *multiple*, as denoting the result of multiplication by fractions as well as by whole numbers.

metry, are thus brought within the range of this definition: it must be kept in mind however, that it is only by considering geometry as thus connected with arithmetic, that such quantities admit of the mode of representation which that definition renders necessary: for there is no geometrical mode of representing the division of one line by another, or the result of such a division: for this result can bear no analogy to the quantities which produce it, being essentially numerical and consequently not capable of being represented by a line, unless in a symbolical sense, which under such circumstances must be different from that in which the other lines are used. It is of great importance to attend to this distinction, as it serves not only to explain the reason why there is no independent definition of ratio in geometry, but also why in comparing different ratios of geometrical lines or areas with each other, with reference to their identity or diversity, we are not at liberty to avail ourselves of the algebraical definition of ratio, unless we first change the mode of representing the quantities which are the objects of the investigation, and resort to the use of the symbols of arithmetic or algebra.

Reason why there is no definition of ratio in geometry.

265. We shall now proceed to the statement of some of the more common propositions concerning ratios, which, though merely properties of arithmetical and other fractions, require, from custom, the use of a new and peculiar phraseology, and are connected with the formation of some important theories.

" Ratios are compared with each other, by comparing the fractions by which they are denoted."

Ratios: how compared.

Thus, the ratios of 3 to 5 and of 5 to 8, are denoted by the fractions $\frac{3}{5}$ and $\frac{5}{8}$: these are identical with the fractions $\frac{24}{40}$ and $\frac{25}{40}$ (Art. 127.): it is the second of these ratios, therefore, which is the greater of the two.

266. A ratio of *greater inequality* is one, whose antecedent is greater than its consequent: a *ratio of less inequality* is one, whose antecedent is less than its consequent: a *ratio of equality* is one, whose antecedent is equal to its consequent: the first corresponds to an improper fraction, the second to a proper fraction, and the third to unity. The following proposition, connected with ratios which are thus denominated, is frequently used.

Ratios of greater or less inequality.

Proposition
respecting
them.
267. "A ratio of greater inequality is diminished and one of less inequality increased, by adding the same number * to both its terms."

Let $\dfrac{a}{b}$ be the primitive and $\dfrac{a+x}{b+x}$ the secondary ratio, formed by adding the same number x to both its terms: these fractions reduced to a common denominator, (Art. 124.) become

$$\frac{ab+ax}{b(b+x)}, \text{ and } \frac{ab+bx}{b(b+x)},$$

respectively: if a be greater than b, or if the primitive ratio be one of greater inequality, the first fraction is the *greater* of the two, which is diminished, therefore, by the addition of the same number to both its terms: but if a be less than b, or if the primitive ratio be one of less inequality, the first fraction is the less of the two, which is increased therefore by the addition of the same number to both its terms.

Meaning of
the sum of
two or
more ratios.
268. If there be several ratios, whose antecedents are multiplied together for a new antecedent, and their consequents together for a new consequent, the resulting ratio is called the *sum* of the component ratios: in other words, the sum of two or more ratios is the product of the fractions which denote them.

Thus, the sum of the ratios of $a:b$ and $c:d$ is $ac:bd$.

When the
consequent
of one ratio
is the ante-
cedent of
the next.
269. If the consequent of one ratio become the antecedent of the next, the sum of any number of such ratios is the ratio of the first antecedent to the last consequent.

If the ratios be $a:b$, $b:c$, $c:d$, and $d:e$; then their sum

$$= \frac{a}{b} \times \frac{b}{c} \times \frac{c}{d} \times \frac{d}{e} = \frac{abcd}{bcde} = \frac{a}{e}.$$

A duplicate
ratio.
270. The sum of two equal ratios, or the *double* of any ratio, is the ratio of the square of the antecedent to the square of the consequent.

For the sum of the ratios $a:b$ and $a:b$ is

$$\frac{a}{b} \times \frac{a}{b} - \frac{a^2}{b^2}.$$

* By number is meant any numerical quantity, whether fractional or integral.

271. In a similar manner, the *triple* of any ratio is the ratio of the cube of its antecedent to the cube of its consequent. *A triplicate ratio.*

For the sum of the ratio of $a : b$, added thrice together, is

$$\frac{a}{b} \times \frac{a}{b} \times \frac{a}{b} = \frac{a^3}{b^3}.$$

272. More generally, the sum of n times any ratio, such as $a : b$, is the ratio of $a^n : b^n$. *n times a ratio.*

For the product of $\frac{a}{b}$ into itself, repeated as a factor n times, is $\frac{a^n}{b^n}$.

In the same sense $a^n : 1$ or $\frac{a^n}{1}$ or a^n simply, is called n times the ratio of $a : 1$.

273. It is in this sense, that the powers of numbers may be considered as *multiples* of the ratios of the simple numbers to 1; thus $10^2 : 1$ or $\frac{10^2}{1}$ or 10^2, may be termed the *double* of the ratio of $10 : 1$; $10^5 : 1$ or $\frac{10^5}{1}$ or 10^5, the *quintuple* of that ratio, and similarly in other cases, the index of the power being the *measure* of the number of simple ratios whose addition forms the compound one: the term *logarithm* means the *number of ratios*, and is therefore equivalent in signification to the index of the number, which forms the *fundamental* ratio. *Logarithm, its primitive meaning.*

Thus if the fundamental ratio be $a : 1$ or $\frac{a}{1}$ or a, then 2 is the *logarithm* of $a^2 : 1$ or of $\frac{a^2}{1}$ or of $a^2 : 3$ is the logarithm of $a^3 : 1$ or of $\frac{a^3}{1}$ or of a^3: and n is the logarithm of $a^n : 1$ or of $\frac{a^n}{1}$ or of a^n.

274. The ratio of $\sqrt{a} : \sqrt{b}$ is called the *half* or the *subduplicate* ratio of $a : b$: for the double of this ratio is *A subduplicate ratio.*

$$\frac{\sqrt{a}}{\sqrt{b}} \times \frac{\sqrt{a}}{\sqrt{b}} = \frac{a}{b}.$$

275. The ratio of $\sqrt[3]{a} : \sqrt[3]{b}$ or $\frac{\sqrt[3]{a}}{\sqrt[3]{b}}$ is called the *subtriplicate* of the ratio of $a : b$ or of $\frac{a}{b}$: for the *triple* of that ratio is $\cdot$ *A subtriplicate ratio.*

$$\frac{\sqrt[3]{a}}{\sqrt[3]{b}} \times \frac{\sqrt[3]{a}}{\sqrt[3]{b}} \times \frac{\sqrt[3]{a}}{\sqrt[3]{b}} = \frac{a}{b}.$$

The sesquiplicate ratio.

276. The ratio of $\sqrt{a^3} : \sqrt{b^3}$. or $\frac{\sqrt{a^3}}{\sqrt{b^3}}$ is called the *sesquiplicate* * (or *ratio sesquialtera*) of $a : b$ or of $\frac{a}{b}$: for the sum of the simple and subduplicate ratio of $a : b$ is

$$\frac{a}{b} \times \frac{\sqrt{a}}{\sqrt{b}} = \frac{\sqrt{a^2} \times \sqrt{a}}{\sqrt{b^2} \times \sqrt{b}} = \frac{\sqrt{a^3}}{\sqrt{b^3}} \dots \text{ (Art. 248.)}$$

Ratios whose terms are unlike surds are not convertible into equivalent ratios, whose terms are rational.

277. The ratios of surds and incommensurable numbers generally, admit of being represented equally with those of commensurable numbers: thus the ratio of $\sqrt{2} : \sqrt{3}$ is represented by $\frac{\sqrt{2}}{\sqrt{3}}$ in the same manner that the ratio of $2 : 3$ is represented by $\frac{2}{3}$: and if we replace $\sqrt{2}$ and $\sqrt{3}$ in this ratio by approximate finite numbers, the ratio which results will approximate to the ratio $\frac{\sqrt{2}}{\sqrt{3}}$: it is only however, when the surds which form the antecedent and consequent of a ratio are reducible to a common surd, that it can be replaced by an equivalent ratio in rational terms: thus the ratio $\sqrt{8} : \sqrt{18}$ or

Ratios whose terms involve like surds are convertible into others whose terms are rational, and conversely.

$\frac{\sqrt{8}}{\sqrt{18}}$ is equivalent to $\frac{2\sqrt{2}}{3\sqrt{2}}$, and therefore to $\frac{2}{3}$: the ratio $\sqrt[3]{81}$: $\sqrt[3]{375}$ or $\frac{\sqrt[3]{81}}{\sqrt[3]{375}}$ is equivalent to $\frac{3\sqrt[3]{3}}{5\sqrt[3]{3}}$, and therefore to $\frac{3}{5}$: and conversely, a ratio whose terms are rational may be converted into an equivalent ratio whose terms are surds, if its terms be multiplied by any common surd, whether we suppose that the rational factors are brought under the sign of the root or not: thus $\frac{7}{11}$ is equivalent to $\frac{7\sqrt{5}}{11\sqrt{5}}$ or to $\frac{\sqrt{245}}{\sqrt{605}}$; and $\frac{2}{13}$ is equivalent to $\frac{2\sqrt[3]{7}}{13\sqrt[3]{7}}$ or to $\frac{\sqrt[3]{56}}{\sqrt[3]{15379}}$.

* The periodic times of any two planets round the Sun are in the *sesquiplicate* ratio of the major axes of their elliptic orbits or of their mean distances from the Sun, a circumstance which gives to this ratio some degree of interest and importance.

The use of fractional indices, which the principles of symbolical algebra will authorize, will enable us to treat ratios which involve the roots of the antecedent and consequent, or powers of them, with much greater clearness and generality than is practicable when mere signs of such surds are allowed to be used.

278. Numbers, whether rational or surd, are essentially discontinuous, and in strictness of language, are incapable of expressing as symbols the properties of continuous magnitude: it is true that if two numbers can be found which represent magnitudes less and greater than the one assigned, others can be found which differ from the representative of the magnitude required less than any number which can be or may be assigned, (Art. 169.) and which in this sense therefore become arithmetically equal to it; but there is an essential distinction between arithmetical equality, as thus defined, and arithmetical identity, and consequently no number can become the absolute representative of an incommensurable magnitude: and though the surd roots of numbers, which are themselves incommensurable, can represent symbolically incommensurable magnitudes, yet any succession of such surd roots must be equally discontinuous with commensurable numbers, and therefore equally incapable of becoming the representatives, except approximately, of every gradation of value of a continuous magnitude included between any assigned limits.

Numbers, whether rational or surd, cannot represent the gradations of value of continuous magnitude.

279. Geometrical magnitudes, being subject to the law of continuity, are capable of representing *symbolically* any magnitudes of the same kind, and therefore also their ratios to each other; but when lines are thus used, as symbols merely, we have no means of ascertaining whether the actual lines which are assumed for this purpose and exhibited to the eye, possess the same relation to each other with the magnitudes which they represent, and under such circumstances, therefore, they are merely equivalent to any other general symbols, whether algebraical or not, which are employed for the same purpose: it is only when they are not used symbolically, but are themselves the magnitudes which they represent, that they become the proper objects of enquiry with respect to their commensurability with each other, or with respect to any other properties which they possess when considered with reference to each other.

Lines may represent continuous magnitude.

280. The process for finding the greatest common measure of two lines is identical with that for finding the greatest common measure of two numbers: for it merely requires us to cut off the less of two lines (the divisor) from the greater (the dividend), as many times as is possible, and then to repeat the same process with the remainder and the last divisor and so on continually, as long as the remainder exists: if the process

Process for ascertaining the commensurability of two lines.

terminates, the lines are commensurable and the last divisor is the greatest common measure required: but if the remainder never disappears, however long the process may be continued, the lines are incommensurable with each other. It may be objected, that this process would not enable us to pronounce two lines to be incommensurable with each other, without an infinite number of operations: but when lines are connected with each other by some assignable geometrical properties, it is generally possible to shew that the process will sooner or later terminate, or that the same relations will recur between the remainder and the divisor, and consequently that the process is interminable, and that the corresponding lines are incommensurable with each other *.

* If it was required to assign a line, the square upon which shall be double of the square upon a given line, it would be easy to shew that such lines would be incommensurable with each other: for if AB be the given line, and if we make BC equal to AB and perpendicular to it, then the square upon AC will be double of that upon AB: from AC cut off $AD=AB$, join BD and draw DE perpendicular to AC meeting BC in E: then it follows that BE, ED and CD are equal to each other: if the remainder CD or BE be taken from the last divisor CB (equal to AB) the remainder CE is greater than CD and bears the same relation to it that AC bears to AB: if CD be taken *twice* from BC, the remainder CF is less than CD, and also CF will bear to CE the same relation that CD bears to AC, however often this process is re-

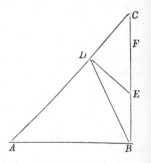

peated: therefore the same relations of the remainder and dividend will be reproduced and consequently the original lines are incommensurable: and as the first quotient is 1 and all those which follow it 2, the ratio in question will be equal to the recurring continued fraction

$$1+\frac{1}{2}+\frac{1}{2}+\frac{1}{2},$$

which represents the square root of 2: in a similar manner, the line, the square upon which is *triple* of that of a given line, may be shewn to be incommensurable with it, and the ratio to be represented by $\sqrt{3}$: the same remark applies to the parts of a line divided in extreme and mean ratio: for if AB be divided in extreme and mean ratio in C, and if we make $CD=CB$, then since

$$AB : AC :: AC : CB,$$
$$AB-AC : AC :: AC-CB : CB,$$
$$\text{or}\quad CB : AC :: AD : CB,$$
$$\text{or}\quad AC :: CD :: CD : AD,$$

and therefore AC is again divided in extreme and mean ratio in D and so on continually: it will follow therefore that the ratio

281.   The quotients of the division of lines by lines, whether considered as symbols or not, are abstract numbers and are therefore neither homogeneous in form, nor in meaning, with the dividend and divisor ; but the quotients of numbers divided by numbers, whether their component units are abstract or concrete, so long as they are the same in both, are necessarily abstract numbers and are therefore homogeneous in form with the dividend and divisor, though they may not be identical in signification : and inasmuch as the processes of arithmetic are equally applicable whatever be the nature of the specific units of the numbers subjected to them, though the interpretation of the results may be different, we are not called upon to change the form or character of our operations, when we pass from the terms of a ratio to the abstract number which we have defined to be its value.

The quotients of the division of lines by lines are numbers.

282.   The case however is altogether different in Geometry, where we have no means of representing *geometrically* the value of a ratio, and consequently no means of reasoning concerning its value when considered absolutely and without reference to other ratios: it is for this reason, as we have before observed, (Art. 264.) that there is no independent definition of ratio in Geometry, and it is only by referring them to other ratios, when they constitute or do not· constitute a proportion as defined geometrically, that we are enabled to consider them and to reason concerning their relative values.

There is no definition of ratio in geometry, inasmuch as its value is not assignable geometrically.

283.   We shall now proceed to the definition of Proportion in Arithmetic, as founded upon the arithmetical definition of ratio.

Arithmetical definition of proportion.

" Proportion consists in the equality of two ratios."

A *proportion* (the term is here used absolutely) is composed of four terms, the first and third of which are the antecedents,

$$\frac{AB}{AC} = 1 + \frac{1}{1} + \frac{1}{1 + \frac{1}{1 + \&c.}}$$

If it was required to assign a line, the cube constructed upon which as an edge is *double* of that which is constructed upon a *given* line as an edge, we should be able to assign no geometrical properties which connect two such incommensurable lines with each other and whose ratio is equivalent to $\sqrt[3]{2}$: neither are the quotients which result from the division of one line by the other *recurrent* in the same order though *interminable*, for if they were so, $\sqrt[3]{2}$ would be expressible as a quadratic surd, which is impossible.   The problem for the duplication of the cube was celebrated amongst the Greek Geometers, and its solution was known to exceed the powers of plane geometry, as it has been commonly defined and limited.

and the second and fourth the consequents, of the ratios which are required to be equal to each other.

284. A proportion in Geometry is expressed by connecting the two ratios, written geometrically, with the sign ::, which is used to denote their identity with each other; thus, if $a : b$ and $c : d$ be the ratios which constitute a proportion, they are written thus,

$$a : b :: c : d.$$

The same method of exhibiting a proportion is very commonly used, both in Arithmetic and Algebra, whatever be the nature of the quantities which compose it.

285. The definition of a ratio which is given in Arithmetic and Algebra, will necessarily lead to a mode of exhibiting a proportion which is appropriate to those sciences: for if $\frac{a}{b}$ and $\frac{c}{d}$ denote the ratios respectively which constitute a proportion, the proportion itself must be expressed by the equation

$$\frac{a}{b} = \frac{c}{d}.$$

It is the equality of these fractions which is the test of proportionality, or of the *equality* of the ratios, which is essential to their forming a proportion: it may be ascertained, therefore, whenever the values of these fractions can be calculated or determined.

286. There is another form of this equation, which is deducible from it, and which expresses therefore the same relation of the quantities involved in it, and which is, generally speaking, more convenient for the purposes of calculation : if the fractions $\frac{a}{b}$ and $\frac{c}{d}$, be reduced to a common denominator, the equation

$$\frac{a}{b} = \frac{c}{d} \text{ becomes } \frac{ad}{bd} = \frac{bc}{bd},$$

or, omitting the common denominator,

$$ad = bc.$$

It appears, therefore, that if four quantities constitute a proportion, the product of the extremes is equal to the product of the means.

287. Conversely, if the product of any two quantities be Its converse. equal to the product of two others, they will be convertible into a proportion, by making the terms of one product the extremes, and the terms of the other product the means.

For if $ad = bc$, we obtain, by dividing these equal quantities by bd,

$$\frac{a}{b} = \frac{c}{d},$$

which is the algebraical mode of expressing the proportion

$$a : b :: c : d,$$
$$\text{or} \qquad c : d :: a : b;$$

in the first of which, a and d are the extremes, and b and c the means; and in the second, c and b are the extremes, and d and a the means.

288. If the two mean terms of a proportion are equal, or Continued proportion. if the consequent of one ratio be the antecedent of the next, the product of the extremes is equal to the square of the mean: for in this case,

$$\frac{a}{b} = \frac{b}{c}, \quad \text{or} \quad \frac{ac}{bc} = \frac{b^2}{bc},$$

and therefore,

$$ac = b^2.$$

In this case, the numbers a, b, and c are said to be in continued proportion.

289. The following Propositions are demonstrated in the Propositions relating to Proportion in the fifth book of Euclid. fifth book of Euclid, in conformity with the geometrical definition of Proportion: they will admit of a much more simple demonstration as will be seen from what follows, from the arithmetical definition of proportion employed in the preceding Articles.

The Propositions in Euclid are frequently quoted in a technical form, as when four quantities are proportionals, they are said to be proportionals also *invertendo, alternando, componendo, dividendo :* we shall refer to these terms and others, in the following Articles, when we are enunciating the propositions Ratios which are the same to the same ratio are the same to one another. which are thus designated.

290. "Ratios which are the same to the same ratio, are the same to one another. (EUCLID, B. v. Prop. xi.)

Let $a : b :: e : f$ and also $c : d :: e : f$, then

$$a : b :: c : d.$$

For if $\dfrac{a}{b} = \dfrac{e}{f}$ and $\dfrac{c}{d} = \dfrac{e}{f}$, then also $\dfrac{a}{b} = \dfrac{c}{d}$, and, therefore,

$$a : b :: c : d.$$

Invertendo. 291. " If four magnitudes be proportionals, they shall be proportionals also *invertendo*, that is, when the terms of the respective ratios are taken in an inverse order."

Let $a : b :: c : d$; then also

$$b : a :: d : c.$$

For if $\dfrac{a}{b} = \dfrac{c}{d}$; and if we divide 1 by each of these equal quantities, we shall get

$$\frac{1}{\left(\dfrac{a}{b}\right)} = \frac{1}{\left(\dfrac{c}{d}\right)}, \text{ or } \frac{b}{a} = \frac{d}{c}, \ldots (\text{Art. 109.})$$

and, therefore,

$$b : a :: d : c.$$

This is Proposition (B) in Simson's EUCLID, Book v.

Alternando. 292. " If four magnitudes be proportionals, they shall be proportionals also *alternando*, or when taken alternately." EUCLID, B. v. Prop. xvi.

Let $\quad a : b :: c : d$, then also

$$a : c :: b : d.$$

For if $\dfrac{a}{b} = \dfrac{c}{d}$, then also $ad = bc$, (Art. 109.) and dividing each of these quantities by dc, we get

$$\frac{ad}{dc} = \frac{bc}{dc}, \text{ or } \frac{a}{c} = \frac{b}{d},$$

and, therefore,

$$a : c :: b : d.$$

Componendo. 293. " If four magnitudes be proportionals, they shall be proportionals also *componendo*, that is, the sum of the first and second shall be to the second as the sum of the third and fourth is to the fourth. (EUCLID, B. v. Prop. xviii.)

Let $\quad a : b :: c : d$, then also

$$a + b : b :: c + d : d.$$

For if $\dfrac{a}{b} = \dfrac{c}{d}$, then also $\dfrac{a}{b} + 1 = \dfrac{c}{d} + 1$, and, therefore,

$$\frac{a+b}{b} = \frac{c+d}{d}, \quad \text{or} \quad a+b : b :: c+d : d.$$

294. "If four magnitudes be proportionals, they shall be Dividendo. proportionals also *dividendo,* that is, the difference of the first and second shall be to the second as the difference of the third and fourth is to the fourth." (EUCLID, B. v. Prop. xvii.)

Let $a : b :: c : d$, then also $a-b : b :: c-d : d$.

For if $\dfrac{a}{b} = \dfrac{c}{d}$, then also $\dfrac{a}{b} - 1 = \dfrac{c}{d} - 1$; and therefore

$$\frac{a-b}{b} = \frac{c-d}{d},$$

or $\quad a-b : b :: c-d : d.$

295. "If four magnitudes be proportionals, they shall be Convertendo. proportionals also *convertendo,* or the first shall be to the difference of the first and second as the third is to the difference of the third and fourth."

Let $a : b :: c : d$, then also $a : a-b :: c : c-d$.

For if $\dfrac{a}{b} = \dfrac{c}{d}$,

then also $\dfrac{a-b}{b} = \dfrac{c-d}{d}$ and $\dfrac{b}{a} = \dfrac{d}{c}$; ... (Art. 291.)

therefore $\dfrac{a-b}{b} \times \dfrac{b}{a} = \dfrac{c-d}{d} \times \dfrac{d}{c}$,

or $\dfrac{a-b}{a} = \dfrac{c-d}{c}$, and *invertendo,* ... (Art. 291.)

$$\frac{a}{a-b} = \frac{c}{c-d},$$

or $\quad a : a-b :: c : c-d.$

This is Proposition (E) in Simson's EUCLID, Book v.

296. "If four magnitudes be proportionals, the sum of the first and second is to their difference as the sum of the third and fourth is to their difference."

Let $a : b :: c : d$,

then also $a+b : a-b :: c+d : c-d$.

For if $\dfrac{a}{b} = \dfrac{c}{d}$,

then also $\dfrac{a+b}{b} = \dfrac{c+d}{d}$, and $\dfrac{a-b}{b} = \dfrac{c-d}{d}$;

therefore $\dfrac{\frac{a+b}{b}}{\frac{a-b}{b}} = \dfrac{\frac{c+d}{d}}{\frac{c-d}{d}}$, and also $\dfrac{a+b}{a-b} = \dfrac{c+d}{c-d}$,

or $a + b : a - b :: c + d : c - d$.

Ex æquali in proportione directâ.

297. " If there be three or any number of magnitudes of the same kind, and as many others, which taken two and two in the same order, have the same ratio: then (*ex æquo* or *ex æquali in proportione directâ*), the first shall be to the last of the first set of magnitudes as the first is to the last of the second set of magnitudes." EUCLID, B. v. Prop. xxii.

Let a, b, c be the first, and a', b', c' the second set of magnitudes; then, if

$$a : b :: a' : b', \text{ and } b : c :: b' : c',$$

we shall also have

$$a : c :: a' : c'.$$

For if $\dfrac{a}{b} = \dfrac{a'}{b'}$, and $\dfrac{b}{c} = \dfrac{b'}{c'}$,

then also $\dfrac{a}{b} \times \dfrac{b}{c} = \dfrac{a'}{b'} \times \dfrac{b'}{c'}$,

and therefore $\dfrac{a}{c} = \dfrac{a'}{c'}$,

or $a : c :: a' : c'$.

A similar demonstration will apply when there are more than three magnitudes in each set.

Ex æquali in proportione perturbatâ.

298. " If there be any number of magnitudes and as many others, which, taken two and two in a *cross* order, have the same ratio; namely, if the first be to the second of the first set of magnitudes as the last but one to the last of the second set of magnitudes, and the second to the third of the first set of magnitudes as the last but two to the last but one of the second set of magnitudes, then (*ex æquo perturbato* or *ex æquali in proportione perturbatâ*), the first of the first set of magnitudes shall be to the last as the first of the second set of magnitudes is to the last." EUCLID, Book v. Prop. xxiii.

Let a, b, c be the first, and a', b', c' the second set of magnitudes; and let

$$a : b :: b' : c',$$
$$\text{and} \quad b : c :: a' : b',$$
$$\text{then} \quad a : c :: a' : c'.$$

For if $\dfrac{a}{b} = \dfrac{b'}{c'}$ and $\dfrac{b}{c} = \dfrac{a'}{b'}$,

then also $\dfrac{a}{b} \times \dfrac{b}{c} = \dfrac{b'}{c'} \times \dfrac{a'}{b'}$; and therefore, $\dfrac{a}{c} = \dfrac{a'}{c'}$

$$\text{or} \quad a : c :: a' : c'.$$

A similar demonstration will apply when there are more than three magnitudes in each set.

299. "If there be three magnitudes in continued proportion (Art. 288.), the first shall have to the last, the *duplicate* ratio (Art. 270.) of the first to the second." Duplicate ratio in Geometry.

Let $a : b :: b : c$, then also $a^2 : b^2 :: a : c$.

For if $\dfrac{a}{b} = \dfrac{b}{c}$,

then also $\dfrac{a}{b} \times \dfrac{a}{b} = \dfrac{b}{c} \times \dfrac{a}{b}$,

or $\dfrac{a^2}{b^2} = \dfrac{a}{c}$;

therefore $a^2 : b^2 :: a : c$.

In Geometry, where there is no independent definition of ratio, it is the enunciation of this proposition which involves the definition of duplicate ratios. EUCLID, B. v. Defin. x.

300. "If there be four magnitudes in continued proportion, the first shall have to the fourth, the *triplicate* ratio, (Art. 271.) of the first to the second." Triplicate ratio in Geometry.

Let $a : b :: b : c :: c : d$, then $a^3 : b^3 :: a : d$.

For if $\dfrac{a}{b} = \dfrac{b}{c} = \dfrac{c}{d}$,

then $\dfrac{a^2}{b^2} = \dfrac{a}{c}$, (Art. 299.) and $\dfrac{a^2}{b^2} \times \dfrac{a}{b} = \dfrac{a}{c} \times \dfrac{c}{d}$, or $\dfrac{a^3}{b^3} = \dfrac{a}{d}$;

therefore $a^3 : b^3 :: a : d$.

It is the enunciation of this proposition which involves the definition of triplicate ratio in Geometry. Euclid, B. v. Def. xi.

301. "If there be four magnitudes, a, b, c, d, which are proportionals, and four others, a', b', c', d', which are proportionals also, then their corresponding products or quotients,

$$aa', \quad bb', \quad cc', \quad dd',$$

$$\text{or} \quad \frac{a}{a'}, \quad \frac{b}{b'}, \quad \frac{c}{c'}, \quad \frac{d}{d'},$$

shall also be proportionals."

For if $\dfrac{a}{b} = \dfrac{c}{d}$, and $\dfrac{a'}{b'} = \dfrac{c'}{d'}$,

then also $\dfrac{a}{b} \times \dfrac{a'}{b'} = \dfrac{c}{d} \times \dfrac{c'}{d'}$;

or $aa' : bb' :: cc' : dd'$.

Again, if $\dfrac{a}{b} = \dfrac{c}{d}$, and $\dfrac{a'}{b'} = \dfrac{c'}{d'}$, and therefore (Art. 291.)

$$\frac{b'}{a'} = \frac{d'}{c'},$$

then $\dfrac{a}{b} \times \dfrac{b'}{a'} = \dfrac{c}{d} \times \dfrac{d'}{c'}$, or $\dfrac{a}{a'} \times \dfrac{b'}{b} = \dfrac{c}{c'} \times \dfrac{d'}{d}$;

and therefore replacing $\dfrac{b'}{b}$ by $\dfrac{1}{\frac{b}{b'}}$ and $\dfrac{d'}{d}$ by $\dfrac{1}{\frac{d}{d'}}$,

we get $\dfrac{\left(\dfrac{a}{a'}\right)}{\left(\dfrac{b}{b'}\right)} = \dfrac{\left(\dfrac{c}{c'}\right)}{\left(\dfrac{d}{d'}\right)}$;

or $\dfrac{a}{a'} : \dfrac{b}{b'} :: \dfrac{c}{c'} : \dfrac{d}{d'}$.

Proportions when thus combined with each other, are said, in geometrical language, to be added together in the first case and subtracted from each other in the second : in the first case, however, they are more commonly said to be *compounded* together.

It is obvious that this proposition may be easily extended to any number of proportions.

302. " If four quantities, a, b, c, d, be proportionals, then a^n, b^n, c^n, d^n, shall also be proportionals."

For if $\dfrac{a}{b} = \dfrac{c}{d}$,

then also $\dfrac{a^n}{b^n} = \dfrac{c^n}{d^n}$,

or $a^n : b^n :: c^n : d^n$.

303. " If there be any number of ratios which are equal to each other, then as one antecedent is to its consequent, so shall all the antecedents together be to all the consequents together." EUCLID, B. v. Prop. xii.

Let $a : b :: c : d :: e : f$,

then also, $a : b :: a + c + e : b + d + f$.

For if $\dfrac{a}{b} = \dfrac{c}{d} = \dfrac{e}{f}$,

then we have $\dfrac{a}{b} = \dfrac{a}{b}$, or $ab = ba$

$\dfrac{a}{b} = \dfrac{c}{d}$, or $ad = bc$ (Art. 287.)

$\dfrac{a}{b} = \dfrac{e}{f}$, or $af = be$,

and consequently

$$ab + ad + af = ba + bc + be ;$$

or, $a(b + d + f) = b(a + c + e)$,

and therefore $\dfrac{a}{b} = \dfrac{a + c + e}{b + d + f}$, (Art. 287.)

or, $a : b :: a + c + e : b + d + f$.

The same demonstration may easily be extended to any number of ratios which are equal to each other.

304. " If there be two or more proportions, which have the same antecedents respectively, then the first antecedent shall have to the sum of all the first consequents, the same ratio which the second antecedent has to the sum of all the second consequents."

For if

$$a : b :: c : d,$$
$$a : b' :: c : d',$$
$$a : b'' :: c : d'' ;$$

then we have

$$a d = c b,$$
$$a d' = c b',$$
$$a d'' = c b'' ;$$

consequently

$$a (d + d' + d'') = c (b + b' + b'') ;$$

and therefore

$$a : b + b' + b'' :: c : d + d' + d''.$$

In a similar manner it might be shewn, that "if there be two or more proportions, which have the same consequents respectively, then the sum of the first antecedents shall have to the first consequent, the same ratio, which the sum of the second antecedents has to the second consequent."

Self-evident consequences of the arithmetical definition of proportion are not always self evident consequences of the geometrical definition.

305. There are many propositions in the fifth book of Euclid, where hypotheses are made concerning ratios as greater and less than, as well as equal to, each other, and the circumstances under which they are so, which are either self-evident, or so nearly self-evident, consequences of the arithmetical definition of ratio, that it will not be necessary to notice them in this place, as distinct propositions to be demonstrated. The case however is very different in a system of Geometry, where the want of a definition of ratio, as disconnected with the definition of proportion, makes it necessary to consider such properties of ratios, as much the objects of demonstration, as any of the properties of proportions or proportionals: thus when it is said that "of unequal magnitudes, the greater has a greater ratio to the same than the less has," (EUCLID, B. v. Prop. viii.) it is required to bring this proposition within the operation of the definition of quantities which are *not* proportionals, and to shew that the conditions are such as coincide with the circumstances under which the first of four magnitudes is defined to have to the second a greater ratio than the third has to the fourth, which is in this case identical with the second: if however we represent algebraically the same three magnitudes by a, b, and c,

where a is greater than c, then the first ratio is represented by $\frac{a}{b}$, and the second by $\frac{c}{b}$: and it is a necessary consequence of the meaning attached to the term *fraction*, which is synonymous with that of ratio, that the first fraction under such circumstances is greater than the second: no formal demonstration could add to the evidence of such a proposition.

The same observation would apply to the following proposition: " if there be six magnitudes, and if the first has to the second the same ratio which the third has to the fourth, but if the third has to the fourth a greater ratio than the fifth to the sixth: then the first has to the second a greater ratio than the fifth to the sixth." (Euclid, B. v. Prop. xiii.)

If the six magnitudes be severally denoted by a, b, c, d, e, f, then the three ratios which are the objects of the proposition are $\frac{a}{b}$, $\frac{c}{d}$ and $\frac{e}{f}$ respectively; if $\frac{a}{b}$ be equal to $\frac{c}{d}$, but if $\frac{c}{d}$ be greater than $\frac{e}{f}$, then we infer immediately that $\frac{a}{b}$ is greater than $\frac{e}{f}$, and no demonstration can add to the evidence of such a conclusion: in the absence however of any geometrical mode of defining, independently of each other, the values of these ratios, it becomes requisite to shew that there are some equimultiples of the first and fifth, and also of the second and sixth, where the multiple of the first is greater than that of the second, but the multiple of the fifth is not greater than that of the sixth: a conclusion by no means self evident, but requiring the authority of a formal demonstration.

306. The contrast, with respect to brevity and clearness, which is presented in the demonstration of the preceding propositions, as founded upon the arithmetical and geometrical definitions of proportion, is so remarkable, as to suggest at once a question with respect to the necessity of adhering to the latter definition in a System of Geometry: to this question we shall now endeavour to give an answer.

The same reasons, in fact, which prevented the transfer of the arithmetical definition of ratio to Geometry, will likewise prevent the similar transfer of the definition of proportion: for it is impossible to ascertain the identity of the fractions which

The arithmetical definition of proportion not transferable to Geometry.

constitute a proportion, if we have no geometrical means of ascertaining the values of the fractions themselves, (Art. 281): it is no answer to this observation to say that the identity of these fractions exists, when their numerators and denominators form the terms of a proportion, in the case of geometrical as well as other quantities: for if geometry be considered as a practical, as well as a theoretical, science, we can avail ourselves of no properties of the quantities which are the objects of its investigation, which are only discoverable by the aid of another science, and which cannot be verified by any geometrical test.

The geometrical definition of proportion must be a consequence of the algebraical definition.

307.   But the arithmetical definition of proportion comprehends geometrical as well as other quantities, and whatever may be therefore the geometrical definition of proportion which we may adopt, it must coincide with the arithmetical definition in its consequences at least, if not in its form: it is for this reason that it will be expedient to examine the consequences of the arithmetical definition of proportion, in order, if possible, to find some one, which admits of the application of a geometrical test, consistent with the prescribed forms of geometrical reasoning, and which is equally applicable to every species of geometrical quantity.

Proposed definition; the rectangle formed by the means equal to the rectangle formed by the extremes.

308.   One of the most immediate and remarkable of these consequences is the equality of the products of the extreme and mean terms of the proportion: if the quantities which were the objects of comparison were geometrical straight lines, the products in question would correspond to rectangles of which these lines were the adjacent sides respectively (EUCLID, B. VI. Prop. xvi.): and such lines would properly form the terms of a proportion, if those rectangles were equal to each other: and inasmuch as the equality or diversity of such rectangles could be ascertained by practical geometrical means (by their conversion into equal squares), we should thus be put into possession of a geometrical test of proportion, which would necessarily coincide with the test supplied by the arithmetical definition.

Objections to it.

309.   Without noticing however other objections to the use of such a geometrical definition of proportion, there is one which is fatal to it: it is not applicable to every species of geometrical quantity: for if the terms of the proportion, two or all of them, were areas or solids, the test in question, would no longer

admit of application: it does not present itself, in short, under a form which is independent of the specific nature of the quantities which constitute each ratio of the proportion; and it is obvious that the same objection would more or less apply to the adoption of any definition, which was founded upon any consequences of the arithmetical definition of proportion, which are independent of, or not immediately connected with, the fractional form of the ratios which compose it.

310. It is for this reason that we shall again recur to the original forms of the fractions which constituted the arithmetical definition of proportion, namely,

$$\frac{a}{b} = \frac{c}{d}:$$

and examine whether there is any modification of their terms, which geometrical quantities could admit of in a system of geometry, which is essentially connected with their equality or diversity: among those might be reckoned any multiples whatsoever of the terms of the ratios, whether lines or areas: thus if we take any equimultiples *whatsoever* (*m*) of the first and third terms of the proportion, and any equimultiples *whatsoever* (*n*) of the second and fourth, we should get

$$\frac{ma}{nb} = \frac{mc}{nd}:$$

A second consequence of the algebraical definition of proportion examined.

and it is obvious that if ma be greater than nb, mc is also greater than nd, and if ma be equal to nb, then mc is also equal to nd, and if ma be less than nb, then mc is also less than nd: for if not, let us suppose mc greater than nb, at the same time that mc is not greater than nd, and it will follow therefore that a ratio of greater inequality (Art. 266.) may be equal to a ratio of equality or to a ratio of less inequality; or in other words, that an improper fraction may be equal to unity or to a proper fraction: and it may be readily shewn that any other conclusion respecting the relation of the terms ma, nb, mc, nd different from those we have mentioned, will lead to similar contradictions.

311. It will follow therefore if a and b, c and d are pairs of geometrical magnitudes of the same kind respectively, whether lines, or areas, or solids, which form the terms of a proportion, and if any equimultiples whatsoever be taken of the first and third, and any equimultiples whatsoever be taken of

Geometrical definition of proportion.

the second and fourth, then if the multiple of the first be greater than the multiple of the second, the multiple of the third will be greater than the multiple of the fourth: if the multiple of the first be equal to that of the second, the multiple of the third will be equal to that of the fourth: and if the multiple of the first be less than that of the second, the multiple of the third will be less than that of the fourth. It is this proposition which is deduced as a necessary consequence of the definition of proportion in arithmetic and algebra, including geometrical as well as other magnitudes, which may be legitimately converted into the definition of proportion in geometry, and which is given for that purpose in the fifth definition of the fifth book of Euclid.

Geometrical definition of quantities which are not proportionals.

312. But this definition is incomplete, unless it can be shewn that it enables us to ascertain not only when four geometrical magnitudes form a proportion, but also when they do not: it follows however as a parallel conclusion, that such magnitudes do *not* form a proportion, which do not, under *all* circumstances, fulfil the conditions which the definition prescribes: or, in other words, four magnitudes do not form a proportion, if, when any equimultiples *whatsoever* are taken of the first and third, and any equimultiples *whatsoever* of the second and fourth, it can be shewn that there exists any multiple of the first which is greater than that of the second, but the corresponding multiple of the third is *not* greater than that of the fourth; or that the multiple of the first is equal to that of the second, but the multiple of the third *not* equal to that of the fourth: or that the multiple of the first is less than that of the second, but the multiple of the third *not* less than that of the fourth.

A consequence also of the algebraical definition.

313. In order to shew that this definition of quantities which are *not* proportionals, is likewise a consequence of the arithmetical definition of proportion, we will suppose the four quantities a, b, c, d, to be so related to each other, that $\frac{a}{b}$ is either greater or less than $\frac{c}{d}$: in the first case, if we make

$$\frac{a-x}{b} = \frac{c}{d}, \quad \text{where} \quad x = \frac{ad-bc}{d},$$

we shall also have

$$\frac{m(a-x)}{nb} = \frac{mc}{nd}:$$

if we now suppose $mc = nd$, we shall also have $ma - mx = nb$, and therefore ma is greater than nb, at the same time that mc is equal to nc: or, in other words, equimultiples of the first and third of four quantities are taken and other equimultiples of the second and fourth, and the multiple of the first is greater than that of the second, but the multiple of the third is *not* greater than that of the fourth. If again, we suppose $\frac{a}{b}$ less than $\frac{c}{d}$, then we may make

$$\frac{a + x}{b} = \frac{c}{d}, \text{ where } x = \frac{bc - ad}{d},$$

and we shall also have

$$\frac{m(a + x)}{nb} = \frac{mc}{nd}:$$

if we now suppose $mc = nd$, we shall also have

$$ma + mx = nb,$$

and, therefore, ma is less than nb, at the same time that mc is not less than nd: or in other words, equimultiples of the first and third of four quantities are taken, and equimultiples likewise of the second and fourth, and the multiple of the first is less than that of the second, but the multiple of the third not less than that of the fourth: it thus appears that the geometrical definition of quantities which are proportionals, as well as of those which are *not* proportionals, are equally consequences of the algebraical definition of proportion.

314. The geometrical definition of proportion is adapted not merely to the peculiar nature of the quantities which are considered in geometry, but likewise to the form under which the reasonings concerning their relations present themselves: for there are no processes in Geometry, beyond the formation of multiples and submultiples, which correspond *generally* to arithmetical multiplication, and none whatever to arithmetical division: the operations of Geometry, as far as they can be called so, and the reasonings connected with them or which are founded upon the definitions, are confined to the comparison of quantities with each other, whether as regards their equality or inequality, or as forming or as not forming the terms of a proportion: the **peculiar** definition, therefore, of proportion in **Geometry has**

The geometrical definition adapted to the forms of geometrical reasonings.

been adopted as much from necessity as from choice, as the only one which was adapted to the form and nature of the processes and reasonings of that science: for we have shewn that there is no other modification of the arithmetical definition of proportion, which possesses the necessary conditions.

General propositions concerning ratios and proportions equally consequences of the two definitions.

315. All general propositions concerning ratios and proportions may be considered as equally necessary consequences, both of the arithmetical and geometrical definitions; for they are both of them equally applicable to every species of quantity, and one of them may be considered as a proposition deducible from the other. If the only object proposed, therefore, in mathematical investigations, was the most speedy establishment or discovery of truths, without any reference to the form of the demonstrations, we should naturally make use of that definition, which conducted us most rapidly and most easily to the conclusions sought for: but such investigations commonly present themselves as parts of some general system, the completeness of which would require consistency in the form of the demonstrations, and consequently a uniform reference to the same system of definitions as the basis of them: it is for this reason, that we ought to adhere uniformly to the arithmetical definition of proportion in a system of Arithmetic or Arithmetical Algebra and to the geometrical definition in a system of Geometry.

Examination of the conformity of the definition of proportion with the popular notions attached to the term.

316. Having established the relations with respect to each other and the appropriate character and applications of the arithmetical and geometrical definitions of proportion, we shall now proceed to explain, at some length, the general agreement of the former definition with the notions which we attach to the term *proportion* and to other equivalent phrases, in ordinary language: we shall then conclude this Chapter with the examination of some of the most important processes in Arithmetic which involve the formation and properties of proportions.

The terms ratio and proportion confounded with each other.

317. In the first place, it may be observed, that we are in the habit of confounding in ordinary language, the terms *ratio* and *proportion* with each other: thus it is equally common to say, that two lines or other quantities are in the *ratio* of 3 to 5, or that they are in the *proportion* of 3 to 5. Both these forms of expression are elliptical, though in different degrees: the first is equivalent to saying, that the ratio of the two lines or quan-

tities is equal to the ratio of 3 to 5, and leaving it to be inferred from thence, that they constitute a proportion: the second may be considered as an abbreviated mode of asserting, that the two lines and the two numbers form the terms of a proportion. In both cases there is the same tacit reference made to the conditions requisite to establish a proportion.

318. The adjective *proportional* is still more variously used, though in all cases it will be found to be equivalent to the assertion of a proportion between certain quantities, either expressed or understood: thus, when we say that the *interest* of money is proportional to the *principal*, we merely express in a very elliptical form the following proposition: "The rate of interest and the time for which it is due being the same, any two principals and their corresponding amounts of interest will constitute the terms of a proportion." Thus, if £100. in one year will produce £5., £700. in the same time and at the same rate will produce £35.; or in other words, 100 and 700, 5 and 35, will form the terms of the proportion, *[side note: Usage of the term proportional.]*

$$100 : 700 :: 5 : 35.$$

319. Another mode of expressing the same proposition will serve to illustrate the efforts made in ordinary language to avoid the tediousness which statements, strictly conformable to the arithmetical definition, would render more or less necessary. When speaking of the dependence of the interest upon the principal, when the rate and time are given, we should say, that "In whatever *proportion* the principal was increased, the *interest* would be increased in the same proportion;" a proposition which might be applied to the preceding example in the following manner: "If there are two principal sums of money, £100. and £700., which form a proportion with the numbers 1 and 7: then the amounts of interest, 5 and 35, of those two principals, will likewise form a proportion with the same numbers 1 and 7: and also the two principals and the two amounts of interest will form a proportion with each other." *[side note: Usage of the phrase "in the same proportion."]*

320. There is no proposition which is more frequently referred to, or which is pregnant with more important consequences than the following: "The effect is always *proportional* to its cause." As this proposition is intimately connected with the subject of our present discussion, we shall endeavour to *[side note: The effect proportional to its cause.]*

explain and illustrate its meaning and applications at some length.

When the dependence is physical.

321. When the connection between cause and effect is physical, and therefore not necessary, the proposition expresses the great law of the permanence and uniformity of the operations of nature, our conviction of the truth of which is the foundation of all our reasonings concerning them : thus, if a given force support a given weight, then the double of that force will support the double of that weight, and any multiple of the same force will support the same multiple of the same weight : the ratio between any two forces, therefore, will be the same as the ratio between the corresponding weights supported; and such forces and weights will form, consequently, the terms of a proportion. It is in this sense that the force would be considered as proportional to the weight, the force corresponding to the cause and the weight to the effect in the general proposition we are illustrating.

Cause and effect convertible terms.

322. The ratios, however, which form the proportion, are convertible, and the terms which correspond to them in the proposition must be convertible likewise. In the particular case, therefore, which we are considering, if the force be considered as proportional to the weight, the weight must likewise be considered as proportional to the force: in whatever sense, therefore, the proportion may require to be interpreted, in order to answer to this change in its form, a corresponding change must take place likewise in the connection between the terms of the proposition.

When the dependence is mathematical.

323. When the connection between the terms of the proposition is mathematical, and therefore determined by definitions, the proposition may be considered as merely an abbreviated form of expressing the corresponding proportion: thus, when we say that the area of a triangle, whose altitude is given, is proportional to its base, we merely assert that the ratio of the area of one triangle to the area of any other triangle possessing the same altitude, is the same as the ratio of the base of the first triangle to the base of the second.

When the dependence is hypothetical.

324. When, however, the connection of the terms of the proposition is neither physically nor mathematically necessary, we must *invest* them with a necessary connection by means of hypotheses, either expressed or understood, which will be equi-

valent to definitions: thus, when we say that the " Work done by labourers is proportional to their number," we take it for granted that each individual labours with the same effect. It is in virtue of such hypotheses, that we conclude, as if with mathematical certainty, that twice or any multiple of the work will be done by twice or the same multiple of the number of men, and consequently, that the quantities of work done in any two cases and the corresponding numbers of men, will constitute the terms of a proportion.

325. The relation of cause and effect, expressed by saying that one is proportional to the other, is more frequently designated by an equivalent phrase, which is, that the *effect varies as the cause*, or conversely: in both cases, an equally enlarged signification is given to the terms cause and effect, and the connection between them is rendered necessary, either by definition or by hypothesis, or by inferences drawn from observation of the general laws of the physical world.

The effect varies as the cause.

326. When the causes or agents which produce an effect are more than one, the effect is said to *vary* conjointly with the causes which produce it. It remains to consider the law of the dependence of the effect and agents in such cases, particularly with reference to the proportion which they form.

Or as the causes or agents conjointly.

327. Thus we should say, that the work done would *vary* conjointly as the number of men employed and the number of days they worked: for if the number of days during which the men worked remained the same, m times the same work would be done by m times the same number of men: and if the number of men remained the same, n times the same work would be done in n times the same number of days: it would follow, therefore, that mn times the original work would be done by m times the original number of men, working for n times the original number of days: and in a similar manner, $m'n'$ times the original work would be done by m' times the original number of men working for n' times the original number of days: the ratio, therefore, of the quantities of work done under these different circumstances, would be that of mn to $m'n'$, which is the ratio of the product of the number of men into the number of days in the first case, to the product of the number of men into the number of days in the second; and

Example of joint variation.

these four quantities, therefore, would form the terms of a proportion.

Independent of the nature and magnitude of the primitive effect and agents.

328. It is obvious, likewise, that the existence and value of the ratios which form this proportion, are perfectly independent of the particular value or peculiar nature of the primitive effect and agents: for if we denote the original work done by w, the original number of men by M, and the original number of days by N, the terms of the first ratio would be mnw and $m'n'w$, and those of the second $mnMN$ and $m'n'MN$, which are clearly identical with each other, inasmuch as w is a common measure of the terms of the first ratio, and MN a common measure of the terms of the second.

Where the agents are more than two.

329. Other conditions or other agents might be introduced into the question we have just been considering, contributing to the effect produced: we might consider, for instance, variations, not merely in the number of men and number of days, but likewise in the number of hours during which they should each of them work, and also in the intensity of their labour: the effect produced or the work done would vary as all these causes or agents *conjointly*: for if we double or otherwise increase the number of hours of labour during each day, we should double or increase at the same rate the work done: and if we should double or otherwise increase the effective industry of the workmen, we should double or increase at the same rate the work done under the same circumstances. If, therefore, $m : m'$ expresses the ratio of the number of men in any two cases, $n : n'$ the ratio of the number of days, $p : p'$ the ratio of the number of working hours each day, and $q : q'$ the ratio of the effective industry of the men under such circumstances, then the ratio of the work done in the two cases would be that of $mnpq$ to $m'n'p'q'$.

Law of dependence of one agent upon the other agents and effect.

330. We have hitherto considered the law of dependence of the effect upon its several agents or causes; and it very rarely happens that they are not sufficiently distinguished from each other by the nature of the question proposed. It is frequently, however, a matter of equal importance, to ascertain the law of dependence of one of the agents upon the other agent or agents, when the effect is the same, or upon the other agents and effect, when the effects in different cases are different from each other.

Thus, the same work is done by different numbers of men Example: in different numbers of days: what is the nature of the relation between the number of men and the number of days?

Let the numbers of men in any two cases be m and m', or let their ratio be that of m to m': let the corresponding numbers of days be n and n'. Then, since the effect or work done varies when the conjointly as the number of men and the number of days, and effect is the since the ratio of the work done under these circumstances, is same. that of 1 to 1: it follows that

$$1 : 1 :: mn : m'n',$$

and therefore

$$mn = m'n', \quad \text{and} \quad \frac{m}{m'} = \frac{n'}{n}; \quad \text{(Art. 287.)}$$

and consequently,

$$m : m' :: n' : n;$$

or the ratio of the numbers of men in the two cases is the Inverse va-
inverse of the ratio of the numbers of days: in other words, riation. the number of men is said to *vary inversely* as the number of days.

If, however, we should suppose the work done in the two When the cases different, and in the ratio of w to w', the first proportion different. would become

$$w : w' :: mn : m'n';$$

and therefore

$$\frac{w}{w'} = \frac{mn}{m'n'}, \quad \text{and} \quad \frac{m}{m'} = \frac{w}{w'} \times \frac{n'}{n} = \frac{\left(\dfrac{w}{n}\right)}{\left(\dfrac{w'}{n'}\right)};$$

and consequently

$$m : m' :: \frac{w}{n} : \frac{w'}{n'}:$$

under such circumstances, the number of men in each case is said *to vary* as the work to be done *directly* and as the number of days *inversely*.

331. In the innumerable questions which present them- Principle of selves as examples of the Rule of Three, direct and inverse, questions in simple and compound, and in most of the applications of the Rule of Arithmetic, it is required to determine the value of one un- Three, &c. known quantity from its connection with three or more known

quantities, when there exists amongst all of them a relation of *cause* or *agent* or *agents* and *effect*, such as we have been considering: the common principle of solution in all such questions is, to reduce all the quantities to the form of a proportion, of which the unknown quantity shall form one term: and if three terms of a proportion be given, the fourth may always be determined: thus, in the proportion

$$a : b :: c : d,$$

we have

$$a = \frac{bc}{d}, \quad d = \frac{bc}{a}, \quad b = \frac{ad}{c}, \quad \text{and} \quad c = \frac{ad}{b};$$

and therefore either of the extreme terms of the proportion may be found by dividing the product of the means by the other extreme; and either of the means may be found by dividing the product of the extremes by the other mean.

Arrangement of the terms of the proportion.

332. In order to arrange the quantities in the question, in the proportion which is necessary for its solution, we must consider, in the first place, whether the unknown quantity can be considered as an effect or an agent; and also, whether it expresses the entire effect or a part of it only: if it be an effect, it must vary as the agent, or jointly as the agents: if it be an agent, it must vary directly as the effect: but if it be one amongst several agents, it must vary as the effect directly, and inversely as the other agents.

Primary agents.

333. The effect may, in some cases, have a separate dependence upon its own agents, as connected with the estimation of its magnitude: thus, the effect may be an area, dependent upon its length and breadth; or a solid, dependent upon its length, breadth and height: and the object of the problem may sometimes require the determination of one of Subordinate agents. these subordinate agents of the entire effect produced by the primary agents: it will vary directly as the primary agents, and inversely as the other subordinate agents.

334. The following are examples:

Examples.

(1) If 3 guns in a battle kill 21 men, how many men would 11 guns kill in the same time?

The *effect* is the number of men killed: the *agent* is the number of *equally* efficient guns.

The effect varies as the agent, and therefore

Men.		Men.		Guns.		Guns.
21	:	x	::	3	:	11;

$$\text{and} \quad x = \frac{11 \times 21}{3} = 77.$$

(2) An elephant consumes 400 lbs. of rice in 3 days: how many lbs. of rice would an elephant, which is $\frac{1}{4}$th greater in every dimension, consume in 5 days?

It is assumed as a mathematical hypothesis, that the consumption of rice by the elephant will vary with his bulk and the number of days, and also that his bulk will vary with his length, breadth and height.

The effect is the consumption of rice, and the unknown quantity is one of the effects.

The agents are the length, breadth and height of the elephant and the number of days.

$$\overset{\text{lbs.}}{400} : \overset{\text{lbs.}}{x} :: \overset{\text{l.}}{1} \times \overset{\text{b.}}{1} \times \overset{\text{h.}}{1} \times \overset{\text{days.}}{3} : \overset{\text{l.}}{\frac{5}{4}} \times \overset{\text{b.}}{\frac{5}{4}} \times \overset{\text{h.}}{\frac{5}{4}} \times \overset{\text{days.}}{5},$$

and therefore

$$x = \frac{625 \times 400}{192} = 1302\frac{1}{12} \text{ lbs.}$$

(3) How much in length which is 4 inches in breadth, will make a yard square?

The effect is the area formed, which is the same in both cases.

The agents are the length and breadth and one therefore varies inversely as the other.

Consequently,

1st length.		2d length.		2d breadth.		1st breadth.
x	:	36	::	36	:	4;

$$\therefore \ x = \frac{36 \times 36}{4} = 324 \text{ inches.}$$

(4) If 132 men can dig a trench which is 100 yards long, 3 deep and 2 wide in 7 days, working during 10 hours each day, how many men will it require to dig a trench 320 yards long, 4 deep and 3 wide in 11 days, working during 12 hours each day?

A A

The effect is the trench, whose subordinate agents are its length, depth and breadth.

The primary agents are the number of men, the number of days and the number of hours in each day.

It is the number of men in the second case which is the agent to be determined.

The number of men varies as the subordinate agents of the effect directly and as the other primary agents inversely.

Therefore,

$$132 : x :: \frac{100 \times 3 \times 2}{7 \times 13} : \frac{320 \times 4 \times 3}{11 \times 12}$$

$$:: 33 : 112 ;$$

$$\therefore x = \frac{112 \times 132}{33} = 448.$$

(5) If 10 men can reap a field in 3 days, whose length is 1200 feet and breadth 800 feet, what is the breadth of a field whose length is 1000 feet, which 12 men can reap in 4 days?

The effect is the area of the field, the subordinate agents of which are its length and breadth: it is the breadth in the second case which is the unknown term of the proportion.

The breadth varies as the number of men and the number of days directly and inversely as the length:

$$800 : x :: \frac{10 \times 3}{1200} : \frac{12 \times 4}{1000}$$

$$:: 25 : 48 :$$

$$\therefore x = \frac{800 \times 48}{25} = 1536.$$

The want of homogeneity in the terms which form the ratios of a proportion will not necessarily lead to erroneous results.

335. In the form of solution of the preceding examples, the terms of the ratios are homogeneous and the values of the ratios are therefore expressible as abstract numbers: but in the ordinary form of solution which is followed in such cases, the terms of the ratios, whether simple or compound, are placed in the order of effects and agents, or conversely,

and consequently the component ratios are not necessarily formed of homogeneous terms. The values of such incongruous ratios are not expressible as abstract numbers, and the arrangement which leads to the employment of them is a manifest violation of propriety: but when it is considered that such an arrangement changes the order of succession of the mean terms of the proportion only, it will be at once manifest that the numerical result, which expresses the value of the unknown term, will be precisely the same as if all the terms were placed in their proper and logical order.

336. Thus the statement of the following question, " if *Example.* the wages of 7 men for 1 week be £10. 10s., what will be the wages of 12 men for the same time and at the same rate?" would be, according to the ordinary practice,

$$\text{Men.} \quad \text{£.} \quad s. \quad \text{Men.} \quad \text{£.}$$
$$7 \; : \; 10 \, . \, 10 \; :: \; 12 \; : \; x :$$

whilst the correct and logical statement, in which the terms of the component ratios are homogeneous, would be

$$\text{Men. Men.} \quad \text{£.} \quad s. \quad \text{£.}$$
$$7 \; : \; 12 \; :: \; 10 \, . \, 10 \; : \; x.$$

The resulting value of x or £18. would be the same in both cases.

337. Inasmuch as the magnitudes which form the several *Numerical* terms of a proportion are expressed by numbers, the nume- *values of* rical value of the unknown term will be the same, whatever *ratios* those numbers represent: and whenever the units which com- *whose* pose the numbers which express homogeneous magnitudes in *terms are* a proportion are the same, the numerical result will express *not homo-* units of the same kind with those of the term which is homo- *geneous.* geneous with it. As far, therefore, as the determination of the numerical value of the unknown term is concerned, we may use the numerical values of the other ratio or ratios, which form a proportion, whether simple or compound, precisely in *Meaning* the same manner as if their terms were perfectly homogeneous. *of the term* Such a practice will be found to be extremely convenient in *rate.* many cases, inasmuch as the terms of such ratios assume a fixed and standard character in extensive classes of questions,

and such standard ratios are expressed in ordinary language by the term *rate*. Thus we are accustomed to speak of the rate of *interest*, of *commission*, of *insurance*, of *exchange*, of *loss* or of *gain*. In other cases, we use the term absolutely, as in speaking of *parochial rates*, *labour rates*, and so on, where it is equivalent to the term *tax*, and becomes the standard ratio which enters into all the proportions which present themselves in the solution of those questions in which they are concerned*.

Various modes of expressing rates of interest, &c.: mean- of the term *per centage*.

338. When all the terms of such proportions are sums of money†, we generally assume the second of the terms of the standard ratio or *rate*, to be either £1. or £100. In the first case, the antecedent of the ratio is the *allowance* (by whatever name called, whether interest, commission, brokerage, &c.) upon £1: in the second case, it is the corresponding allowance upon £100. and is therefore called the *per centage*. It is this second mode of expressing the rate, which is most commonly used, as being best adapted to the popular expression of its meaning and to the ordinary arithmetical processes, which are employed for solving questions in which it is involved: the following table will exhibit the values of this standard ratio or rate, in various cases of its occurrence.

* The phrase, which is so commonly used, in questions of proportions, "at the same rate" merely expresses the mathematical character of *permanency*, (Art. 324.) which becomes the basis of their solution.

† In such a case, the terms of the standard ratio are homogeneous, though differently designated: thus one term is *interest* and the other *principal* (or otherwise denominated though similarly connected with each other) and though they are expressed by identical units, are essentially distinguished from each other, when considered with reference to the question to be solved.

Standard Ratios.	Per Centage.	Rate (r).	
$1 \ : 100$	1	$\dfrac{1}{100} = .01$	Table of rates.
$2 \ : 100$	2	$\dfrac{2}{100} = .02$	
$3 \ : 100$	3	$\dfrac{3}{100} = .03$	
$4 \ : 100$	4	$\dfrac{4}{100} = .04$	
$5 \ : 100$	5	$\dfrac{5}{100} = .05$	
$10 \ : 100$	10	$\dfrac{10}{100} = .1$	
$1\frac{1}{2} : 100$	$1\frac{1}{2}$	$\dfrac{1.5}{100} = .015$	
$2\frac{1}{2} : 100$	$2\frac{1}{2}$	$\dfrac{2.5}{100} = .025$	
$3\frac{1}{2} : 100$	$3\frac{1}{2}$	$\dfrac{3.5}{100} = .035$	
$4\frac{1}{2} : 100$	$4\frac{1}{2}$	$\dfrac{4.5}{100} = .045$	
$\frac{1}{8} \ : 100$	$\frac{1}{8}$	$\dfrac{.125}{100} = .00125$	
$\frac{3}{4} \ : 100$	$\frac{3}{4}$	$\dfrac{.75}{100} = .0075$	
$105 \ : 100$	105	$\dfrac{105}{100} = 1.05$	
$92\frac{1}{2} : 100$	$92\frac{1}{2}$	$\dfrac{92.5}{100} = .925$	

339. If the proportion, one of whose ratios (r) is such a standard ratio, be simple, and if a and c express the antecedent and consequent of the second ratio which involves the unknown term, then we shall find

Rule for the solution of questions involving *rates.*

$$\frac{a}{c} = r,$$

and therefore

$$a = cr \quad \text{or} \quad c = \frac{a}{r},$$

according as the antecedent or the consequent is the unknown term. If the value of r be expressed as a number, and not as a ratio with both its terms, we at once multiply c by r, to obtain a, or we divide a by r, to obtain c: but if r be expressed as a ratio, and not as a number, we find the unknown term by the ordinary arithmetical process: the following are examples.

(1)   To find the commission on £187. 10s. 6d. at $2\frac{1}{2}$ per cent.

$$c = £187. \ 10s. \ 6d. = £187. \ 525,$$

$$r = .025,$$

$$a = cr = 187.525 \times .025$$

$$= 4.688125 = £4. \ 13s. \ 9\tfrac{3}{20}d.$$

Or, otherwise,

```
   £.      £.   s.   d.              £.          £.
a  :    187 . 10 . 6      ::     2½    :      100
          20                                   20
        ─────                                ─────
        3750                                 2000
          12                                   12
        ─────                                ─────
       45006                                24000
          2½
       ─────
       90012
       22503
 ─────────────────
24.000) 112.515 ( 4.688125
         96       20
        ─────     ───────
        165       13.7625
        144          12
        ─────     ───────
        211        9.15
        192
        ─────
        195
        192
        ─────
          30
          24
        ─────
          60
          60
        ─────
         120
         120
```

or £4. 13s. $9\tfrac{3}{20}d.$, the answer.

(2) To find the value, in sterling money, of £650. consols at $90\frac{3}{8}$ per cent.

$$c = 650, \quad r = .90375,$$
$$a = cr = £587.4375 = £587.\ 8s.\ 9d.$$

The ordinary statement is

$$
\begin{array}{cccc}
£. & £. & £. & £. \\
a & : 650 :: & 90\frac{3}{8} & : 100.
\end{array}
$$

(3) What will the rates of a parish, whose rental is £1764. 10s. 6d., amount to, at $6\frac{3}{4}d.$ per pound?

$$c = £1764.525, \quad r = \frac{6\frac{3}{4}}{12 \times 20} = .028125,$$

$$a = cr = £49.6273\ldots$$

$$= £49.\ 12s.\ 6\frac{1}{2}d., \text{ nearly.}$$

In multiplying 1764.525 and .028125 together, it will be most convenient to take the digits of the multiplier from right to left, and to put down no digits in the several partial products which are lower than the fourth place of decimals*: the process would stand thus;

$$
\begin{array}{r}
1764.525 \\
.028125 \\
\hline
352905 \\
141162 \\
1765 \\
353 \\
88 \\
\hline
49.6273 \\
20 \\
\hline
12.546 \\
12 \\
\hline
6.552 \\
4 \\
\hline
2.208
\end{array}
$$

* For 1 farthing $= .00104166$, and consequently decimal digits in places below the fourth can very rarely influence the lowest denomination of units in the result.

(4) To find the interest of £230. 10s. for 1 year at 4 per cent.

$$c = £230.5,$$
$$r = .04,$$
$$a = cr = 9.22 = £9. \ 4s. \ 4\tfrac{3}{4}d., \text{ nearly.}$$

The ordinary statement is

£.   s.

$$a : 230 . 10 :: 4 : 100.$$

Computation of simple interest for periods different from that with respect to which the rate is estimated.

340. When *simple* interest is required to be determined for any period different from that upon which the per centage or rate is estimated, we may consider both the *per centage* and the *time* as agents of the effect or *interest,* and proceed as in ordinary cases of compound proportion: but inasmuch as a period of *one* year or *unity* forms generally one of the terms of the ratio of the *times* and the number of years (t) (number being taken in its most general sense) the other, it will follow that this number (t) will express the value of this ratio, and therefore

$$\frac{a}{c} = rt \quad \text{and} \quad a = crt, \quad \text{or} \quad c = \frac{a}{rt}:$$

it follows therefore that we must multiply the interest of one year by t, in order to get the interest for t years, a conclusion which is deducible likewise from more simple considerations.

Example.   Thus, let it be required to find the interest of £427. 10s. for $2\tfrac{1}{2}$ years at $4\tfrac{3}{4}$ per cent.

$$c = 427.5$$
$$r = .0475$$
$$cr = 20.30625$$
$$t = 2.5$$

$$a = crt = 50.765625$$
$$= £50. \ 15s. \ 3\tfrac{3}{4}d.,$$

which is the amount of interest for the period in question. The ordinary statement would be

£.   £.   s.

$$a : 427 . 10 :: 4\tfrac{3}{4} : 100 \left.\begin{array}{c} \\ \\ \end{array}\right\}$$
$$:: 2\tfrac{1}{2} : 1$$

£.   £.   s.

or $a : 427 . 10 :: 4\tfrac{3}{4} \times 2\tfrac{1}{2} : 100 \times 1.$

341.   The interest upon money generally becomes due yearly Compound
interest. or half-yearly; and in ordinary cases it is either paid when due, or added or presumed to be added, to the principal, whose increased amount becomes the agent of the interest for the next succeeding period: the interest, which thence arises, is greater than the *simple* interest, which is estimated upon the original and unaltered principal, and is therefore denominated *compound* interest.   The calculation of the amount of *compound* interest, at least for periods which are entire multiples of the subordinate periods, whether years or half-years, at the ends of which interest becomes due, depends upon the simple composition of given ratios and is entirely within the domain of arithmetic: but inasmuch as the questions connected with the anticipated or deferred payments of money and the consequent deductions (discount) or additions (interest) which must affect the original principal concerned, belong to a very extensive class, involving in many cases very complicated relations, where algebraical formulæ of solution are more convenient for use and their deduction and application more easily understood, than the rules which are given in books of Arithmetic, we shall reserve the further consideration of them for a subsequent chapter: it would, in fact, be quite impossible to treat this very important subject, with sufficient generality, without the aid of the principles of Symbolical Algebra.

Questions relating to compound interest, discount, &c. most easily calculated by formulæ.

342.   In the examples considered in the preceding articles, we have been required to determine *one* unknown quantity, which formed one of the terms of a proportion, whether simple or compound: but many questions will present themselves, in which *two* or *more* unknown quantities are involved, which, though connected with each other, require to be determined by different proportions: and others, in which one unknown quantity only is required to be determined through the medium of others, which, by presenting themselves both in the antecedents and consequents of ratios which are compounded together, disappear altogether from the final result.   Questions which, in books of Arithmetic, are referred to generally under the head of Single and Double Fellowship, belong to the first of these classes; and those relating to Exchanges and other analogous subjects, belong to the second.

Questions involving two or more unknown quantities, which are solved by means of proportions.

Two great classes of such questions.

Examples. 343. The following are examples of the first class:

Question in Single Fellowship. (1) " *A* and *B* have gained in trade £182: *A* put in £300, and *B* £400: what is each person's just share of the profit?"

The hypothesis, implied in the use of the term *just*, is, that the *joint* will bear to the *separate* profit, the same ratio which the *joint* will bear to the *separate* stock: if we call therefore *x* the profit of *A* and *y* the profit of *B*, we shall find

$$\text{£.} \quad \text{£.} \quad \text{£.}$$
$$700 : 300 :: 182 : x,$$
$$700 : 400 :: 182 : y.$$

Consequently, we obtain from the first proportion $x = £78$, and from the second $y = £104$.

This is an example of Single Fellowship.

Question in Double Fellowship. (2) " Two troops of horse rent a field, for which they pay £82: one of the troops sent into it 64 horses for 25 days: the other, 56 horses for 30 days: what portion of the rent must each troop pay?"

If we call *x* the portion of the rent which should be paid by the first troop, and *y* the portion which should be paid by the second, we shall find

$$\text{£.}$$
$$64 \times 25 + 56 \times 30 : 64 \times 25 :: 82 : x,$$
$$64 \times 25 + 56 \times 30 : 56 \times 30 :: 82 : y.$$

Consequently, $x = £40$ and $y = £42$.

Reducible to one in Single Fellowship. The hypothesis is, that the consumption of grass is jointly proportional to the number of horses and the number of days: or otherwise, if we consider the *unit* of consumption to be the *feed* of *one* horse for *one* day, the quantity consumed by each troop would be represented by 64×25 and 56×30, or by 1600 and 1680, respectively, and the *joint* or *entire* consumption by their sum or 3280: the question, when thus analysed, becomes a case of Single Fellowship.

The following question is of a similar kind:

Question in Double Fellowship. (3) " A ship's company take a prize of £1000, which is to be divided amongst them, *according to their pay and to the time during which they have served:* now the officers, four in number, have 40s. each a month, and the midshipmen, 12 in number, have 30s. each a month, and they have all served 6 months: the sailors, who are 110 in number, have each 22s. a month, and have been on board 3 months. What will be the share of each class?"

The pay due to each class of claimants for the period of their service, will be found by multiplying together the number of persons, the monthly pay (in shillings), and the number of months of service: the resulting sums will be $4 \times 6 \times 40$, $12 \times 6 \times 30$, and $110 \times 3 \times 22$, or 960s., 2160s., and 7260s. respectively, and the sum of the whole of them 10380s.: if we now designate the unknown shares of prize-money due to each class by x, y and z respectively, we shall find

$$\begin{array}{ccc} s. & s. & \pounds. \\ 10380 : & 960 :: & 1000 : x, \\ 10380 : & 2160 :: & 1000 : y, \\ 10380 : & 7260 :: & 1000 : z. \end{array}$$

We thus find
$$\begin{aligned} x &= \pounds 92. \ 9s. \ 8\tfrac{1}{2}d. \\ y &= \pounds 208. \ 1s. \ 10\tfrac{1}{4}d. \\ z &= \pounds 699. \ 8s. \ 5\tfrac{1}{4}d. \end{aligned}$$

It will necessarily follow that $x + y + z = \pounds 1000$, inasmuch as the antecedents of the ratios in the three proportions are the same; and therefore (Art. 304)

$$10380 : 960 + 2160 + 7260 :: 1000 : x + y + z;$$

and since $10380 = 960 + 2160 + 7260$, therefore also $1000 = x + y + z$: the same remark applies to the two examples preceding.

The separate shares distributed will together amount to the whole sum to be distributed.

344. In the second class of questions, which was noticed above, (Art. 342.) there is only *one* unknown quantity which is required to be finally determined, though other unknown quantities are involved as intermediate terms of comparison or otherwise, whose actual determination will not be necessary, if they can be introduced both into the antecedents and consequents of the ratios, which are compounded together in order to form the final proportion.

Questions in which unknown quantities present themselves as intermediate terms only.

The following are examples:

(1) "If I buy tobacco at £10. 10s. per *cwt.*, at how much per *lb.* must I sell it, so as to gain 12 per cent.?"

Question in Profit and Loss.

Let x be the *cost* price per *lb.* of the tobacco, and y its *sale* price, so as to answer the required conditions: consequently

$$\text{lb.} \quad \text{£.} \quad s. \quad \text{lb.} \quad s.$$
$$112 : 10 . 10 :: 1 : x,$$
$$\text{£.} \qquad \text{£.}$$
$$100 : 112 :: x : y;$$

therefore compounding the proportions,

$$\text{£.} \quad s.$$
$$100 : 10 . 10 :: 1 : y,$$
$$\text{or} \quad y = 2.1s. = 2s. \ 1\tfrac{4}{5}d.$$

In this case, the cost price (x) is an intermediate term only, whose value it is not necessary to determine: the incongruity of the terms of the ratios in the first of the two proportions given above has been noticed before (Art. 335).

Another question in Profit and Loss.

(2) " Sold a repeating watch for £52. 10s. and by so doing lost 17 per cent.: whereas by fair trading I should have cleared 20 per cent.: how much was it sold under its just value?"

Let x be the cost price, and y the trading price at which it should have been sold: we then get

$$\text{£.} \qquad \text{£.} \qquad \text{£.} \qquad \text{£.} \quad s.$$
$$100 : 83 :: x : 52 . 10$$
$$120 : 100 :: y : x$$

$$\overline{}$$
$$120 : 83 :: y : 52 . 10$$

and therefore $y = £75. \ 18s. \ 0\tfrac{3}{4}d.$

from which, if £52. 10s. be subtracted, we get £23. 8s. $0\tfrac{3}{4}d.$, which is the answer to the question proposed.

In this case, as in the former, the cost price is an intermediate term, which disappears by the composition of the proportions.

Questions on barter and exchanges considered as introductory to the *chain-rule.*
Question of barter solved by composition of proportions.

345. In questions of barter and exchanges we generally find a series of quantities, either expressed or implied, which become merely terms of comparison, all of which, except the object of research, disappear in the composition of the proportions. This disappearance of several intermediate terms will be best understood from the following example:

" If 3lbs. of tea be worth 4lbs. of coffee, and if 6lbs. of coffee be equal to 20lbs. of sugar, how many lbs. of sugar may be had for 9lbs. of tea?"

For greater clearness, let us denote the cost price of a lb. of tea by A, of a lb. of coffee by B, and of a lb. of sugar by C, and let x be the number of lbs. of sugar required to be determined: we then get the following proportions:

$$A : B :: 4 : 3$$
$$B : C :: 20 : 6$$
$$C : A :: 9 : x$$
$$1 : 1 :: 4 \times 20 \times 9 : 3 \times 6 \times x.$$

Therefore $3 \times 6 \times x = 4 \times 20 \times 9,$

or $x = \dfrac{4 \times 20 \times 9}{3 \times 6} = 40.$

In this example the proportions are derived, by resolving the several equations $3A = 4B$, $6B = 20C$, and $xC = 9A$, which are immediately furnished by the question, into their equivalent proportions (Art. 287.): in practice, however, it is much more convenient to dispense with the proportions altogether, retaining the equations only, which are written underneath each other, as follows: *The same question solved by the chain-rule.*

$$3A = 4B,$$
$$6B = 20C,$$
$$xC = 9A.$$

If we strike out A, B and C, which occur upon both sides of these equations, and if we multiply together those numerical coefficients which are severally placed underneath each other, we shall get the equation

$$3 \times 6 \times x = 4 \times 20 \times 9,$$

from which the value of x is determined as before.

346. The second process of solution of the preceding example, contains the principle of the *chain-rule*, which is so useful in the calculation and arbitration of exchanges, in the comparison of the standards of weight, measure and capacity of different countries, and in almost all the transactions of international commerce: the class of questions to which it is applicable, as well as the rule itself, may be stated generally as follows. *The principle of the chain-rule.*

If there be any number of quantities A_1, $A_2 \ldots A_n$, which are so related to each other, that

$$a_1 A_1 = a_1 A_2,$$

$$a_2 A_2 = a_2 A_3,$$

$$a_3 A_3 = a_3 A_4,$$

$$\ldots \ldots \ldots$$

$$a_{n-1} A_{n-1} = a_n A_n,$$

where a_1, a_2, $a_3 \ldots a_{n-1}$, and a_1, a_2, $a_3 \ldots a_n$, are given numbers, then it is required to find what number (x) of A_n shall be equal to a given number (a_n) of A_1.

The value of x, which is required, may be expressed by the formula

$$x = \frac{a_1 \, a_2 \, \ldots \, a_n}{a_1 a_2 \ldots a_{n-1}}.$$

Or, if expressed in words, *the number required, is equal to the quotient which arises from dividing the continued product of the given numbers on the right-hand side of the several equations, by the continued product of the given numbers on the left: the unknown number being supposed to be placed on the right-hand side of the equations, and it being understood that the same intermediate term, whether* A_1, $A_2 \ldots A_n$, *appears once only on the same side of the several equations.*

347. The quantities A_1, $A_2 \ldots A_n$, though they may be specifically different from each other, will admit of comparison with each other, through the medium of some common element of value. Thus, different commodities can bear a real ratio to each other, through the medium of the prices at which they can be purchased or sold: coins and measures of weight, length, capacity, &c. whether of the same or different countries, become comparable with each other by reference to given standards or through the known multiples of subordinate units, by which their various denominations are known or presumed to be connected with each other.

348. The proof of the *chain-rule*, as stated in Art. 346, though otherwise deducible from very obvious and simple considerations, admits of immediate demonstration from the composition of proportions (Art. 301.): for if we resolve the several

equations, which are furnished by the enunciation of the question, into their equivalent proportions, we get

$$A_1 : A_2 :: \alpha_1 : a_1$$
$$A_2 : A_3 :: \alpha_2 : a_2$$
$$\dots\dots\dots\dots\dots$$
$$A_{n-1} : A_n :: \alpha_{n-1} : a_{n-1},$$
$$A_n : A_1 :: \alpha_n : x,$$

which, when compounded together, furnish the final proportion

$$1 : 1 :: \alpha_1 \alpha_2 \dots \alpha_n : a_1 a_2 \dots a_{n-1} x ;$$

and, therefore,

$$a_1 a_2 \dots a_{n-1} x = \alpha_1 \alpha_2 \dots \alpha_n,$$

$$\text{or} \quad x = \frac{\alpha_1 \alpha_2 \dots \alpha_n}{a_1 a_2 \dots a_{n-1}}.$$

349. The following are examples of the application of this very important and comprehensive rule. Examples.

(1) How much sugar at 8d. per lb. must be given in barter for 20 cwt. of tobacco at £3. per cwt.? Exchange or barter of commodities.

The successive equations are

$$8d. = 1 \text{ lb.},$$
$$1s. = 12d.,$$
$$£1 = 20s.,$$
$$1 \text{ cwt.} = £3,$$
$$x \text{ lb.} = 20 \text{ cwt.}$$

Consequently

$$x = \frac{12 \times 20 \times 3 \times 20}{8}$$

$$= 1800 \text{ lbs. of sugar.}$$

The several equations which enter into this question might be expressed in words at length, as follows:

8d. is the price of 1 lb. of sugar,

one shilling contains or equals 12 pence,

one pound sterling contains or equals 20 shillings,

one cwt. costs 3 pounds sterling,

x lbs. of sugar are equal in price to 20 cwt. of tobacco.

A question
in simple
proportion. (2) " What ought a person to spend in a week, whose expenditure is £700 per annum?"

$$52 \text{ weeks} = £700,$$

$$£x = 1 \text{ week}.$$

Consequently

$$x = \frac{£700}{52} = £13. \ 9s. \ 2\tfrac{3}{4}d.$$

In other words, the expenditure of 52 weeks is equal to £700, and £x is equal to the expenditure of one week.

This is an example of the application of the *chain rule* to a simple Rule of Three question.

A question
in reduc-
tion. (3) " To reduce £2. 10s. 6d. to farthings."

$$£1 = 20s.,$$

$$1s. = 12d.,$$

$$1d. = 4 \text{ farthings } (f),$$

$$xf. = £2. \ 10s. \ 6d.,$$

$$= 2 \times 4 \times 12 \times 20 + 10 \times 4 \times 12 + 6 \times 4,$$

or $x = 624$ (farthings).

This is an example of reduction, where a quantity expressed by units of different denominations appears in the last equation: in such a case it is very obvious that the successive units of higher denomination must be expressed in multiples of units of the lowest denomination, which, when added together, produce a homogeneous result.

A question
on the com-
parison of
standards
of length. (4) " Required the relation between the French *mêtre* and the Rhynland *foot*, supposing the French mêtre equal to 39.371 English inches, and that 37 English feet are equal to 36 Rhynland feet."

$$1 \text{ mêtre} = 39.371 \text{ inches},$$

$$12 \text{ inches} = 1 \text{ English foot},$$

$$37 \text{ English feet} = 36 \text{ Rhynland feet},$$

$$x \text{ Rhynland feet} = 1 \text{ mêtre}.$$

Consequently

$$x = \frac{39.371 \times 36}{12 \times 37}$$

$$= 3.192 \text{ (Rhynland feet)}$$

$$= 1 \text{ (mêtre)}.$$

(5) "What is the course of exchange between London and Paris, if the price of an ounce of standard gold in London be 78 shillings and if the premium on gold in Paris be 8 francs in the thousand?"

This is a question for the determination of the course of exchange between London and Paris from the price of bullion at those places: it is expressed by the relation between a pound sterling and a franc, which are the primary standards or units of value of the English and French coinage respectively: in defining the course of exchange between other countries, we merely replace a pound sterling and a franc, by the primary coins of those countries.

A gold standard is adopted in England and a silver standard in France: it is for this reason that silver in one country and gold in the other, may bear a premium or discount with reference to their respective standards of circulation.

The *mint* or *tariff* price of a *kilogramme* of *fine* gold in France is 3434.44 francs; a kilogramme contains 32.154 English ounces.

The mint price of an ounce of *standard* gold in England is £3. 17s. 10½d. or £3.89375: the *standard* gold of the coinage being 22 carats, or rather being alloyed in such a manner, that 12 ounces of *standard* are equal in value to 11 ounces of *fine* gold.

With these preparatory explanations and facts, the solution of the question will stand as follows:

$$£1. = 20s.$$

$$78s. = 1 \text{ ounce standard gold,}$$

$$12 \text{ ounces standard} = 11 \text{ ounces fine gold,}$$

$$32.154 \text{ ounces fine} = 1 \text{ kilogramme fine gold,}$$

$$1 \text{ kilogramme fine} = 3434.44 \text{ francs tariff,}$$

$$1000 \text{ francs tariff} = 1008 \text{ francs with premium,}$$

$$x \text{ francs with premium} = £1. \text{ sterling.}$$

Consequently,

$$x = \frac{20 \times 11 \times 3434.44 \times 1008}{12 \times 32.154 \times 1000 \times 78} = 25.30:$$

or £1. sterling is equivalent to 25 francs 30 centimes, which is the *course of exchange*.

Fixed numbers in exchanges.

350. In considering the fluctuations of the course of exchange between London and Paris, the only variable quantities will be the premium (per 1000 francs) upon gold in Paris and the price of standard bullion in England: every other number involved in the expression for x, which is given above, will be fixed and invariable: the value of

$$\frac{20 \times 11 \times 3434.44}{12 \times 32.154 \times 1000} = 1.95823$$

Their use.

is called the *fixed number* in the regulation of the exchanges between London and Paris, and, when once determined, may be used, for the same two places, in all cases whatsoever. Thus if the premium on gold at Paris be 10 francs per thousand, and the price of an ounce of standard gold be 77s. 9d. we shall find

$$x = 1.95823 \times \frac{1010}{77.75} = 25.45, \text{ nearly,}$$

or the pound sterling would be equal to 25 francs 45 centimes *.

Similar *fixed* numbers, dependent upon the relations of the subdivisions, weights and fineness of the primary standards of circulation of different countries, may be determined and similarly used, for the purpose of calculating the course of exchange from the prices of bullion at any two places whatsoever.

Simple arbitration of exchange.

351. *Simple arbitration of exchange* is the determination of the course of exchange between B and C when the course of exchange between A and B and also between A and C is given: the following is an example.

---

* The *par of exchange* between London and Paris is the price of a pound sterling in francs, when the prices of gold in Paris and of standard bullion in London are at the tariff or mint prices, or at a proportionate premium or discount in both countries: this *par of exchange*, in the case under consideration, is 25.15 francs nearly ; and in order to find the course of exchange, we must multiply the *par of exchange* by the ratios of the premium price of gold in Paris (per thousand francs) to 1000, and of the price of an ounce of standard bullion in England to the mint price. Thus, in the last case considered in the text, the course of exchange

$$= 25.15 \times \frac{1010}{1000} \times \frac{77.875}{77.75} .$$

Similar remarks may be applied to the determination of the course of exchange between London and any other place.

" If the course of exchange of London on Paris be 25 francs 60 centimes, and of London on Cadiz be 41d. the piastre, how many francs are equal to a doubloon of 4 piastres? or in other words, what is the course of exchange between Paris and Cadiz, the standard coins being francs and doubloons?"

$$1 \text{ doubloon} = 4 \text{ piastres},$$
$$1 \text{ piastre} = 41d.,$$
$$12d. = 1s.,$$
$$20s. = \pounds1. \text{ sterling},$$
$$\pounds1. \text{ sterling} = 25.60 \text{ francs},$$
$$x \text{ francs} = 1 \text{ doubloon}.$$

Consequently,

$$x = \frac{4 \times 41 \times 25.60}{12 \times 20}$$

$$= 17.49,$$

or 17 francs 49 centimes are equal to one doubloon.

The fixed number is here $\dfrac{4}{12 \times 20} = .0125.$

352. *Compound arbitration of exchange* is where the course of exchange between A and B, B and C, C and D is given, to find the course of exchange between A and D. It is obviously a repetition of simple arbitration: for in the case proposed we may find the course of exchange between A and C by simple arbitration, and subsequently by the same process that between A and D, from our knowledge of the course of exchange between A and C, and C and D: or the whole may be effected by one operation with the *chain rule*.

Compound arbitration of exchange.

The following is an example.

" The exchange between London and Amsterdam is $35\frac{1}{2}$ shillings Flemish per pound sterling, between Amsterdam and Lisbon is 43 pence Flemish per old crusade, and between Lisbon and Paris is 483 rees for 3 francs: required the arbitrated course of exchange between London and Paris?"

Question in compound arbitration of exchange.

In one' old crusade there are 400 rees.

$$\text{£1. sterling} = 35\tfrac{1}{2} \text{ shillings Flemish,}$$
$$1 \text{ shilling Flemish} = 12 \text{ pence Flemish,}$$
$$43 \text{ pence Flemish} = 1 \text{ old crusade,}$$
$$1 \text{ old crusade} = 400 \text{ rees,}$$
$$483 \text{ rees} = 3 \text{ francs,}$$
$$x \text{ francs} = \text{£1. sterling.}$$

Consequently,

$$x = 24.61, \text{ nearly,}$$

or the arbitrated course of exchange between London and Paris is 24 francs 61 centimes the pound sterling.

General object proposed by circular exchanges.

353. Simple and compound arbitration (the latter is rarely practised) of circular exchanges enable merchants to compare the arbitrated with the direct and declared course of exchange, and thus to judge of the most advantageous mode of receiving or transmitting money or bills. In forming such a judgment, however, many other circumstances must be taken into consideration, such as the time required for obtaining returns, the interest of money, the relative security of the transactions, and so on: a complete knowledge and rapid appreciation of such particulars would require long and careful study, and constitute in fact the education and the occupation of the most accomplished merchants*. Our object, in the very slight and imperfect notice of this subject which we have given in the preceding Articles, has been the illustration of a very useful and comprehensive arithmetical rule, in some of the most important examples of its application.

* On the subject of exchange transactions of every kind, the student may consult Kelly's " Universal Cambist," a very useful and elaborate work.

CHAPTER V.

ON THE SOLUTION OF EQUATIONS.

354. THE general object proposed in the solution of questions in Arithmetic, is the determination of some number, concrete or abstract, which was previously unknown, as the final result of certain operations with given numbers, which the conditions of the question require or direct to be performed: of this kind are the sums, remainders, products and quotients, which result from the fundamental operations of addition, subtraction, multiplication and division, as well as the other results which arise from their repetition or combination in any order: the square, cube and other roots of given numbers: and the unknown term in a proportion which is determined by known and defined operations, and of which such varied examples have been considered in the last Chapter.

The general object proposed in arithmetical processes.

355. The general character of arithmetical processes requires that *the unknown quantity which is sought for in the solution of the question, should not be involved in the course of the operations which are required for its determination.*

In arithmetical processes, the unknown quantity sought for is not involved in the processes which lead to its determination.

This condition, though not always strictly adhered to, will sufficiently define the classes of questions which may be treated by arithmetical processes alone, without requiring any aid from the use of symbolical language or from other less simple processes of reasoning, conducted by means of ordinary language, by which the use of symbols may sometimes be superseded: the following example will serve to illustrate the distinction to which we refer.

356. " To find a number, the sum of whose double and whose half shall be equal to 25."

An algebraical problem.

Its statement.

If we call x the unknown number, then its double will be represented by $2x$ and its half by $\frac{x}{2}$: their sum or

$$2x + \frac{x}{2} = 25.$$

Its solution.

Since " the doubles of equals are equal," it follows that if we multiply both sides of this equation by 2, we shall get

$$4 + 2 \times \frac{x}{2} = 50,$$

$$\text{or} \quad 4x + x = 50,$$

$$\text{or} \quad 5x = 50,$$

$$\text{or} \quad x = \frac{50}{5} = 10,$$

for it is obvious that if 5 times x be equal to 50, x will be equal to one-fifth part of 50 or to 10.

Difficulty of disentangling the complicated relations of unknown numbers by means of ordinary language.

357. It would not be difficult to solve a simple question like this by means of reasonings conducted in ordinary language, without the use of signs or symbols, by following the order of the process which is given above: innumerable problems, however, might be proposed, in which common minds would be totally bewildered in the attempt to comprehend at one view the entire conditions, when expressed in ordinary language, which the unknown number must satisfy, or to follow out, by means of it, the successive steps by which those conditions are finally reduced to one, which furnishes the solution of the question.

An arithmetical problem.

358. If we should interchange the known and unknown number in the problem proposed in Art. 356, it would be enunciated as follows.

" To find the number, which shall be equal to the sum of the double and the half of the number 10."

This is a proper arithmetical problem, in which the unknown number is *not* involved in the operations which are required for its determination: the process of solution, conducted without signs or symbols, would stand as follows:

Its solution.

10

2

20, the double of 10.

2)10

5, the half of 10.

20

5

25, their sum or the number required
to be determined.

359. When a question is proposed for solution, in which The symbolical enunciation of a problem leads to an equation. the unknown quantity or number is itself involved in the conditions which are proposed for its determination, then the expression of those conditions by means of signs and symbols will always terminate in an equation, which may be considered as the symbolical enunciation of the problem proposed. For assuming that the signs of Algebra are competent to express all the operations of Arithmetic, and that a symbol, such as x or y, may express the unknown number (all other numbers involved in the question being known and expressed by digits and zero), it is obvious that no known number can be assigned as the *necessary* result of any series of operations which involve this unknown number, unless they make it disappear, in which case its value is altogether arbitrary and indifferent *: it will consequently follow that the conditions of the question must *assign* a result, which is either a given number, or a second symbolical expression also involving the unknown number or its symbol, but which is not reducible to identity with

---

* Thus if the unknown number or any multiple of it be both added and subtracted, or if one multiple of it be divided by another, and if it be not otherwise involved, it will altogether disappear and will in no respect influence the other conditions of the question: thus $7 + x - x$ or $7 + 4x - 4x$, or $\dfrac{7x}{x}$ or $\dfrac{21x}{3x}$ are all of them equally identical with the number 7, and consequently in all such cases a *known* arithmetical result *necessarily* follows from a series of operations which involve an unknown number whatever its value may be.

the former: and it is obvious that the condition which asserts that the first of these expressions is equivalent to the second, which is symbolized by the interposition of the sign = between them, will in all cases convert them into an equation.

Meaning of identical equations.

360. Equations are said to be *identical* when the two expressions, connected by the sign =, which compose them, are identical or are reducible to identity by the performance of the operations which are indicated in them: under such circumstances, any quantity which is contained in them, which is unknown and therefore indicated by a symbol, will continue unknown or indeterminate, as far as its value can be inferred or determined from its connection with such an equation.

Equations absolutely identical.

361. The following equations are absolutely identical without requiring any preparatory reduction to make them so.

(1) $x = x$.

(2) $x + 5 = x + 5$.

(3) $3x + 7 = 3x + 7$.

(4) $4 + 5x - \dfrac{7ab}{4} = 4 + 5x - \dfrac{7ab}{4}$.

It is obvious that these equations will continue to be identical, whatever value is assigned to the symbols which they involve, so long as such values are the same upon both sides of the several equations.

Equations reducible to identity.

362. The following equations are reducible to identity by the actual performance of the operations which are indicated in them.

$$(1) \quad 3x + 4x = 7x.$$

In this case it is merely necessary to add together $3x$ and $4x$, Art. 31, in order to make the first member of the equation identical with the second.

$$(2) \quad \frac{25 - x^2}{5 - x} = 5 + x.$$

The second member of this equation is the result of the division of $25 - x^2$ by $5 - x$, an operation which is indicated by the fraction $\dfrac{25 - x^2}{5 - x}$.

$$(3) \quad \frac{a^3 - {}^3x}{a - x} - ax = a^2 + x^2.$$

The division of $a^3 - x^3$ by $a - x$, which is indicated by the fraction $\dfrac{a^3 - x^3}{a - x}$, gives us $a^2 + ax + x^2$, from which if ax be subtracted (an operation which is indicated by the sign − which is placed before it), we shall get $a^2 + x^2$ for the result, which is the second member of the equation: it follows therefore that the two members of the original equation are reducible to identity with each other.

363.   The solution of problems which are beyond the proper province of arithmetic, will require their algebraical enunciation in the form of equations and the subsequent reduction of the equations thus formed, so that the unknown symbol or symbols may be altogether insulated, when possible, from any connection with other operations or numbers.   These two processes, though involved in the solution of every problem, are quite distinct from each other; but it is the second of them which is alone concerned in the classification of equations or which presents any very peculiar difficulties to be overcome: it is for this reason that we shall begin by assuming that the equations are already formed and proceed at once to the consideration of the rules for their reduction and solution.

The formation and reduction of equations are distinct processes.

It is quite impossible, however, to advance to any great extent in the theory of the solution of equations, without the aid of Symbolical Algebra; and in the present chapter we shall confine our attention exclusively to the solutions of equations of the first and second degrees, as far as they can be effected by the principles of arithmetical algebra alone.   We shall begin with the statement of some general rules for the preliminary reduction of equations which are equally applicable to equations of all degrees, and which are founded upon the most simple principles.

The solution of equations generally requires the aid of symbolical algebra.

364.   *Numbers, symbols, or terms may be transferred from one side of an equation to the other, by merely changing the algebraical signs which precede them, + into − and − into +.*

Rule for the transposition of terms from one side of an equation to another.

Thus if
$$a - c = b,$$
then
$$a = b + c :$$
and also

if
$$a + c = b,$$
then likewise
$$a = b - c.$$

Proof.   For since, if "equals be added to equals, the wholes are equal," it follows that if
$$a - c = b,$$
then, by adding c to both the equals $a - c$ and b, we get
$$a - c + c = b + c,$$
$$\text{or} \qquad a = b + c,$$
$$\text{since} \qquad a - c + c = a. \qquad \text{(Art. 15.)}$$

Again, since if "equals be taken from equals, the remainders are equal," it follows, that if
$$a + c = b,$$
then, by subtracting c from both the equals $a + c$ and b, we get
$$a + c - c = b - c,$$
$$\text{or} \qquad a = b - c,$$
$$\text{since} \qquad a + c - c = a, \qquad \text{(Art. 15.)}$$

All the significant terms of an equation may be transferred to one side.   365. This is a most important principle in the reduction of equations to new and more commodious forms, insomuch as it enables us to transfer *any* or *all* the terms of one of the members of an equation to the other and conversely: and it follows as an immediate consequence of it, that every equation may admit of such a transposition of its terms, that all its significant terms may be made to form one of its members and *zero* the other: thus if
$$a = b,$$
then $\qquad\qquad\qquad a - b = b - b = 0. \qquad \text{(Art. 16.)}$

If $\qquad\qquad\qquad a + c = b,$

then $\qquad\qquad\qquad a + c - b = b - b = 0.$

If $\qquad\qquad\qquad a - c = b,$

then $\qquad\qquad\qquad a - b - c = b - b = 0.$

Examples.   366. The following are examples of the application of the preceding rule.

(1)   Let $7 - 3x = 5 - 2x$: and let it be required to transpose the term $2x$ from the right to the left-hand side of the equation.

Add $2x$ to both sides, and we get

$$7 - 3x + 2x = 5 - 2x + 2x,$$

or $\qquad\qquad 7 - 3x + 2x = 5,$

or $\qquad\qquad\qquad 7 - x = 5.$ (Arts. 31. and 32.)

(2)   Let $4x - \dfrac{x}{2} - 3 = 9x + \dfrac{x}{2} - 15$: and let it be required

to transpose $\dfrac{x}{2}$ and 15 from the right to the left-hand side of the equation.

Subtract $\dfrac{x}{2}$ from, and add 15 to, both sides of the equation, and we get

$$4x - \frac{x}{2} - 3 - \frac{x}{2} + 15 = 9x + \frac{x}{2} - 15 - \frac{x}{2} + 15,$$

or $\qquad 4x - \dfrac{x}{2} - 3 - \dfrac{x}{2} + 15 = 9x,$

or $\qquad\qquad 4x - x + 12 = 9x,$

or $\qquad\qquad\qquad 3x + 12 = 9x.$

If we wish to transfer $3x$ from the left to the right-hand side of this reduced equation, we shall get, by subtracting $3x$ from both sides of it,

$$3x + 12 - 3x = 9x - 3x,$$

or $\qquad\qquad\qquad 12 = 6x.$

(3)   Let $7x - 4 - \dfrac{2x}{3} = \dfrac{x}{3} + 14$; and let it be required to transpose all the significant terms to one side of the equation.

Subtract $\dfrac{x}{3}$ and 14 from both sides of the equation, and we get

$$7x - 4 - \frac{2x}{3} - \frac{x}{3} - 14 = \frac{x}{3} + 14 - \frac{x}{3} - 14,$$

or $\qquad\qquad 7x - 4 - x - 14 = 0,$

or $\qquad\qquad\qquad 6x - 18 = 0.$

The members of an equation may be multiplied by any number or expression.

367. *If both sides of an equation be multiplied by the same number, symbol, or expression, the resulting products will continue equal to each other.*

For if

$$a = b,$$

then also

$$ac = bc,$$

whatever c may be.

This conclusion is equivalent to the axiom that "equi-multiples of equals are equal to one another," the term multiple being taken in its largest sense, whether as signifying a whole or a fractional number.

Rule for clearing an equation of fractions.

368. An equation, one or both of whose members involve fractional terms, may be reduced to an equivalent equation, without fractions, *by multiplying*, in conformity with the principle in the last Article, *both its members by the least common multiple of all the denominators of the fractional terms:* for it is obvious that the denominators of every fractional term in the original will disappear in the reduced equation, inasmuch as its numerator has been multiplied by a multiple of its denominator, and is therefore reducible to an equivalent number or expression without a denominator.

Reason for employing the least common multiple of the denominators.

The same reduction may be effected by multiplying both members of the equation successively by the several denominators of the fractions which they involve, destroying successively those fractions whose denominators are the multipliers: but a single multiplication by the *least common multiple* of all the denominators, will not only effect this reduction at once, but will furnish a reduced equation in its most simple form, a consideration of great importance when the coefficients of one or more of its terms would otherwise be large numbers.

Examples.

369. The following are examples:

$$(1) \quad \frac{x}{2} + 3 = 6.$$

Multiply both sides of this equation by 2, and we get

$$x + 6 = 12,$$

an equation without fractions.

$$(2) \quad \frac{x}{2} + \frac{x}{3} = 5.$$

Multiply both sides of the equation by 6, the least common multiple of the two denominators 2 and 3, and we get

$$3x + 2x = 30.$$

For $6 \times \dfrac{x}{2} = 3x$ and $6 \times \dfrac{x}{3} = 2x.$

$$(3) \quad \frac{x}{2} + \frac{x}{3} + \frac{x}{4} = 13.$$

Multiply both sides of the equation by 12, which is the least common multiple of 2, 3 and 4: we thus get

$$6x + 4x + 3x = 156,$$

$$\text{or} \quad 13x = 156.$$

For $12 \times \dfrac{x}{2} = 6x, \quad 12 \times \dfrac{x}{3} = 4x, \quad 12 \times \dfrac{x}{4} = 3x,$ and $12 \times 13 = 156$:

it also follows that $6x + 4x + 3x$ is equal to $13x$. (Art. 31.)

$$(4) \quad \frac{12}{x} + 2 = \frac{4}{x} + 4.$$

Multiply both sides of the equation by the only denominator x, and we get

$$12 + 2x = 4 + 4x.$$

$$(5) \quad \frac{30}{x+2} = \frac{15}{x-1}.$$

Multiply both sides of this equation by $(x+2)\ (x-1)$, which gives us

$$30x - 30 = 15x + 30.$$

For $\dfrac{30}{x+2} \times (x+2)\ (x-1)$ is equal to $30 \times (x-1) = 30x - 30,$

and $\dfrac{15}{x-1} \times (x+2)\ (x-1)$ is equal to $15 \times (x+2) = 15x + 30.$

$$(6) \quad \frac{10}{x} - \frac{3}{x+2} = \frac{6}{x+1}.$$

Multiply both sides of the equation by $x\,(x+2)\,(x+1)$, which gives us

$$10\,(x+1)\,(x+2) - 3\,x\,(x+1) = 6\,x\,(x+2),$$
$$\text{or} \quad 10\,x^2 + 30\,x + 20 - 3\,x^2 - 3\,x = 6\,x^2 + 12\,x.$$

The members of an equation may be divided by any number.

370. *If both sides of an equation be divided by the same number, symbol, or expression, the resulting quotients will be equal to each other.*

For, if

$$a = b,$$

then also

$$\frac{a}{c} = \frac{b}{c},$$

whatever c may be.

Examples.

371. The following are examples of the application of this rule.

(1) $3\,x = 12$; divide both sides of this equation by 3, and we get

$$x = 4.$$

(2) $13\,x = 156$: divide both sides of this equation by 13, and we get

$$x = 12.$$

(3) $\dfrac{90}{x} - \dfrac{27}{x+2} = \dfrac{54}{x+1}$: divide both sides of this equation by 9, which is the greatest common measure of the several numerators 90, 27 and 54, and we get

$$\frac{10}{x} - \frac{3}{x+2} = \frac{6}{x+1}.$$

The form of an equation may be always simplified, as in this example, by dividing both its members by any common measure of its several terms or of their numerators, when they appear under a fractional form.

Like terms in an equation collected into one.

372. The rule for the combination of like terms into one (Art. 31.) will enable us to reduce equations, when cleared of fractional terms, by collecting severally into one those like terms which are on one side of the sign = or which are transferable to one side of it, by the rule of transposition, (Art. 364.): the following are examples:

$$(1) \quad 15x - 3x - 5x = 105.$$

Collecting the like terms $15x$, $3x$ and $5x$ into one, we get

$$7x = 105.$$

$$(2) \quad 3x - 10 = 8 + x.$$

Transposing x from the right-hand side of the equation to the left, we get

$$3x - x - 10 = 8,$$

$$\text{or} \quad 2x - 10 = 8.$$

If we further transpose 10 from the left-hand side of the equation to the right, we get

$$2x = 8 + 10 = 18.$$

$$(3) \quad 7x^2 - 10x = 120 + 4x^2 - 19x.$$

Transposing $4x^2$ and $19x$ from the right-hand side of this equation to the left, we get

$$7x^2 - 4x^2 - 10x + 19x = 120;$$
or
$$3x^2 + 9x = 120.$$

In this equation, there are two sets of *like* terms, one involving x and the other x^2.

373. If the square or higher roots of the unknown quantity or *of any expression which involves it*, be found in an equation, it may be removed from it by transposing the terms, when necessary, in such a manner, that the radical term *alone* may be found upon one side of the equation: if we then raise both sides of the equation to the power which the radical denominates, the radical will disappear, and the equation will admit of further reduction, when necessary, by the preceding rules.

Equations may be cleared from radicals.

374. The following are examples:

Examples.

$$(1) \quad \sqrt{x} = 4.$$

Squaring both sides of the equation, we get

$$x = 16.$$

$$(2) \quad \sqrt[3]{x} + 7 = 10.$$

Transposing 7, we get

$$\sqrt[3]{x} = 10 - 7 = 3.$$

Cubing both sides of this equation, we get

$$x = 27.$$

$$(3) \quad \sqrt{(x - 16)} = 2.$$

Squaring both sides of this equation, we get

$$x - 16 = 4,$$

or, transposing 16,

$$x = 4 + 16 = 20.$$

$$(4) \quad x + \sqrt{(3x^2 - 4x + 12)} = 6.$$

Transposing x, from the left to the right-hand side of the equation, we get

$$\sqrt{(3x^2 - 4x + 12)} = 6 - x.$$

Squaring both sides of this equation, we get

$$3x^2 - 4x + 12 = (6 - x)^2,$$
$$= 36 - 12x + x^2.$$

Transposing known terms to one side of this equation and unknown terms to the other, we get

$$3x^2 - 4x + 12x - x^2 = 36 - 12.$$

Collecting sets of like terms into one, we find

$$2x^2 + 8x = 24.$$

Equations which involve more radical terms or expressions than one.

375. Equations may be proposed which involve more radical terms or expressions than one, which may be made to disappear by means of various expedients: the following is an example:

$$\sqrt{(x - 7)} = 2\sqrt{x} - 5.$$

Squaring both sides of this equation, we get

$$x - 7 = 4x - 20\sqrt{x} + 25.$$

The equation thus reduced, involves one radical term only: transposing this radical term to the left and all the other terms to the right-hand side of the equation, we get

$$20\sqrt{x} = 4x - x + 25 + 7,$$
$$= 3x + 32.$$

Squaring both sides, we get

$$400x = 9x^2 + 192x + 1024.$$

376. The rules of reduction, which have been given in the eleven last Articles, may be combined into the following general rule, which is equally applicable to the reduction of equations of all degrees.

" Clear the equation of fractional terms, by multiplying both members of it successively by the several denominators of the fractions, or *at once* by the least common multiple of them." Arts. 368, 369.

" Transpose the known terms to one side of the equation, and the unknown terms to the other: and combine the like terms severally into one." Arts. 364, 365, 366.

" If there be a radical term in the equation, let it be removed when possible, by the rules given in Arts. 372, 373, 375."

" If there be terms in the equation thus reduced, which involve different powers of the unknown quantity or symbol, place them, *when possible,* in the order of the several powers; and divide both sides of the equation by the coefficient of the highest power of the unknown symbol." Arts. 370, 371.

" If the simple or first power only of the unknown symbol be involved in the reduced equation, the operation last indicated will *insulate* the unknown symbol and furnish the solution of the equation (Arts. 370, 371): but if the equation involve higher powers of the unknown symbol than the first, then the determination of its value or values, *or the solution of the equation,* will require the application of rules or formulæ which will be the objects of subsequent investigation."

377. The degree of an equation, *when reduced*, will be determined by the highest power of the unknown symbol which it involves: thus, if it involves the *simple* power of it only, it is a *simple* equation: if it involves the second power of the unknown symbol, with or without the simple power, it is an equation of the *second* degree or a *quadratic* equation: if it involves the third power of the unknown symbol, with or without inferior powers of it, it is an equation of the *third* degree or a *cubic* equation: if it involves the *fourth* power of the unknown symbol, with or without inferior powers of it, it is an equation of the *fourth* degree, or a *biquadratic* equation: and so on, for equations of the *fifth, sixth,* and *higher* degrees.

218

The solution of equations generally will require the aid of the principles of Symbolical Algebra.

378. The theory of the solution of all equations, when considered in their most general form, will require a considerable, and in most cases, a profound knowledge of the principles of Symbolical Algebra: in the present chapter, we shall confine our attention to such simple and quadratic equations only, as admit of solution by the aid of the principles of Arithmetical Algebra alone.

Examples of the solution of simple equations which involve one unknown symbol only.

379. We shall begin with the solution of simple equations, involving one unknown number or symbol only.

$$(1) \quad \text{Let } 7x - 10 = 5x - 4.$$

Transposing the unknown terms to one side and the known terms to the other, (Arts. 364 and 366), we get

$$7x - 5x = 10 - 4.$$

Collecting like terms into one, (Art. 372), we find

$$2x = 6.$$

Dividing both sides of this equation by 2 (Art. 370), the coefficient of x, we get

$$x = 3,$$

where x is completely *insulated* and its value therefore determined.

$$(2) \quad 5x + 4 = 9x + 1.$$

Therefore, (Art. 364),

$$4 - 1 = 9x - 5x;$$

or,

$$9x - 5x = 4 - 1 *;$$

or, (Art. 372),

$$4x = 3;$$

or, (Art. 370),

$$x = \frac{3}{4};$$

which is the solution of the equation, furnishing that value of the unknown symbol which alone satisfies the conditions proposed.

$$(3) \quad 70x - 42x + 42 + 280 = 700 - 35x - 60x + 80 + 56x - 56.$$

* The right-hand member of an equation may obviously be made the left and the left-hand member may be made the right, without disturbing or affecting their equality: it is usual to place the unknown symbols on the left hand.

Therefore,

$$70x - 42x + 35x + 60x - 56x = 700 + 80 - 56 - 42 - 280 \ldots (1),$$
$$165x - 98x = 780 - 378 \ldots \ldots \ldots \ldots \ldots (2),$$
$$67x = 402 \ldots \ldots \ldots \ldots \ldots \ldots (3),$$
$$x = \frac{402}{67} = 6 \ldots \ldots \ldots \ldots \ldots \ldots (4).$$

When the unknown terms have been transposed to one side of the equation and the known terms to the other (1), we add together the terms, on each side, which have the same sign (2), subtract the resulting sums respectively from each other, (3), and finally divide the remainders by the single coefficient of the unknown term (4)*.

(4)   Let $\dfrac{x}{4} + 5 = 9$.

Multiply both sides of the equation by 4, and we get
$$x + 20 = 36;$$
or (Art. 366),
$$x = 36 - 20 = 16.$$

(5)   Let $30 - \dfrac{x}{10} = 52 - \dfrac{5x}{6}$.

Multiply both sides of the equation by 30, which is the least common multiple of the denominators 10 and 6, (Art. 368), and we get
$$900 - 3x = 1560 - 25x.$$

Transposing known terms to one side and unknown terms to the other (Art. 364), we get
$$25x - 3x = 1560 - 900;$$

---

* The following are similar examples:

(1) $x - 10 + 8 = 70 - x,$
$\qquad x = 36.$

(2) $3000 - 50x = 5400 - 100x + 2x,$
$\qquad x = 50.$

(3) $3x + x + 48x - 3600 = 48x,$
$\qquad\qquad x = 900.$

(4) $2x - 3x + 120 = 4x - 6x + 132,$
$\qquad\qquad x = 12.$

(5) $7x + 4 - 15x = 6x + 2,$
$\qquad\qquad x = \dfrac{1}{7}.$

or (Art. 372),

or (Art. 370),

$$22x = 660 \; ;$$

$$x = \frac{660}{22} = 30 \; .$$

(6)   Let $\dfrac{5}{x} + \dfrac{9}{4} = 16.$

Multiply both sides of the equation by $4x$, the least common multiple of the denominators x and 4, and we get

$$20 + 9x = 64x \; ;$$

or, subtracting $9x$ from both sides and interchanging the members, the right to the left and the left to the right,

$$64x - 9x = 20 \; ;$$

or

$$55x = 20 \; ;$$

or

$$x = \frac{20}{55} = \frac{4}{11} \; .$$

(7)   Let $\dfrac{4x-21}{9} + 3\dfrac{3}{4} + \dfrac{57-3x}{4} = 241 - \dfrac{5x-96}{12} - 11x.$

Multiply both sides of this equation by 36, which is the least common multiple of the denominators 9, 4 and 12 (Art. 364), and we get

$$16x-84+135+513-27x=8676-15x+288-396x.$$

Consequently

$$16x - 27x + 15x + 396x = 8676 + 288 + 84 - 135 - 513 \; ;$$

or

$$427x - 27x = 9048 - 648 \; ;$$

or

$$400x = 8400 \; ;$$

or

$$x = \frac{8400}{400} = 21.$$

Important rule and caution.

· In reducing equations, which involve fractions, we multiply the numerators of the several fractions by the *quotients of the least common multiple of the denominators divided by the proper denominator of each fraction, omitting the denominator :* thus in the example just given, we multiply the numerator $4x - 21$ of the fraction $\dfrac{4x-21}{9}$ by $\dfrac{36}{9}$ or 4, and we omit 9; the numerator 3 of the fraction $\dfrac{3}{4}$ by $\dfrac{36}{4}$ or 9, and we omit 4; the numerator

$57 - 3x$ of the fraction $\dfrac{57 - 3x}{4}$ by $\dfrac{36}{4}$ or 9, and we omit 4;

the numerator $5x - 96$ of the fraction $\dfrac{5x - 96}{12}$ by $\dfrac{36}{12}$ or 3, and we omit 12 : and it should be carefully kept in mind, that whenever a fraction is preceded by a negative sign, as is the case with the fraction $\dfrac{5x - 96}{12}$, we change *both* the signs of the product of $5x - 96$ by 3, writing down $-15x$ instead of $+15x$ and $+288$ instead of -288 : in all other cases, where the fraction is preceded by no sign or by the sign $+$, we leave the signs of the terms of the numerator unchanged, after the multiplications, required for the reduction of the equation, are performed*.

$$(8)\quad \text{Let } \sqrt{(7x - 13)} = 8.$$

Squaring both sides, we get

$$7x - 13 = 64.$$

Therefore
$$7x = 77,$$

$$x = \frac{77}{7} = 11.$$

---

* The following examples are similar to those just given :

$(1)\quad \dfrac{x}{3} - \dfrac{x}{4} + \dfrac{x}{6} = 3.$

The least common multiple is 12 ;
$$x = 12.$$

$(2)\quad 3x + \dfrac{2x + 6}{5} = \dfrac{11x - 37}{20} + \dfrac{x - 7}{7} + 23.$

The least common multiple is 140 ;
$$x = 7.$$

$(3)\quad \dfrac{x}{7} - \dfrac{x}{5} + 12 = \dfrac{x}{5} - \dfrac{x}{3} + 28.$

The least common multiple is 105 ;
$$x = 210.$$

$(4)\quad \dfrac{7x + 9}{8} - \dfrac{3x + 1}{7} = \dfrac{9x - 13}{4} - \dfrac{249 - 9x}{14}.$

The least common multiple is 56 ;
$$x = 9.$$

$(5)\quad \dfrac{x}{10} + 10x = \dfrac{x}{2} + \dfrac{x}{5} + \dfrac{x}{40} - \dfrac{10 - x}{7} + 93\tfrac{3}{4}.$

The least common multiple is 280 ;
$$x = 10.$$

$$(9) \quad \text{Let} \quad \sqrt[3]{(10\,x + 7)} = 3.$$

Cubing both sides, we get

$$10\,x + 7 = 27.$$

Therefore

$$10\,x = 20,$$

and

$$x = 2.$$

Equations may be possible and impossible.

380. The equations, which have been proposed above, are all of them possible, being capable of being satisfied by real arithmetical values of the unknown symbols, whether whole or fractional: but equations may be proposed which no value of the unknown symbol can satisfy, and which are therefore, properly speaking, impossible: the following are examples:

$$(1) \quad \text{Let} \quad \frac{x + 3}{5} + 11\,x = \frac{3\,x + 13}{4} - 34.$$

Multiply both sides of this equation by 20, and we get

$$4\,x + 12 + 220\,x = 15\,x + 65 - 680.$$

Therefore

$$209\,x = 65 - 680 - 12,$$
$$= 65 - 692.$$

The operation of subtracting a greater number (692) from a less (65) is obviously impossible, and consequently no real arithmetical value of x can satisfy the conditions of this equation.

$$(2) \quad \text{Let} \quad \frac{100 - x}{11} + \frac{11\,x}{10} = \frac{2\,x + 6}{7} + 1 \text{ *}.$$

Multiply both sides of this equation by 770, and we get

$$7000 - 70\,x + 847\,x = 220\,x + 660 + 770,$$
$$847\,x - 70\,x - 220\,x = 660 + 770 - 7000,$$
$$557\,x = 1430 - 7000.$$

Which is obviously an impossible equation, inasmuch as 7000 cannot be subtracted from 1430.

---

* In Symbolical Algebra, this operation becomes possible and the result is written -627: the corresponding value of x is -3: a similar observation applies to the example which follows.

381. When a problem is proposed, it is rarely possible to predict with certainty whether it admits or does not admit of solution in the precise sense in which it was proposed, or, in other words, whether the corresponding equation can be satisfied by any assignable value of the unknown symbol.

The possibility of the solution of a problem cannot always be predicted.

The solution of such an equation, as we have seen in the preceding examples, will involve a more or less extensive series of arithmetical operations for the purpose of insulating the unknown symbol, and will be possible as long as those operations are possible in their proper arithmetical sense, and impossible in all other cases. In Symbolical Algebra, as we shall afterwards find, a great extension of meaning will be given to such operations, and they will become, by the introduction of negative and other quantities, whether capable of interpretation as real existences or not, practicable under circumstances in which they would be altogether impossible and unintelligible in Arithmetic.

382. The equations, which we have hitherto considered, are simple equations, involving, when reduced, the simple power *only* of the unknown symbol: in *quadratic* equations, we shall find the square of the unknown symbol, with or without its simple power, and the rule of reduction, which is given in Article 376, directs us to transpose, when possible, all the unknown terms to one side of the equation and the known terms to the other, to collect like terms severally into one, and to divide both sides of the resulting equation by the coefficient of the square of the unknown symbol: the following are examples of quadratic equations when thus reduced.

Quadratic equations: forms which they will assume, when reduced.

$$(1) \quad x^2 + 6x = 16,$$
$$(2) \quad x^2 - 6x = 16,$$
$$(3) \quad 6x - x^2 = 8.$$

383. If we denote the coefficient of the simple power of x by $2a$, and the known term by b, the general forms of reduced quadratic equations will be as follows:

General forms of reduced quadratic equations.

$$(\alpha) \quad x^2 + 2ax = b,$$
$$(\beta) \quad x^2 - 2ax = b,$$
$$(\gamma) \quad 2ax - x^2 = b.$$

384. In order to prepare quadratic equations when thus reduced, for solution, we add both the members to, in the two first forms (a and β), and we subtract both of them from, in the third form (γ), the square (a^2) of half the coefficient of the simple power of the unknown symbol (x): we thus obtain, in the two first cases,

$$(a') \quad x^2 + 2\,a\,x + a^2 = a^2 + b,$$
$$(\beta') \quad x^2 - 2\,a\,x + a^2 = a^2 + b,$$

and in the third case,

$$(\gamma') \quad x^2 - 2\,a\,x + a^2 = a^2 - b.$$

But $x^2 + 2\,a\,x + a^2 = (x+a)^2$, (Art. 62); and $x^2 - 2\,a\,x + a^2 = (x-a)^2$, (Art. 64); and consequently the forms (a'), (β'), (γ'), become

$$(a') \quad (x + a)^2 = a^2 + b,$$
$$(\beta') \quad (x - a)^2 = a^2 + b,$$
$$(\gamma') \quad (x - a)^2 = a^2 - b.$$

Again, if two numbers be equal to each other, their square roots are also equal to each other, and consequently the extraction of the square roots of both members of the equations (a'), (β'), (γ'), will reduce that severally to the simple equations,

$$(a') \quad x + a = \sqrt{(a^2 + b)},$$
$$(\beta') \quad x - a = \sqrt{(a^2 + b)},$$
$$(\gamma') \quad x - a = \sqrt{(a^2 - b)}.$$

The solution of these simple equations will give us

$$(a') \quad x = \sqrt{(a^2 + b)} - a,$$
$$(\beta') \quad x = \sqrt{(a^2 + b)} + a,$$
$$(\gamma') \quad x = \sqrt{(a^2 - b)} + a.$$

385. Thus in the examples, (1), (2), (3), given in Art. 382, we get, by *adding* both the members of the equations (1) and (2) *to* 9, which is the square of half the coefficient (6) of $6x$, and by *subtracting* both the members of the equation (3) *from* 9,

$$(1') \quad x^2 + 6x + 9 = 9 + 16 = 25,$$
$$(2') \quad x^2 - 6x + 9 = 9 + 16 = 25,$$
$$(3') \quad x^2 - 6x + 9 = 9 - 8 = 1.$$

If we now extract the square root of both members of these several equations, we shall get the simple equations

$$(1') \quad x + 3 = \sqrt{25} = 5,$$

$$(2') \quad x - 3 = \sqrt{25} = 5,$$

$$(3') \quad x - 3 = \sqrt{1} = 1,$$

by the solution of which we readily obtain

$$(1') \quad x = 5 - 3 = 2.$$

$$(2') \quad x = 5 + 3 = 8.$$

$$(3') \quad x = 1 + 3 = 4.$$

386. In considering more attentively the forms of the trinomials $x^2 + 2ax + a^2$ and $x^2 - 2ax + a^2$, which are given in Art. 384, it is obvious that they will continue to be identical in value, when their terms are written in a contrary order; or in other words, that $x^2 + 2ax + a^2 = a^2 + 2ax + x^2$ and that $x^2 - 2ax + a^2 = a^2 - 2ax + x^2$: but though these trinomials are respectively identical in value, their square roots in the second case, which are $x - a$ and $a - x$ respectively, are not so *; and whilst the value of x is unknown, there is no reason for the selection of one of them in preference to the other : it remains to consider, in what manner and in what cases, the ambiguity which thence arises can be removed.

The third (γ) of the general forms given in Art. 384 is ambiguous.

There is no ambiguity in the second form (β); (Art. 384); for if we suppose the root of the trinomial $x^2 - 2ax + a^2$ or of its equivalent $a^2 - 2ax + x^2$ to be $a - x$ instead of $x - a$, we should get

$$a - x = \sqrt{(a^2 + b)},$$

and therefore,

$$x = a - \sqrt{(a^2 + b)};$$

consequently the greater quantity or number $\sqrt{(a^2 + b)}$ must be subtracted from the less a, which is impossible† : it follows therefore that in this case we are restricted to the choice of the root $x - a$ alone.

---

* The square root of $x^2 + 2ax + a^2$ is $x + a$ and of $x^2 + 2ax + x^2$ is $a + x$; these roots are identical in value, and involve no ambiguity : in other words, the solutions of the equation $x + a = \sqrt{(a^2 + b)}$ and $a + x = \sqrt{(a^2 + b)}$, will give the same value of x.

† For it is obvious that the square root of $a^2 + b$ is greater than the square root of a^2, which is a.

But there is an ambiguity in the third form (γ), (Art. 384): for whether we suppose the root of the trinomial $x^2 - 2ax + a^2$, or of its equivalent $a^2 - 2ax + x^2$ to be $x - a$ or $a - x$, we can in both cases, get a possible result: for in the first case, we get

(γ') $\quad x - a = \surd\,(a^2 - b)$ and therefore $x = a + \surd\,(a^2 - b)$;

and in the second, we get

(γ') $\quad a - x = \surd\,(a^2 - b)$ and therefore $x = a - \surd\,(a^2 - b)$,

both of which values are possible *, and consequently both of them will equally satisfy the conditions of the original equation, or of the problem of which it is the algebraical enunciation.

Examples of unambi guous and ambiguous solutions.

387. Thus in the particular examples considered in Art. 385, we find, admitting the *double* form of the root of the first member of each equation,

$$(1'') \quad x + 3 = 3 + x = 5,$$
$$\text{or} \quad x = 2.$$

In this case we get the same value of x from both the roots $x + 3$ and $3 + x$ of $x^2 + 6x + 9$ and of $9 + 6x + x^2$.

$(2'')$ The first form of the root $x - 3$ of $x^2 - 6x + 9$, gives us

$$x - 3 = 5;$$
$$\text{or} \quad x = 8,$$

which is a real and possible value.

The second form of the root $3 - x$ of $9 - 6x + x^2$, gives us

$$3 - x = 5,$$
$$\text{or} \quad x = 3 - 5,$$

which is not a real value, since it involves an impossible operation.

$(3'')$ The first form of the root $x - 3$ of $x^2 - 6x + 9$, gives us

$$x - 3 = 1;$$
$$\text{or} \quad x = 3 + 1 = 4,$$

which is a real and possible value.

The second form of the root $3 - x$ of $9 - 6x + x^2$, gives us

$$3 - x = 1,$$
$$\text{or} \quad x = 3 - 1 \quad \text{or} \quad 2,$$

which is also a real and possible root.

---

* For $\surd(a^2 - b)$ is less than a, and therefore in the second case, a less number is subtracted from a greater: it is also taken for granted, in the third form of quadratic equations, that b is less than a^2, otherwise the operation of subtracting b from a^2, as well as that of extracting the square root of the remainder, would be impossible.

388. The generalizations of Symbolical Algebra, which make operations practicable under all circumstances, will enable us to assign two roots or values of the unknown symbol in every quadratic equation, whether they be possible and such as can be considered and interpreted in Arithmetic, or not: but in the view which we have given of such equations in the preceding Articles, we must regard such double values of x, whenever they occur, as marks of indeterminateness in the problems which furnish the equations, or in the equations themselves: for they indicate the existence of two values of the symbol or number sought for, which equally answer the proposed conditions, and consequently shew that those conditions are not sufficient to furnish its absolute and unambiguous determination.

The existence of double arithmetical roots in a quadratic equation is a mark of indeterminateness.

389. The following are examples of the reduction and solution of quadratic equations:

Examples of the reduction and solution of quadratic equations.

(1)   Let $5x^2 - 20x = 105$.

Divide (Art. 382) both sides of the equation by 5, which is the coefficient of x^2, and we get

$$x^2 - 4x = 21.$$

Add 4, the square of 2, or of half the coefficient of x, to both sides of the equation (Art. 384), and we get

$$x^2 - 4x + 4 = 21 + 4 = 25.$$

Extract the square root (Art. 384) of both sides, and we get

$$x - 2 = 5,$$
$$\text{and} \quad x = 7,$$

which is the root of the equation or value of x required.

(2)   Let $19x - 39 - 2x^2 = 6x - 33$.

Transposing the known terms to one side and the unknown to the other (Art. 382), we get

$$13x - 2x^2 = 6.$$

Dividing both sides of this equation by 2, the coefficient of x^2 (Art. 382), we get

$$\frac{13}{2}x - x^2 = 3.$$

Subtracting both members of this equation from $\left(\dfrac{13}{4}\right)^2$ or $\dfrac{169}{16}$, which is the square of half the coefficient of x (Art. 384), we get

$$\frac{169}{16} - 13x + x^2 = \frac{169}{16} - 3 = \frac{169 - 48}{16} = \frac{121}{16}.$$

Extracting the square root of both members of this equation (Art. 384), we get

$$\frac{13}{4} - x = \frac{11}{4},$$

$$\text{or} \quad x = \frac{2}{4} \text{ or } \frac{1}{2}. \qquad \bullet$$

But if we reverse the order of the terms of $\dfrac{169}{16} - 13x + x^2$, (Art. 386), which will furnish the root $x - \dfrac{13}{4}$, we shall get

$$x - \frac{13}{4} = \frac{11}{4};$$

$$\text{or} \quad x = \frac{13 + 11}{4} = \frac{24}{4} = 6.$$

There are therefore *two real and possible* values of x, which are 6 and $\dfrac{1}{2}$: the solution is consequently ambiguous.

$$(3) \quad \text{Let} \quad \frac{x+7}{x} + \frac{x}{x+7} = \frac{5}{2}.$$

Multiply both sides of this equation by $2x(x+7)$ or $2x^2 + 14x$, and we get

$$2x^2 + 28x + 98 + 2x^2 = 5x^2 + 35x.$$

Transposing known terms to one side of this equation and unknown to the other, we get

$$x^2 + 7x = 98.$$

Adding $\dfrac{49}{4} = \left(\dfrac{7}{2}\right)^2$ or the square of half the coefficient of x to both sides of the equation, we get

$$x^2 + 7x + \frac{49}{4} = 98 + \frac{49}{4} = \frac{441}{4}.$$

Extracting the square root of both members of this equation, we find

$$x + \frac{7}{2} = \frac{21}{2}.$$

or $\quad x = \frac{14}{2} = 7,$

which is the only root of the equation.

(4) Let $\dfrac{40}{x-5} + \dfrac{27}{x} = 13.$

Clearing the equation of fractions, we find

$$40x + 27x - 135 = 13x^2 - 65x.$$

Transposing known terms to one side and unknown terms to the other, we get

$$132x - 13x^2 = 135.$$

Dividing both sides by the coefficient of x^2, we get

$$\frac{132}{13}x - x^2 = \frac{135}{13}.$$

Subtracting both members of this equation from $\left(\dfrac{66}{13}\right)^2$ or $\dfrac{4356}{169}$, the square of half the coefficient of x, we get

$$\frac{4356}{169} - \frac{132}{13}x + x^2 = \frac{4356}{169} - \frac{135}{13} = \frac{2601}{169}$$

Extracting the square root of both members of this equation, we get

$$\frac{66}{13} - x = \frac{51}{13},$$

or $\quad x = \frac{15}{13}.$

Otherwise, if the equation be put under the equivalent form

$$x^2 - \frac{132}{13}x + \frac{4356}{169} = \frac{2601}{169};$$

and if the square root of both its members be extracted, we get

$$x - \frac{66}{13} = \frac{51}{13},$$

or $\quad x = \frac{117}{13} = 9.$

The solution is therefore ambiguous.

(5)   Let $\dfrac{x+4}{x+1} - \dfrac{3x-12}{x+8} = 6.$

Clearing the equation of fractions, we get
$$x^2 + 12x + 32 - 3x^2(-3x + 9x + 12x) + 12 = 6x^2 + 54x + 48.$$

If we attempt to transpose the known terms to one side of the equation and the unknown to the other, we shall find
$$8x^2 + 33x = 44 - 48\,^*,$$
which involves an impossible operation: we conclude therefore that there are no possible values of x which will satisfy the conditions of this equation †.

* The two roots of this equation in Symbolical Algebra would be -4 and $-\dfrac{1}{8}$; they are neither of them quantities which can be considered or interpreted in Arithmetic.

† The following are other examples of quadratic equations:

(1) $x^2 + 3x = 70,$
$x = 7.$

(2) $.x^2 - 3x = 70,$
$x = 10.$

(3) $7x - x^2 = 12,$
$x = 3$ or $x = 4.$

(4) $11x^2 - 10x = 469,$
$x = 7.$

(5) $64x^2 + 8x = 56,$
$x = \dfrac{7}{8}.$

(6) $\dfrac{x}{x+60} = \dfrac{7}{3x-5},$
$x = 14.$

(7) $\dfrac{3x+4}{5} - \dfrac{30-2x}{x-6} = \dfrac{7x-14}{10}$
$x = 36$ or $12.$

(8) $\dfrac{90}{x} - \dfrac{27}{x+2} = \dfrac{90}{x+1},$
$x = 4.$

(9) $\dfrac{x^2}{361} + 32 + \dfrac{7x}{19} = x,$
$x = 152$ or $76.$

(10) $\dfrac{12}{5-x} + \dfrac{8}{4-x} = \dfrac{32}{x+2},$
$x = 2$ or $\dfrac{58}{13}.$

(11) $4x - x^2 = 6.$
The values of x are impossible, for 6 cannot be subtracted from 2^2 or 4.

390. The theory of the solution of numerical equations of higher orders than the second and the discussion of the circumstances under which such solutions are possible, whether ambiguous or unambiguous, and also whether such ambiguity, when it exists, applies to two or to a greater number of values, is full of difficulties and cannot be treated with sufficient generality without a considerable knowledge of the principles of Symbolical Algebra. In the theory of the extraction of compound roots, which is given in Chap. III. Art. 241., &c. we have considered some examples of the method of approximating to the values of such roots, when the limits or whole numbers between which they were situated were given: such methods, however, can be considered as auxiliary only to the theorems by which the limits of the root, when the solution is ambiguous, or of the root, when the solution is unambiguous, can be assigned in all cases.

Difficulties in the solution of numerical equations of higher orders.

391. Problems proposed for solution, as we have already had occasion to remark, Art. 342, may involve two or more unknown numbers, and the conditions given, when the problem is determinate, will be sufficient for their determination: in translating such problems into symbolical language, we shall find as many equations as there are unknown numbers or symbols: thus, if there be two unknown numbers or symbols, there will be two independent equations, which involve them either separately or combinedly: if there be three unknown symbols, there will be three independent equations, which involve them either separately or combinedly: and similarly for a greater number of unknown symbols. The necessity which exists for this equality, between the number of *independent* equations and the number of unknown symbols, in all determinate problems, will be made sufficiently manifest in the process which will be employed for their solution in the following Articles.

Determinate problems which involve two or more unknown numbers will lead to the same number of independent equations.

392. The following is an example of such a problem, involving two unknown numbers and leading to two independent equations.

Problem involving two unknown numbers.

"What two numbers are those whose sum is equal to 10, and of which twice the greater exceeds three times the less by 5?"

If we denote the greater of these unknown numbers by x, and the less of them by y, and translate the conditions into

Leads to two independent equations.

symbolical language, in the order which they are presented in the problem, we shall find

$$(1) \qquad x + y = 10$$
$$(2) \qquad 2x - 3y = 5$$

which are the two equations required: and these equations are independent of each other, inasmuch as the second is not derivable * from the first.

Meaning of simultaneous equations.

393. The unknown symbols x and y express the same numbers whenever they are referred to in the problem proposed, and they therefore possess the same values in both the equations (1) and (2): such pairs or sets of equations in which the same unknown symbols appear, which are assumed to possess the same values throughout, are called *simultaneous* equations: whenever equations, involving the same unknown symbols, are considered in connection with each other, they are assumed to be simultaneous.

Rule for the reduction of simultaneous equations.

394. When simultaneous equations are proposed for solution, they are reduced, when necessary, in conformity with the following rule.

Clear the several equations of fractions and transpose, when possible, the known terms to one side of each equation and the unknown to the other.

Example.

Thus, if the simultaneous equations furnished by the problem be

$$(1) \qquad \frac{x}{2} + \frac{y}{3} - 2 = \frac{x}{5} + 5.$$

$$(2) \qquad \frac{7x}{10} + \frac{5y}{6} - 12 = x + \frac{y}{12} - 6,$$

we multiply both members of the first equation by 30, (the least common multiple of 2, 3 and 5), and of the second equation

---

* Thus the equations $2x + 2y = 20$, $3x + 3y = 30$, &c. are immediately derivable from the first equation $x + y = 20$, by multiplying both its members by 2, 3, &c.: such derived equations furnish no new conditions, and are not therefore independent equations: in a similar manner, the equation which arises from adding or subtracting any multiple of one equation to or from any multiple of the other, will not be an independent equation.

by 60, (the least common multiple of 10, 6 and 12,) which gives us

$\quad$ (1) $\quad 15x + 10y - 60 = 6x + 150.$

$\quad$ (2) $\quad 42x + 50y - 720 = 60x + 5y - 360.$

Transposing the known terms to one side of each of these equations and the unknown to the other, we get

$\quad$ (1) $\quad 9x + 10y = 210.$

$\quad$ (2) $\quad 45y - 18x = 360;$

which are the reduced equations required.

Again, if the original simultaneous equations be

$\quad$ (1) $\quad x - \dfrac{3x + 5y}{17} + 17 = 5y + \dfrac{4x + 7}{3}$

$\quad$ (2) $\quad \dfrac{22 - 6y}{3} - \dfrac{5x - 7}{11} = \dfrac{x + 1}{6} - \dfrac{8y + 5}{18};$

by multiplying the first equation by 51 and the second by 198, we get

$\quad$ (1) $\quad 51x - 9x - 15y + 867 = 255y + 68x + 119.$

$\quad$ (2) $\quad 1452 - 396y - 90x + 126 = 33x + 33 - 88y - 55.$

By transposing respectively the known terms to one side of each of these equations and the unknown to the other, we finally get the reduced equations:

$\quad$ (1) $\quad 26x + 270y = 748\,^{*}.$

$\quad$ (2) $\quad 123x + 308y = 1600.$

395. The following rule will furnish the solution of all simultaneous equations with two unknown symbols, when thus reduced, which are of the first degree or which involve neither the product, square or higher powers of the unknown symbols. *Rule for solving simultaneous equations of the first degree.*

Let the two unknown symbols be x and y, and let it be required to determine x.

---

* This equation may be simplified by dividing all its terms by 2, which reduces it to

$$13x + 135y = 374:$$

and in general all equations may be simplified, by dividing them by any common measure of all their terms, whenever such a common measure exists.

G G

Find the least common multiple of the two coefficients of **y**, *and multiply each equation by the quotient which arises from dividing this least common multiple by the successive coefficients of* **y** : *the derived equations, which result, will present the term involving* **y** *with the same coefficient**.

Subtract these equations from each other (the less from the greater) when the identical coefficients of **y** *have the same sign, and add them together, when their signs are different : the final resulting equation will involve* **x** *only, whose value can therefore be immediately determined.*

The value of **y** *may be found by a similar process, replacing generally, in the rule just given, the symbol* **y** *by the symbol* **x**, *and* **x** *by* **y** : *or otherwise, we may substitute the value of* **x** *found by the first process, in either of the given equations, which will thus become a given equation with one unknown symbol only, which may be solved by the ordinary rules.*

Process of elimination.

396.   The process described in the preceding rule, by which *one* final equation with *one* unknown symbol is deduced from *two* equations with *two* unknown symbols, is generally designated by the term *elimination*.   The essence of this process does not consist in the mere form of the rule which is followed for this purpose, which may be greatly varied, but in the reduction of two equations into one, from which one of two unknown symbols has been *eliminated* or made to disappear : the same term is applied generally to the processes by which symbols are made to disappear from equations, whatever be their number.

We shall give a few examples in illustration of the rule in the last Article, before we proceed to consider its extension to three or more equations with three or more unknown symbols.

Examples.

397.   (1)   Let   (1) $3x + 7y = 33$
(2) $2x + 3y = 17$.

---

* For if b and b' be the coefficients of y in the given equations, and if m be their least common multiple, then the coefficient of y will be $\dfrac{mb}{b}$ or m in one equation, and $\dfrac{mb'}{b'}$ or m in the other.

Multiply the first equation by $3 \left(= \dfrac{3 \times 7}{7} \right)$, and the second equation by $7 \left(= \dfrac{3 \times 7}{3} \right)$, and we get

$$(3) \quad 9x + 21y = 99.$$
$$(4) \quad 14x + 21y = 119.$$

Subtract (3) from (4), and we get

$$5x = 20 \quad \text{or} \quad x = 4.$$

Again, multiply (1) by $2 \left(= \dfrac{2 \times 3}{3} \right)$ and (2) by $3 \left(= \dfrac{2 \times 3}{2} \right)$, and we get

$$(5) \quad 6x + 14y = 66.$$
$$(6) \quad 6x + 9y = 51.$$

Subtract (6) from (5), and we get

$$5y = 15,$$
$$\text{or} \quad y = 3;$$

consequently $x = 4$, $y = 3$ are the only two values of x and y, which *simultaneously* answer the conditions of the equations (1) and (2).

$$(2) \quad \text{Let} \quad (1) \quad 17x + 15y = 335.$$
$$(2) \quad 13x - 10y = 20.$$

The least common multiple of 15 and 10 is 30: multiply (1) by $2 \left(= \dfrac{30}{15} \right)$, and (2) by $3 \left(= \dfrac{30}{10} \right)$, and we get

$$(3) \quad 34x + 30y = 670.$$
$$(4) \quad 39x - 30y = 60.$$

Since the identical coefficients of y have *different* signs, we add together (3) and (4), which gives us

$$73x = 730,$$
$$\text{or} \quad x = 10.$$

Again, multiply (1) by $13 \left(= \dfrac{13 \times 17}{17} \right)$, and (2) by 17, $\left(= \dfrac{13 \times 17}{13} \right)$, and we get

$$(5) \quad 221x + 195y = 4355.$$
$$(6) \quad 221x - 170y = 340.$$

Since the identical coefficients of x have the *same* sign, we subtract (6) from (5), which gives us

$$365y = 4015,$$

$$y = \frac{4015}{365} = 11.$$

The values of x and y, which simultaneously answer the conditions of the equations (1) and (2), are $x = 10$ and $y = 11$.

This value of y would be much more readily obtained by substituting in equation (1) the number 10 for x, which gives

$$170 + 15y = 335,$$

$$\text{or} \quad 15y = 165,$$

$$y = \frac{165}{15} = 11 \, *$$

$$(3) \quad \frac{x}{8} + 8y = 194, \qquad (1).$$

$$\frac{7}{8} + 8x = 131. \qquad (2).$$

---

* The first pair of equations given in Art. 394, as examples of the method of reduction, is

$$(1) \qquad 9x + 10y = 210.$$
$$(2) \qquad 45y - 18x = 360.$$

Eliminating x in the first place (the process being more simple than in the case of y), we get

$$(3) \qquad 18x + 20y = 420.$$
$$(4) \qquad 45y - 18x = 360.$$

Adding (3) and (4) together, we get

$$65y = 780,$$

$$\text{or} \quad y = 12.$$

Substituting this value of y in equation (1), we find

$$9x + 120 = 210,$$

$$9x = 90,$$

$$x = 9.$$

The second pair of equations, in the same article, is,

$$(1) \quad 13x + 135y = 374, \; \Big\}$$
$$(2) \quad 123x + 308y = 1600, \Big\}$$

from which we find, by a similar process,

$$x = 8 \text{ and } y = 2.$$

Clearing these equations of fractions, we get

$$(3) \quad x + 64y = 1552.$$

$$(4) \quad y + 64x = 1048.$$

Multiply (3) by 64 $\left(= \dfrac{64 \times 1}{1}\right)$, and (2) by 1 $\left(= \dfrac{64 \times 1}{64}\right)$, and we get

$$64x + 4096y = 99328$$
$$y + 64x = 1048$$
$$\overline{4095y = 98280}$$
$$y = 24.$$

Substitute this value of y in (3), and we get

$$x + 1536 = 1552,$$

$$\text{or} \quad x = 16 \,^*.$$

---

* The following are other examples of pairs of simple simultaneous equations :

$$(1) \quad \left. \begin{aligned} 5x + 4y &= 96, \\ 4x + 5y &= 93, \end{aligned} \right\}$$

$$\therefore \quad x = 12 \text{ and } y = 9.$$

$$(2) \quad \left. \begin{aligned} \frac{x+2}{y+6} &= \frac{1}{2}, \\ \frac{x-2}{y+3} &= \frac{1}{3}, \end{aligned} \right\}$$

$$\therefore \quad x = 7 \text{ and } y = 12.$$

$$(3) \quad \left. \begin{aligned} \frac{x}{6} + \frac{y}{4} &= \frac{1}{6}, \\ 4x + 3y &= 3, \end{aligned} \right\}$$

$$\therefore \quad x = \frac{1}{2} \text{ and } y = \frac{1}{3}.$$

$$(4) \quad \left. \begin{aligned} \frac{x+11}{10} + \frac{y-4}{6} &= x - 7, \\ \frac{x+5}{7} - \frac{y-7}{3} &= y - x, \end{aligned} \right\}$$

$$\therefore \quad x = 9 \text{ and } y = 10.$$

$$(5) \quad \left. \begin{aligned} \frac{3}{x} + \frac{4}{y} &= 2, \\ \frac{9}{x} - \frac{8}{y} &= 1. \end{aligned} \right\}$$

Consider $\dfrac{1}{x}$ and $\dfrac{1}{y}$ as the unknown symbols, or replace them, in the first instance by other unknown symbols, such as z and u respectively,

$$\therefore \quad x = 3 \text{ and } y = 4.$$

Two equations, involving two or **more** symbols, **are** reduced to one by the elimination of one of them.

398. Two equations, with three or a greater number of unknown symbols, are reduced to one by the elimination of any one of them: for if we severally multiply two such simple equations by the quotients which arise from dividing the least common multiple of the coefficients of the *same* symbol by its coefficient in each equation, the derived equations which result will involve this symbol with the same coefficient, (Art. 395,) which will therefore disappear when they are added together or subtracted from each other, an operation which reduces the two equations into one.

Example.

Thus, if the two simultaneous equations involving three unknown symbols x, y and z, be

$$\left. \begin{aligned} (1) \quad & 7x + 9y + 12z = 61 \\ (2) \quad & 5x + 4y + 15z = 58 \end{aligned} \right\},$$

and if we multiply (1) by $5 \left(= \dfrac{60}{12} \right)$, and (2) by $4 \left(= \dfrac{60}{15} \right)$, we get

$$\left. \begin{aligned} (3) \quad & 35x + 45y + 60z = 305 \\ (4) \quad & 20x + 16y + 60z = 232 \end{aligned} \right\}$$

If we subtract equation (4) from (3), we get

$$(5) \quad 15x + 29y = 73 ;$$

a single equation, from which the symbol z is eliminated. A similar operation would eliminate either of the other unknown symbols x and y from the original pair of equations, but the two remaining symbols would always present themselves in the final resulting equation.

Thus, if we should eliminate the symbol y from equations (1) and (2), we should get

Equations with more unknown symbols than one are indeterminate, if the number of equations are less than the number of unknown symbols.

$$(6) \quad 17x + 87z = 278 ;$$

and, if we should eliminate the symbol x from the same equations, we should get

$$(7) \quad 45z - 17y = 101.$$

399. If there be two equations *only* involving severally *three* unknown symbols, the single equation which results from the elimination of any one of them, will always contain two unknown symbols, and will not be sufficient for their determina-

tion*. But if the number of independent equations be exactly equal to the number of unknown symbols, we shall be enabled to reduce the number of equations severally by *unity* by the elimination of the successive symbols, so as to obtain finally a single equation with a single unknown symbol.

400.   Thus if we have the three simultaneous equations   Example.

$$(1) \quad 7x + 9y + 12z = 61,$$
$$(2) \quad 5x + 4y + 15z = 58,$$
$$(3) \quad 3x + 10y + 20z = 83,$$

involving three unknown symbols x, y and z, we shall obtain, by eliminating z from (1) and (2), as we have shewn in Art. 398,

$$(4) \quad 15x + 29y = 73;$$

and if we proceed to eliminate in the same manner, the same symbol z from equations (1) and (3), we shall get

$$(5) \quad 26x + 15y = 56.$$

The equations (4) and (5) are simultaneous, involving the same pair of symbols x and y; and consequently if we eliminate one of them y by the rule given in Art. 395, we shall obtain a single final equation

$$529x = 529,$$
$$\text{or} \quad x = 1.$$

We hence readily find from equations (4) or (5), $y = 2$, and from equations (1), or (2), or (3), $z = 3$.

401.   In the example just given, we have eliminated z from the pairs of equations (1) and (2), (1) and (3), in order to obtain the equations

$$(4) \quad 15x + 29y = 73,$$
$$(5) \quad 26x + 15y = 56;$$

from which the values of x and y have been determined: if we had eliminated z from the equations (2) and (3), we should have obtained a third equation

$$(6) \quad 14y - 11x = 17.$$

---

* Thus in the example considered in the preceding Article, we obtain from *two* equations (1) and (2) with *three* unknown symbols, the three equations (5), (6) and (7), which severally involve *different* pairs of symbols, and which are consequently incompetent to furnish us, by further *elimination*, single equations with one unknown symbol only.

This equation however is not an independent equation, being derived by subtracting equation (5) from equation (4): it cannot therefore be made the foundation of any conclusions which are not derivable from equations (4) and (5).

The number of independent equations must not exceed the number of unknown symbols.

402. If there be three equations which severally involve the same *two* unknown symbols only, we can make three combinations of pairs of such equations, which are severally sufficient to determine their values: if the three equations be independent or not derivable from each other, the values of the pairs of symbols which are derived from the several pairs of equations which are thus combined, will have no necessary connection with each other, and consequently may not be the same for the different combinations: and if the resulting pairs of values are found to be identical, one of the three equations is not only superfluous, but may be shewn, as we shall afterwards see, to be derivable from the other two.

The number of independent equations must exactly equal the number of unknown symbols.

403. From the preceding considerations it will follow, that the number of equations must be exactly equal to the number of unknown symbols, in order that the process of elimination may lead successively to as many final equations as there are unknown symbols and no more, in each of which one of these unknown symbols is involved: if the number of such equations be less than the number of unknown symbols, the final equations which result from the process of elimination described in the preceding Articles, will involve more unknown symbols than one, which are, therefore, indeterminate: but if the number of such equations be greater than the number of unknown symbols, we shall be able by the same process, to obtain more final equations than one, which involve the same unknown symbol, and which will not be consistent with each other, unless a number of those equations which is equal to the excess above the corresponding number of unknown symbols, be derivable from the other equations.

Examples.

404. The following are examples of independent simultaneous equations, with more unknown symbols than one.

$$\text{Let} \quad 3x + 7y + 10z = 61 \dots \dots \dots (1).$$
$$4x - 13y + 9z = 10 \dots \dots \dots (2).$$
$$7x - 20y + 12z = 22 \dots \dots \dots (3).$$

Combining equations (1) and (2) we get, by eliminating z,

$$27x + 63y + 90z = 549$$
$$40x - 130y + 90z = 100$$

$$193y - 13x \qquad = 449 \ldots\ldots\ldots(4).$$

Combining equations (1) and (3), we get

$$18x + 42y + 60z = 366$$
$$35x - 100y + 60z = 110$$

$$142y - 17x \qquad = 256 \ldots\ldots\ldots(5).$$

Lastly, combining equations (4) and (5), we obtain

$$1846y - 221x = 3328$$
$$3281y - 221x = 7633$$

$$1435y = 4305$$
$$\text{or} \quad y = 3.$$

From equations (4) or (5), by replacing y by 3, we easily get $x = 10$: and from equations (1), (2) or (3), by replacing x by 10 and y by 3, we get $z = 1$.

If we had combined equations (2) and (3), we should have got, by eliminating z,

$$16x - 52y + 36z = 40$$
$$21x - 60y + 36z = 66$$

$$5x - 8y \qquad = 26 \ldots\ldots\ldots(6).$$

If we combine this equation with either of the equations (5) or (6), it will furnish the same values of x and y which we have already found from their combination with each other. The fact is, that equation (6) is deducible from equations (4) and (5), by multiplying the first of them by $\frac{2}{5}$, the second by $\frac{3}{5}$, and subtracting the second resulting equation from the first*.

* In order to discover these multipliers, if they exist, we may multiply equation (4) by an unknown number m, and equation (5) by an unknown number n, which gives us the equations

$$193my - 13mx = 449m,$$
$$142ny - 17nx = 256n;$$

and subtracting them from each other, we find

$$(17n - 13m)x - (142n - 193m)y = 449m - 256n \ldots\ldots\ldots(7).$$

In

(2)   Let $\dfrac{x}{3} - \dfrac{y}{6} + \dfrac{z}{12} = \dfrac{z-x}{9}$ .... (1),

$$\frac{3x-9}{5} + \frac{2y-6}{6} + \frac{7z-84}{11} = \frac{z-3y+4x}{6} \quad \ldots \ldots (2),$$

$$\frac{x+y-9}{11} - \frac{z-2y}{12} = 3 + \frac{3z-10y}{8} \ldots \ldots \ldots (3).$$

Multiplying equations (1), (2) and (3) by 36, 330 and 264 respectively, which are the least common multiples of their respective sets of denominators, and transposing the known terms to one side and the unknown terms to the other, we get the reduced equations

$$16x - 6y - z = 0 \ldots \ldots \ldots (4),$$

$$275y + 155z - 22x = 3444 \ldots \ldots (5),$$

$$24x + 398y - 121z = 1008 \ldots \ldots (6).$$

Combining the equations (4) and (5), (4) and (6), respectively together and eliminating x from each pair, we get

In order that this equation (7) may coincide with equation (6) given in the text, we must suppose the coefficients of x and y, as well as the final terms, to be respectively identical with each other in the two equations: we thus get the three equations

$$17n - 13m = 5 \ldots \ldots \ldots \ldots (8),$$
$$142n - 193m = 8 \ldots \ldots \ldots \ldots (9),$$
$$449n - 256m = 26 \ldots \ldots \ldots \ldots (10);$$

combining equations (9) and (10), we get, by the ordinary process of elimination,

$$2414n - 1846m = 710$$
$$2414n - 3281m = 136$$
_____
$$1435m = 574$$

or $m = \dfrac{574}{1435} = \dfrac{2}{5}$.

And substituting this value of m in equations (8) or (9), we find

$$n = \frac{14637}{24395} = \frac{3}{5} \, .$$

If we make use of these values of m and n, we shall also find

$$449n - 256m = 26,$$

so that every term and member of equation (6) is derivable from equations (4) and (5).

The necessary identity of the three pairs of equations derived from different combinations of the original equations will be immediately manifest from their general solution. See the Notes and Additions at the end of this volume.

$$176x - 66y - 11z = 0$$
$$2200y + 1240z - 176x = 27552$$

$$2134y + 1229z = 27552 \ldots (7).$$

$$48x - 18y - 3z = 0$$
$$48x + 796y - 242z = 2016$$

$$814y - 239z = 2016 \ldots (8).$$

If we further eliminate y from equations (7) and (8), we get

$$78958y + 45473z = 1019424$$
$$78958y - 23183z = 195552$$

$$68656z = 823872$$
$$\text{or} \quad z = 12.$$

If we substitute 12 for z in equations (7) or (8), we get $y = 6$: and if we substitute 12 for z and 6 for y, in equations (4), (5) or (6), we get $x = 3$.

(3)   Let $2x + 3y + 4z + 5u = 30 \ldots (1).$

$$7y - 3x + 5z - 3u = 16 \ldots (2).$$
$$9z - 4x - 3y + 11u = 4 \ldots (3).$$
$$47u - 5x - 4y - 3z = 9 \ldots (4).$$

Eliminating x from equations (1) and (2), (1) and (3), (1) and (4) respectively, we get

$$23y + 22z + 9u = 122 \ldots (5).$$
$$3y + 17z + 21u = 64 \ldots (6).$$
$$7y + 14z + 119u = 168 \ldots (7).$$

Eliminating y from the pairs of equations (5) and (6), (6) and (7), we get

$$325z + 456u = 1106 \ldots (8).$$
$$210u - 77z = 56 \ldots (9).$$

If we further eliminate z from equations (8) and (9), we get

$$103362u = 103362,$$
$$\text{or} \quad u = 1.$$

From equations (8) or (9) we find $z = 2$; from equations (5), (6) or (7), we find $y = 3$: and from equations (1), (2), (3) or (4), we find $x = 4$ *.

Simultaneous equations of higher degrees.

405. We have hitherto confined our attention to the solution of simultaneous equations of the first degree only: the solution of those of higher degrees will involve peculiar difficulties which cannot be easily overcome without the aid of the principles of Symbolical Algebra. There is one case, however, in which one

Case in which they are reducible to a final quadratic equation with one unknown symbol.

of the simultaneous equations *only* ascends to the second degree, where the process of elimination will easily lead us to a quadratic equation with one unknown symbol, admitting of solution by the ordinary methods: the mode of effecting this reduction will be best understood from one or two examples.

Examples.

406. (1) Let the simultaneous equations be

$$\left. \begin{array}{r} 2x + 3y = 15 \\ x^2 + y^2 - xy = \ \ 9 \end{array} \right\},$$

the second of which is of the second degree.

From the first equation, find the value of y in terms of x†, which gives us

$$y = 5 - \frac{2x}{3}.$$

---

* The following are other examples of simultaneous equations with more unknown symbols than two.

(1)
$$\left. \begin{array}{r} 3x + 5y + 7z = 169, \\ 7x + 4y + 11z = 246, \\ 10x + 12y + 5z = 292, \end{array} \right\}$$

$\therefore \ x = 10, \ \ y = 11, \ \ z = 12.$

(2)
$$\left. \begin{array}{r} 10x + 12y + 2z = 4.148, \\ 4x + 5y - z = 1.177, \\ x + 3y + 5z = 2.102, \end{array} \right\}$$

$\therefore \ x = .151, \ \ y = .172, \ \ z = .287.$

(3)
$$\left. \begin{array}{r} 3x + 4y = 34, \\ 5y + 6z = 74, \\ 9z + 11u = 202, \\ 7x + 4z = \ \ 78, \end{array} \right\}$$

$\therefore \ x = 6, \ \ y = 4, \ \ z = 9, \ \text{and} \ u = 11.$

† Every equation with two unknown symbols may be solved with respect to one of them, by transposing all the terms, excepting that which involves the

Substitute this *indeterminate* value of y in the second equation, and we get

$$x^3 + \left(5 - \frac{2x}{3}\right)^2 - x\left(5 - \frac{2x}{3}\right) = 9,$$

or $\quad x^2 + 25 - \dfrac{20x}{3} + \dfrac{4x^2}{9} - 5x + \dfrac{2x^2}{3} = 9,$

or $\quad 9x^2 + 225 - 60x + 4x^2 - 45x + 6x^2 = 81 \ldots$(Art. 368),

or $\quad 105x - 19x^2 = 144 \ldots$(Art. 366),

or $\quad \dfrac{105}{19}x - x^2 = \dfrac{144}{19} \ldots$(Art. 364).

Subtracting both members of this equation from $\left(\dfrac{105}{38}\right)^2$, (Art. 384), we get

$$\frac{11025}{1444} - \frac{105}{19}x + x^2 = \frac{81}{1444},$$

or $\quad x^2 - \dfrac{105x}{10} + \dfrac{11025}{1444} = \dfrac{81}{1444}.$

In the first case we get, by extracting the square root of both members,

$$\frac{105}{38} - x = \frac{9}{38} \quad \text{or} \quad x = \frac{96}{38} = \frac{48}{19}:$$

unknown symbol in question, to one side of the equation, and dividing both members of the resulting equation by its coefficient: thus, in the example in the text, we transpose $2x$ from the left-hand side of the equation to the right, and we get

$$3y = 15 - 2x;$$

and dividing both members of this equation by 3, we get

$$y = 5 - \frac{2x}{5};$$

In a similar manner, if we should solve the same equation with respect to x, we should get

$$x = \frac{15 - 3y}{2}.$$

Such solutions are obviously *indeterminate*, inasmuch as one unknown symbol is expressed in terms of the other, and no conclusion can be drawn with respect to the value of one of them, without assigning or assuming the value of the other: it is only by supposing that the values of x and y necessarily denote whole numbers, that the extent of this *indetermination* will be variously limited: the solution of such indeterminate equations, under such limitations, will form the subject of a distinct chapter.

and in the second,

$$x - \frac{105}{38} = \frac{9}{38} \text{ or } x = 3.$$

If $x = 3$, the corresponding value of $y = 5 - \frac{2x}{3}$ is 2.

If $x = \frac{48}{19}$, the corresponding value of y is $\frac{63}{19}$.

(2) Again, let the simultaneous equations be

$$\left. \begin{array}{c} x + y = 7 \\ xy = 12 \end{array} \right\}$$

The first equation, solved with respect to y, gives us

$$y = 7 - x,$$

which substituted in the second equation, gives us the quadratic equation

$$x(7 - x) = 12,$$
$$\text{or} \quad 7x - x^2 = 12.$$

Subtracting both its members from $\left(\frac{7}{2}\right)^2$, we get

$$\frac{49}{4} - 7x + x^2 = \frac{49}{4} - 12 = \frac{1}{4},$$
$$\text{or} \quad x^2 - 7x + \frac{49}{4} = \frac{1}{4}.$$

From the first of these equations, we get, by extracting the square root,

$$\frac{7}{2} - x = \frac{1}{2} \text{ or } x = 3;$$

and from the second,

$$x - \frac{7}{2} = \frac{1}{2} \text{ or } x = 4.$$

If $x = 3$, the corresponding value of y is 4: and if $x = 4$, the corresponding value of y is 3: and it may be observed that the values of x and y are *commutable* in all cases in which they are *symmetrically* involved, as in the present case, in the proposed simultaneous equations.

The same equations may be otherwise solved as follows.

Since $x + y = 7$, by squaring both sides, we get (Art. 62),

$$x^2 + 2xy + y^2 = 49 \dots\dots\dots\dots\dots\dots\dots\dots\dots (1),$$

and since $xy = 12$, and therefore $4xy = 48$, it follows that

$$x^2 + 2xy + y^2 - 4xy = x^2 - 2xy + y^2 = 49 - 48 = 1 \ldots \ldots (2).$$

If we extract the square root of both members of this equation, we get

$$\left. \begin{array}{l} x - y = 1, \\ \text{but} \quad x + y = 7 \, ; \end{array} \right\}$$

consequently, by adding these equations together, we get

$$2x = 8 \quad \text{or} \quad x = 4,$$

and by subtracting them from each other,

$$2y = 6 \quad \text{or} \quad y = 3.$$

The values of x and y thus given are simultaneous: but if we change the order of succession of x and y in the equations (1) and (2), and extract their square roots respectively, we shall get

$$y + x = 7,$$
$$y - x = 1,$$

and therefore $\qquad y = 4$ and $x = 3$ *.

---

* The following are other examples of simultaneous equations which lead to a single final equation of the second degree, with one unknown symbol only,

$$(1) \qquad \left. \begin{array}{l} x + y = 10, \\ x^2 + y^2 = 82, \end{array} \right\}$$

The final equation is

$$10x - x^2 = 9 \, ;$$
$$\therefore \quad x = 9 \quad \text{and} \quad y = 1, \quad \text{or} \quad x = 1 \quad \text{and} \quad y = 9.$$

$$(2) \qquad \left. \begin{array}{l} x - y = 8, \\ x^2 + y^2 = 82. \end{array} \right\}$$

The final equation is

$$x^2 - 8x = 9 \, ;$$
$$\therefore \quad x = 9 \quad \text{and} \quad y = 1 :$$

the values of x and y are no longer commutable in these simultaneous equations, inasmuch as they are not symmetrically involved in them.

$$(3) \qquad \left. \begin{array}{l} x - y = 8, \\ x^2 - y^2 = 80. \end{array} \right\}$$

The final equation is

$$16x - 64 = 80,$$

which is a simple equation: this arises from the divisibility of $x^2 - y^2$, the first
member

Equations
of higher
orders will
in most
cases re-
quire for
their so-
lution an
extensive
knowledge
of their
general
theory.

407. We shall not attempt the solution of equations, whether single or simultaneous, which exceed the second degree, though many examples of such equations may be proposed which either possess or are reducible to, such a form, as to admit of easy solution by the direct extraction of roots or other expedients: but it is only through the aid of the principles of Symbolical Algebra, and the results of a very extensive and difficult theory, that the arithmetical rules for the general solution of numerical equations of all orders can be deduced or demonstrated; it is for this reason that we shall defer the investigation and application of such rules to a subsequent volume of this work, in which the whole theory of equations will be considered in its most general form: the rules and examples which we have given will be sufficient to enable a student to solve extensive classes of problems which lead to equations, and to give him that familiar command of the rules for the reduction of symbolical expressions, as well as of the limits of their application, which forms the best preparation for the study and just appreciation of the principles of Symbolical Algebra.

member of the second equation, by $x - y$, the first member of the first: we thus reduce the second equation to

$$\frac{x^2 - y^2}{x - y} = x + y = 10,$$

which is a simple equation.

$$(4) \qquad \begin{aligned} x + y &= 5, \\ x^3 + y^3 &= 35. \end{aligned} \Big\}$$

The second equation is of the third degree, but since $x^3 + y^3$ is divisible by $x + y$, (Art. 86. Ex. 16.), it is reducible to an equation of the second degree, which is

$$\frac{x^3 + y^3}{x + y} = x^2 - xy + y^2 = 7.$$

The final equation is

$$5x - x^2 = 6,$$

and $x = 3$ and $y = 2$, or $x = 2$ and $y = 3$.

$$(5) \qquad \left. \begin{aligned} \frac{7x - 3y}{5} - \frac{y - x}{4} &= x + y - 11, \\ \frac{x^2 - 3y^2}{23} + 2x &= y - 7. \end{aligned} \right\}$$

The final equation in terms of y is

$$862 y^2 + 1959 y = 55951,$$

from which we get $y = 7$, and therefore $x = 3$.

408. We shall now proceed to the consideration of the general Symbolical enunciation of problems. rules for the symbolical enunciation of problems, (Art. 359.), in which the unknown number or numbers are more or less involved in the conditions which are required for their determination; and it will tend to facilitate this enquiry, if we classify, very generally, the problems which present themselves for solution, with reference to the unknown number or numbers which they severally involve.

There are three great classes of such problems to be considered.

First Class. Problems which involve one unknown number Classification of problems. only, which is throughout the subject of the conditions proposed for its determination.

Second Class. Problems which involve two or more unknown numbers, which are so related to each other by the conditions of the problem as to be expressed or immediately expressible in terms of one of them only.

Third Class. Problems which involve two or more unknown numbers which are not immediately expressible in terms of one of them, but require to be denoted by distinct symbols.

We shall consider and exemplify in succession the rules for the symbolical enunciation of these different classes of problems.

409. In the first of the preceding classes we commonly General rules for the symbolical enunciation of the first class of problems. express the unknown number by one of the last letters of the alphabet, such as x, and we proceed to symbolize, by the known forms and signs of Algebra, the successive conditions to which it is subject: thus the unknown number or its symbol may require to be multiplied or divided, to be increased or diminished, by given numbers: or it may require to be raised to a given power or a given root of it to be extracted: and similar operations may require to be performed with or upon expressions, already formed, which involve it. The result of all such operations must be likewise declared in one of the conditions of the problem, otherwise they would lead to the mere formation of an algebraical expression in which the unknown symbol would remain as indeterminate as when first assumed*: but if the result of such

---

* Thus, if the problem merely said that an unknown number, expressed by x, was to be multiplied by 3, forming $3x$, and the result to be divided by 5, forming $\frac{3x}{5}$, which was subsequently to be increased by 7, forming the

expression

operations be stated to be equal either to a simple number or to a symbolical expression formed by similar operations as that first obtained, though not deducible as a necessary consequence from it, we symbolize this condition, or in other words, we express the equivalence in value of the two expressions thus formed, by the interposition of the sign of equality between them, and we thus obtain the equation which is the symbolical enunciation of the problem proposed, from whose reduction and solution the unknown number may be determined.

In some cases the conditions may be symbolized in the order in which they present themselves in the problem, by an immediate translation of ordinary into symbolical language: in others, they will be involved in such a manner, that the discovery of their relation and succession and their consequent symbolical expression will present difficulties, which can only be overcome by close attention and a clear insight into the relations of the numbers and magnitudes which they involve; for such cases general rules are nearly useless, and the student must trust to the diligent and patient study and analysis of examples alone for the acquisition of those habits of mind which will guide his course in their symbolical enunciation.

expression $\frac{3x}{5} + 7$, and if all the declared conditions of the problem should now be exhausted, we should be in possession of no means of determining x, since the same series of operations may be performed, and the same expression formed, whatever x may be: but if it was further asserted that the result of the preceding operations should be equal to the number 13, we should symbolize this last condition by placing the sign $=$ between $\frac{3x}{5} + 7$ and 13, which would form the equation

$$\frac{3x}{5} + 7 = 13,$$

from which the value of x might be determined.

Again, if, instead of asserting that the expression first formed or $\frac{3x}{5} + 7$ was equal to 13, it was said that it was equal to twice x diminished by 7, or to $2x - 7$, we should place the sign $=$ between $\frac{3x}{5} + 7$ and $2x - 7$, thus forming the equation

$$\frac{3x}{5} + 7 = 2x - 7.$$

410. The following are examples of problems which belong Examples. to the first of the three classes enumerated in the last Article.

(1) What number is that, two-thirds of which increased by 4, shall be equal to four-fifths of it diminished by 2?

If we denote the unknown number by x and symbolize the successive conditions as they arise, the same problem may be written as follows.

What number (x) is that, two-thirds of which $\left(\dfrac{2x}{3}\right)$, increased by $4 \left(\dfrac{2x}{3} + 4\right)$ shall be equal $(=)$ to four-fifths of it $\left(\dfrac{4x}{5}\right)$ diminished by $2 \left(\dfrac{4x}{5} - 2\right)$?

If we now confine ourselves to symbolical language only, following the same order of succession in the symbolization of the conditions of the problem, we shall get

$$\frac{2x}{3} + 4 = \frac{4x}{5} - 2\ldots\ldots\ldots\ldots(1),$$

which is the symbolical enunciation of the problem required.

If we clear this equation (1) of fractions, we get

$$10x + 60 = 12x - 30;$$

and transposing known terms to one side of the equation and the unknown to the other, we find

$$2x = 90,$$

$$\text{or} \quad x = 45,$$

which is the number which answers the conditions of the problem *.

---

* The following problems are of a similar nature :

(1) What number is that, the treble of which is as much above 40 as its half is below 100?

The equation is

$$3x - 40 = 100 - \frac{x}{2},$$

$$x = 40.$$

(2) What number is that, which is less than the sum of its half, its third and its quarter by 1 ?

$$\frac{x}{2} + \frac{x}{3} + \frac{x}{4} = x + 1,$$

$$x = 12.$$

(2)   A gamester loses one-half his money, and then gains 6*s*: he afterwards loses one-third of what remains, and then gains 12*s*: he lastly loses one-fourth of what remains, and finds that he has 2 guineas remaining: what sum had he at first?

The units, in which the gamester's losses and gains are expressed, are shillings, of which he had 42 remaining: let x express the number of shillings he had at first, and let us symbolize the conditions as they present themselves in the problem.

His first loss is $\frac{x}{2}$: there remains $x - \frac{x}{2}$, or $\frac{x}{2}$, after which he wins 6*s*., which added to $\frac{x}{2}$, gives $\frac{x}{2} + 6$ for the money which he possessed at the end of his first adventure; he then loses one-third of $\frac{x}{2} + 6$, which is $\frac{x}{6} + 2$, and which subtracted from $\frac{x}{2} + 6$ leaves him $\frac{x}{2} + 6 - \frac{x}{6} - 2$, or $\frac{x}{3} + 4$: he afterwards wins 2*s*., which added to $\frac{x}{3} + 4$, makes $\frac{x}{3} + 4 + 12$, or $\frac{x}{3} + 16$, for the money he possessed at the end of his second adventure: he now loses one-fourth of $\frac{x}{3} + 16$, or $\frac{x}{12} + 4$, which subtracted from $\frac{x}{3} + 16$, leaves $\frac{x}{3} + 16 - \frac{x}{12} - 4$, or $\frac{x}{4} + 12$, and which, by the conditions of the problem, is equal to 42: consequently

$$\frac{x}{4} + 12 = 42,$$

$$\frac{x}{4} = 30,$$

$$x = 120,$$

which is the sum which he first possessed.

If we omit all explanations in common language, and express the conditions throughout symbolically, reducing the expressions as they are formed, we shall get

(1) x.

(2) $x - \frac{x}{2} = \frac{x}{2}$: an identical equation, (Art. 362).

(3) $\dfrac{x}{2} + 6.$

(4) $\dfrac{x}{6} + 2.$

(5) $\dfrac{x}{2} + 6 - \dfrac{x}{6} - 2 = \dfrac{x}{3} + 4:$ an identical equation.

(6) $\dfrac{x}{3} + 4 + 12 = \dfrac{x}{3} + 16:$ an identical equation.

(7) $\dfrac{x}{12} + 4.$

(8) $\dfrac{x}{3} + 16 - \dfrac{x}{12} - 4 = \dfrac{x}{4} + 12:$ an identical equation.

(9) $\dfrac{x}{4} + 12 = 42.$

(10) $\dfrac{x}{4} = 30.$

(11) $x = 120.$

The solution of this problem involves no difficulty beyond the symbolical expression of the most common operations, the reduction of fractions and a close attention to the succession of conditions expressing the fortunes of the gamester, in the order in which they are presented in the problem: it further requires the reduction of the several expressions as they are formed to their most simple equivalent forms: if such reductions were neglected and the operations throughout were merely indicated and not performed, the succession of steps would stand as follows:

(1) $x.$

(2) $x - \dfrac{x}{2}.$

(3) $x - \dfrac{x}{2} + 6.$

(4) $\dfrac{1}{3}\left(x - \dfrac{x}{2} + 6\right).$

(5) $x - \dfrac{x}{2} + 6 - \dfrac{1}{3}\left(x - \dfrac{x}{2} + 6\right).$

(6) $x - \dfrac{x}{2} + 6 - \dfrac{1}{3}\left(x - \dfrac{x}{2} + 6\right) + 12.$

(7) $\quad \dfrac{1}{4}\left\{x-\dfrac{x}{2}+6-\dfrac{1}{3}\left(x-\dfrac{x}{2}+6\right)+12\right\}.$

(8) $\quad x-\dfrac{x}{2}+6-\dfrac{1}{3}\left(x-\dfrac{x}{2}+6\right)+12-$

$\qquad \dfrac{1}{4}\left\{x-\dfrac{x}{2}+6-\dfrac{1}{3}\left(x-\dfrac{x}{2}+6\right)+12\right\}=42.$

(9) $\quad x-\dfrac{x}{2}+6-\dfrac{x}{3}+\dfrac{x}{6}-2+12-\dfrac{x}{4}+\dfrac{x}{8}-\dfrac{6}{4}+\dfrac{x}{12}-\dfrac{x}{24}$

$\qquad +\dfrac{6}{12}-3=42.$

(10) $\quad 24x-12x+144-8x+4x-48+288-6x+3x-36$

$\qquad +2x-x+12-72=1088.$

(11) $\quad 6x=720.$

(12) $\quad x=120.$

It will hence appear how much the final equation is simplified, by a proper attention to the reduction of the expressions to their most simple forms at the moment of their first formation *.

(3) **Two men** A **and** B **can do a piece of work in 12 days: but** B **alone can do it in 30 days: in what number of days can** A **do the work alone?**

---

* The following problems are of a similar nature:

(1) In a battle, one-fourth of the men within 500 were killed: one-half of the remainder within 1400 were wounded: one-sixth of the remainder together with 500 were taken prisoners, and there only remained 4000 men: what was the number of men in the army before the battle?

The final equation, if the expressions are reduced, when formed, will be

$$\frac{5x}{16}+875=4000.$$
$$x=10000.$$

(2) In a naval engagement, one-third of the fleet are taken, one-sixth sunk, and two burnt: in a storm after the action, one-seventh of the remainder are lost and only 24 escape: of what number of ships did the fleet originally consist?

The final equation is

$$\frac{x}{2}-2-\frac{x}{14}+\frac{2}{7}=24,$$
$$\text{or}\quad x=60.$$

Let x be the number of days, in which A can do the work alone.

If we further represent the whole work by 1, the portion of it which will be done by A in one day will be represented by $\frac{1}{x}$, the portion done by B in one day by $\frac{1}{30}$, and the portion done by A and B together in one day by $\frac{1}{12}$.

The conditions of the problem give us the equation

$$\frac{1}{x} + \frac{1}{30} = \frac{1}{12}*.$$

* For if A, in one day, can do a piece of work represented by $\frac{1}{x}$, in x days he can do x times as much, which will therefore be denoted by $x \times \frac{1}{x}$ or 1 : in other words, he would do the whole work or 1 in that time.

We might represent the entire work to be done by any number, whether 1, 2, 3, &c.: thus, if we represented it by 2, the work done in one day by A would be denoted by $\frac{2}{x}$, by B in one day by $\frac{2}{30}$, and by both of them together in one day by $\frac{2}{12}$: the final equation would thus become

$$\frac{2}{x} + \frac{2}{30} = \frac{2}{12},$$

which is reducible, by dividing all its terms by 2, to

$$\frac{1}{x} + \frac{1}{30} = \frac{1}{12},$$

the same equation as is given in the text : as it is indifferent therefore by what number we choose to denote the entire work done, it is most convenient and most simple to denote it by 1.

The following problem is of a similar nature :

(1) Seven horses and four cows consume a stack of hay in 10 days, and two horses can eat it alone in 40 days : in how many days will one cow be able to eat it?

The final equation is

$$\frac{7}{80} + \frac{4}{x} = \frac{1}{10},$$

$$x = 320.$$

Therefore clearing the equation of fractions, by multiplying both its members by $60x$, (Art. 268.), we get

$$60 + 2x = 5x,$$

$$3x = 60,$$

$$x = 20.$$

(4) A hare, 50 leaps before a greyhound, takes four leaps to the greyhound's three: but two of the greyhound's leaps are equal to three of the hare's. How many leaps must the greyhound take to catch the hare?

Let x be the number of leaps taken by the greyhound: $\dfrac{4x}{3}$ will be the corresponding number of leaps taken by the hare*.

Let 1 represent the space covered by the hare in one leap †: then $\dfrac{3}{2}$ will be the corresponding space covered by the greyhound in one leap ‡.

Therefore $\dfrac{4x}{3} \times 1 = \dfrac{4x}{3}$ § will be whole space passed over by the hare before she is caught: and $x \times \dfrac{3}{2}$ or $\dfrac{3x}{2}$ will be the

---

* For the number of (x) greyhound's leaps is to that of the hare :: 3 : 4, and therefore the number of hare's leaps $= \dfrac{4x}{3}$.

† We may assume 1 or any given number whatever to represent the length of the hare's leap: thus if we assumed 10 to represent it, the final equation would be

$$\frac{3x}{2} \times 10 - \frac{4x}{5} \times 10 = 50 \times 10,$$

every term of which is divisible by 10, thus reducing it to the same equation as if 1 had been assumed to represent the length of the hare's leap, as in the text.

‡ For the length of the greyhound's leap is to that of the hare (1) :: 3 : 2, and therefore the greyhound's leap $= \dfrac{3}{2}$, that of the hare being 1.

§ For the whole space passed over will be equal to the product of the number of leaps and the length of each of them.

corresponding space passed over by the greyhound: the difference between them, by the conditions of the problem, will
be 50×1 or 50: consequently

$$\frac{3x}{2} - \frac{4x}{3} = 50,$$

$$\text{or} \quad x = 300 \text{ *}.$$

(5) What number is that, which multiplied into itself when
increased by 4, will give a product equal to 45?

Let x represent the required number: then $x + 4$ is the
expression for that number increased by 4: the conditions of
the problem assert that

$$x (x + 4) = 45,$$

$$\text{or} \quad x^2 + 4x = 45,$$

a quadratic equation.

If we complete the square, by adding 2^2 or 4 to both its
members, we shall find

$$x^2 + 4x + 4 = 49,$$

and extracting the square roots of both members, we get

$$x + 2 = 7,$$

$$\text{or} \quad x = 5.$$

(6) A person bought a number of oxen for £120., and
found that if he had bought 3 more with the same money,
he would have paid £2. less for each. How many oxen did
he buy?

Let x represent the number of oxen bought: then the
price of each will be found by dividing the entire cost by

---

* The following problem is of a similar kind:

Two couriers A and B leave the same place and travel in the same direction,
but A starts 3 days later than B: A travels 65 leagues a-day and B only 60: after
how many days will A overtake B?

The final equation is
$$65 (x - 3) = 60x,$$
$$x = 39.$$

This problem may be very easily varied; in its most general form, it is generally
called the problem of the *couriers*, the discussion of which will be found hereafter to be extremely instructive, as illustrating the meaning of algebraical signs,
when used independently, in Symbolical Algebra.

the number bought, which is therefore $\dfrac{120}{x}$: if he had purchased 3 more $(x+3)$ for the same money, the price of each would have been $\dfrac{120}{x+3}$: and the conditions assert that the first price would exceed the second by £2.: consequently

$$\frac{120}{x} - \frac{120}{x+3} = 2.$$

Clearing the equation of fractions, by multiplying both its members by $x(x+3)$, we get

$$120x + 360 - 120x = 2x^2 + 6x,$$

or
$$2x^2 + 6x = 360,$$

or
$$x^2 + 3x = 180,$$

a quadratic equation.

If we complete the square, by adding $\left(\dfrac{3}{2}\right)^2$ to both its members, we shall find

$$x^2 + 3x + \frac{9}{4} = \frac{729}{4}.$$

Extracting the square roots of both its members, we get

$$x + \frac{3}{2} = \frac{27}{2},$$

$$x = 12^*.$$

Problems, which produce quadratic equations, will rarely present, previously to their symbolical enunciation and reduction, any very definite or easily definable character by which they can be

---

* If the conditions of the problem had been varied, by changing *buying* into *selling, more* into *fewer, greater* into *less* and *paying* into *receiving,* it would have stood as follows :

"A person *sold* a number of oxen for £120, and if he had *sold* 3 *fewer* for the same money, he would have *received* £2. more for each. How many oxen did he *sell*?"

The final equation in this case would be

$$x^2 - 3x = 180,$$

whose root is 15 : this number with its sign changed (-15) would be the second root of the equation given in the text, as determined by the principles of Symbolical Algebra.

distinguished from those which produce simple equations merely, and the course which must be followed for translating their conditions into symbolical language will be nearly, if not entirely, the same in both cases: it is for this reason that we have not considered it necessary to refer them to a distinct class.

The solutions of the two preceding problems are perfectly unambiguous: the one which follows will present an example of an ambiguous solution, which a slight change of the conditions will render in one case unambiguous and in others impossible.

(7) By selling a horse for £24. I lose as much per cent. as the horse cost me. What was the prime cost of the horse?

Let x be the prime cost of the horse, and therefore $x-24$ will express the loss incurred by the sale: and it is asserted that this loss $(x-24)$ bears the same ratio to the prime cost (x) of the horse, that the prime cost (x) of the horse bears to £100.: consequently

$$x - 24 : x :: x : 100,$$

or $$100x - 2400 = x^2, \quad \text{(Art. 286.)}$$

or $$100x - x^2 = 2400.$$

Subtracting both members of this equation from 50^2 or 2500, we get

$$2500 - 100x + x^2 = 2500 - 2400 = 100,$$

or $$x^2 - 100x + 2500 = 100.$$

If we extract the square roots of both members of these equations respectively, we shall get, in the first case,

$$50 - x = 10, \quad \text{or} \quad x = 40,$$

and in the second,

$$x - 50 = 10, \quad \text{or} \quad x = 60.$$

It appears therefore that the prime cost is ambiguous, inasmuch as £40. and £60. will equally answer the conditions of the problem: for it may be easily seen that both these numbers will equally satisfy the proportions,

$$40 - 24 \text{ or } 16 : 40 :: 40 : 100,$$

$$60 - 24 \text{ or } 36 : 60 :: 60 : 100.$$

If we had supposed the sale price of the horse to have been £25., this ambiguity would no longer exist: for in this case, the proportion asserted in the problem becomes

$$x - 25 : x :: x : 100,$$

or $$100x - 2500 = x^2,$$

or $$100x - x^2 = 2500,$$

or $$2500 - 100x + x^2 = 0,$$

or $$x^2 - 100x + 2500 = 0.$$

If we extract the square roots, we get, in the first case,

$$50 - x = 0, \quad \text{or} \quad x = 50,$$

and in the second,

$$x - 50 = 0, \quad \text{or} \quad x = 50.$$

It appears therefore that there is one price £50. *only*, which will answer the conditions of the problem.

But if we had supposed the sale price of the horse to have been £26., we should have found,

$$x - 26 : x :: x : 100,$$

or $$100x - 2600 = x^2,$$

or $$100x - x^2 = 2600,$$

and if we subtract both members of this equation from $50^2 = 2500$, we should find,

$$2500 - 100x + x^2 = 2500 - 2600,$$

which is impossible, inasmuch as we are required to subtract a greater number 2600 from a less 2500: there is no value of x therefore which can satisfy the conditions of this equation *.

Problems of the se-cond class.
411. In the second class of problems, conformably to the distribution which we have made of them, we shall find more

* For if there was a real and possible value of x, there would be a real and possible value of $50 - x$, if x was less than 50, or of $x - 50$, if x was greater than 50, and therefore also of their squares $2500 - 100x + x^2$ and $x^2 - 100x + 2500$, which are identical in value: but it appears from the equation

$$2500 - 100x + x^2 = 2600 - 2500,$$

that there is no such possible value of $2500 - 100x + x^2$, inasmuch as its value can only be found by an impossible operation.

unknown numbers than one, which are related to each other in such a manner, that one of them being given, the rest may be assigned in terms of it, without the solution of subsidiary equations: it will follow, therefore, that if we represent one of these unknown numbers by a symbol, the conditions of the problem will enable us to express *explicitly** the other unknown numbers in terms of that symbol and of known numbers. It is for this reason that it will be unnecessary, in such cases, to represent the several unknown numbers by as many different symbols and consequently to form as many distinct equations as there are unknown symbols to be determined. (Art. 403.)

412. Thus if the problem involves two unknown numbers, whose sum is equal to 10, we may represent one of them by x and the other by $10 - x$: if there be two numbers whose product is equal to 10, we may represent one of them by x and the other by $\frac{10}{x}$†: if there be two numbers, of which one exceeds the other by 2, we may represent the greater by x and the less by $x - 2$, or we may represent the less by x and the greater by $x + 2$: if there be two numbers, of which the first is equal to one-third of four times the excess of the first above 5, we shall represent the first by x and the second by $\frac{4x - 5}{3}$, which is the immediate result of the translation of those conditions of the problem into symbolical language: and generally whenever there are

The selection of the unknown number which is to be represented by a symbol exemplified.

---

* By the use of the term *explicit* as applied to the expression of one symbol in terms of another, we mean that the equation is solved with respect to that symbol, (Note, p. 245): thus if

$$y = \frac{3x + 7}{4},$$

we say that the equation is solved with respect to y, or that y is expressed *explicitly* in terms of x: but in the equivalent equation

$$4y - 3x = 7,$$

the equation is not solved with respect to y, though capable of being so, and the expression of y in terms of x being *implied*, it is said that y is given *implicitly* in terms of x.

† In these cases, the connection of the two unknown numbers is rather *implied* than *expressed*: but the connection is so simple, and the expression of one in terms of the other so immediate, that it would be a very unnecessary refinement to separate such cases from those which follow.

two unknown numbers, of which one is the result of operations upon the other which are capable of being immediately symbolized, we shall represent the subject of those operations by x and the other by its corresponding and appropriate expression in terms of x.

A similar course is followed, if there be more than two unknown numbers, which have a similar connection with one of them: thus if there be three unknown numbers of which the first exceeds the second by 2 and the second exceeds the third by 3, we represent the first by x, the second by $x-2$, and the third by $(x-2)-3$ or $x-5$: if there be three unknown numbers of which the second exceeds the first by 3 and is less than the third by 5, we represent the second (which is the subject) by x, and therefore the first by $x-3$, and the last by $x+5$: if there be four unknown numbers which are as the numbers 1, 3, 5, 7, we shall represent the first by x, and therefore the others by $3x$, $5x$, and $7x$ respectively: if there be four numbers of which one-third of the first shall be equal to one-fourth of the second, and one-half of the second to one-fifth of the third, and one-sixth of the third to one-seventh of the fourth, we represent the first by x, and therefore the second by $\frac{4x}{3}$, the third by $\frac{10x}{3}$, and the fourth by $\frac{35x}{9}$*: and similarly in other cases.

413. The following are examples:

Examples.   (1) The greater of two numbers exceeds the less by 3, and four times the greater diminished by seven times the less is equal to 3. What are the numbers?

---

* In cases like this, where the conditions which connect the unknown numbers with one of them are considerably involved and not easily capable of explicit expressions in terms of their subject, it is most convenient to denote, *temporarily at least*, the several unknown numbers by separate symbols: thus, if we represent them in this case by x, y, z, u respectively, the conditions of the problems will give us $\frac{x}{3} = \frac{y}{4}$, $\frac{y}{2} = \frac{z}{5}$, $\frac{z}{6} = \frac{u}{7}$ and therefore $y = \frac{4x}{3}$, $z = \frac{5y}{2} = \frac{10x}{3}$ and $u = \frac{7z}{6} = \frac{35x}{9}$.

. Let x denote the greater of the two numbers: then $x - 3$ will denote the less: but the conditions of the problem assert that

$$4x - 7(x - 3) = 3,$$
$$4x - 7x + 21 = 3,$$
$$3x = 18,$$
$$x = 6,$$
$$\text{and} \quad x - 3 = 3.$$

The numbers are therefore 6 and 3.

If we denote the greater of the two numbers by x and the less by y, we shall immediately get the two equations,

$$\left. \begin{array}{c} x - y = 3 \\ 4x - 7y = 3 \end{array} \right\}.$$

Therefore, $\qquad 4x - 4y = 12$

$$\underline{4x - 7y = 3}$$

$$3y = 9 \quad \text{or} \quad y = 3$$
$$x = y + 3 = 6.$$

(2) A sum of money was distributed amongst four poor persons: the second received 10d. more, the third 5d. less, and the fourth 14d. more, than the first: and the whole sum distributed was less by 1d. than five times what the first received. What were the respective sums distributed?

Let x be the sum (in pence) given to the first: therefore,

$x + 10 = $ sum given to the second,

$x - 5 = \dots\dots\dots\dots$ third,

$x + 14 = \dots\dots\dots\dots$ fourth.

The whole sum distributed is

$$x + x + 10 + x - 5 + x + 14,$$

which is equal, by the conditions of the problem, to $5x - 1$: therefore,

$$x + x + 10 + x - 5 + x + 14 = 5x - 1,$$
$$4x + 19 = 5x - 1,$$
$$x = 20.$$

The sums distributed are therefore 20d., 30d., 15d., and 34d. respectively.

If we should represent the respective sums distributed by x, y, z, u, we should find

$$x + y + z + u = 5x - 1,$$
$$y = x + 10,$$
$$z = x - 5,$$
$$u = x + 14,$$

which are the four equations given to determine the four unknown symbols $x, y, z,$ and u: but $y, z,$ and u, by the conditions of the problem, are given *explicitly* in terms of x, and therefore the four equations may be immediately reduced to one by the substitution of the values of $y, z,$ and u in the first equation.

(3) A labourer is engaged to work for 30 days on condition of receiving 2*s.* for every day he worked, and of forfeiting 6*d.* for every day he was idle: at the end of the time he received 35*s.* How many days did he work, and how many was he idle?

Let x be the number of days he worked, and therefore $30 - x$ is the number of days that he was idle: the conditions of the question state that he received $2x$ shillings for his work, and forfeited $\dfrac{30 - x}{2}$ shillings for his idleness, and that the first sum exceeded the second by 35*s.*: consequently,

$$2x - \frac{30 - x}{2} = 35,$$

$$4x - 30 + x = 70,$$

$$5x = 100,$$

$$x = 20, \quad \text{and} \quad 30 - x = 10.$$

He therefore worked 20 days and was idle 10.

(4) Two travellers A and B start at the same time from two places, whose distance is 180 miles, to meet each other. A travelled 6 miles a-day more than B, and B travelled as many miles each day as was equal to twice the number of days before they met. How many miles did each of them travel each day?

Let x be the number of miles travelled each day by B, and therefore $x + 6$ the number travelled by A: the whole number of miles travelled by both of them together each day would be therefore $2x+6$: the whole number of days before they met is therefore $\dfrac{180}{2x+6}$, which, by the conditions of the question, is equal to $\dfrac{x}{2}$: consequently,

$$\frac{180}{2x+6} = \frac{x}{2},$$

or $\quad x^2 + 3x = 180.$

Adding $\left(\dfrac{3}{2}\right)^2$ or $\dfrac{9}{4}$ (Art. 384) to both members of this equation, we get

$$x^2 + 3x + \frac{9}{4} = 180 + \frac{9}{4} = \frac{729}{4},$$

and extracting the square root on both sides, we find

$$x + \frac{3}{2} = \frac{27}{2},$$

or $\quad x = 12,$

which is the number of miles travelled each day by B: and therefore $x+6$ or 18 is the number travelled by A.

If we had denoted the two unknown numbers by x and y respectively, the equations would have been

$$y = x + 6,$$

$$\frac{180}{x+y} = \frac{x}{2}.$$

The substitution of $x+6$ for y in the second equation will give us the same equation which we have otherwise obtained above*.

---

* The following are other problems belonging to the same class:

(1) A and B begin to trade, A's stock exceeding B's by £100. They each gain £50, which makes their stocks, when thus increased, in the proportion of 6 to 5. What were their original stocks?

Let $x = B$'s stock and therefore $x + 100 = A$'s stock: the equation is

$$\frac{x + 150}{x + 50} = \frac{6}{5},$$

$x = 450$ or B's stock, and $x + 100 = 550$ or A's stock.

L L

(2) To

Problems of the third class.

414. Problems of the third and last class in the general distribution which we have given of them (Art. 408), will involve two or more unknown numbers, which are not expressed nor easily and immediately expressible in terms of one of them and of known numbers: under such circumstances we assume distinct symbols to represent the several unknown numbers, or at least as many of them as are not explicitly expressed or immediately expressible in terms of others, and we form as many equations as there are unknown symbols to be determined.

Problems of the second class might be included in those of the third.

Problems of the second class might be included in the third, and they might be solved, as we have already seen, in a similar manner: the distinction however which we have established between them, though very slightly and imperfectly marked in principle, is quite sufficiently so in practice: for in one case we proceed at once to the formation of the final equation, which is the result of the elimination of one or more symbols from two or more equations, in the other.

(2) To divide the number 108 into four such parts that the first increased by 2, the second diminished by 2, the third multiplied by 2, and the fourth divided by 2, may be all equal to each other.

Let x be the first, then $x + 4$ is the second, $\dfrac{x+2}{2}$ the third, and $2x + 4$ the fourth; the equation is

$$x + x + 4 + \frac{x+2}{2} + 2x + 4 = 108,$$

and the four parts are 22, 26, 12 and 48.

(3) Required to mix two sorts of wine at 6s. and 5s. a quart, so that the mixture may be worth 5s. 4d. a quart. How much of each sort must be taken, so as to make one quart of the mixture?

Let x be the quantity of the first sort, and therefore $1 - x$ of the other: the final equation is

$$72x + 60 - 60x = 64,$$

$$\text{or} \quad x = \frac{1}{3} \quad \text{and} \quad 1 - x = \frac{2}{3}.$$

(4) Bought two flocks of sheep for £15. in one of which there were 5 more than in the other: the sheep in one flock cost as many shillings as there were sheep in the other and conversely. How many sheep were there in each flock?

Let x be the number of sheep in the least of the two flocks, and therefore $x + 5$ the number in the other: the final equation is

$$2x^2 + 10x = 300,$$

and therefore $x = 10$ and $x + 5 = 15$, are the numbers required.

415. The following are examples:

(1) What fraction is that which becomes, when its numerator is increased by 7, equal to $\frac{3}{2}$, and when its denominator is increased by 10, equal to $\frac{1}{2}$?

Let x represent the numerator and y the denominator of the fraction: if the numerator (x) be increased by 7, the denominator remaining unchanged, the fraction becomes $\frac{x+7}{y}$: and if the denominator y be increased by 10, the numerator remaining unchanged, the fraction becomes $\frac{x}{y+10}$: the conditions of the problem say that

$$\frac{x+7}{y} = \frac{3}{2} \quad (1)$$
$$\frac{x}{y+10} = \frac{1}{2} \quad (2)$$

Clearing these equations of fractions and transferring known terms to one side and unknown to the other, we get

$$3y - 2x = 14 \quad (3)$$
$$2x - y = 10 \quad (4)$$

Adding these equations together, we get

$$2y = 24, \quad \text{and} \quad y = 12.$$

Substituting this value of y in the second equation (4), we get

$$2x - 12 = 10,$$
$$2x = 22, \quad \text{and} \quad x = 11.$$

The fraction is therefore $\frac{11}{12}$.

(2) There is a number, consisting of two digits, which exceeds five times the digit in the unit's place by 6: and if 27 be added to it, the sum will be expressed by the same digits in an inverted order.

Let x be the digit in the place of tens and y the digit in the place of units: then $10x + y$ is the number which by the conditions of the problem exceeds $5y$ by 6: consequently,

$$10x + y = 5y + 6,$$

$$\text{or} \quad 10x - 4y = 6 \ldots \ldots \ldots \ldots (1).$$

Again, if 27 be added to $10x + y$, making $10x + y + 27$, the sum will be equal to the number expressed by the digits x and y in an inverted order: therefore,

$$10x + y + 27 = 10y + x,$$

or $$9y - 9x = 27,$$

or $$y - x = 3 \ldots \ldots \ldots \ldots (2).$$

The two equations are therefore,

$$\left. \begin{array}{c} 10x - 4y = 6 \\ y - x = 3 \end{array} \right\}$$

Multiplying the second equation by 4, we get

$$\left. \begin{array}{c} 10x - 4y = 6, \\ 4y - 4x = 12. \end{array} \right\}$$

Adding these equations together, we get

$$6x = 18,$$

$$x = 3,$$

and $$y = x + 3 = 6.$$

The number is therefore 36.

(3) A boy spends $5s.$ in apples and oranges, buying the first at 6 and the second at 4 a penny. Afterwards he sold two-thirds of his apples and half his oranges for $3s.$ How many of each sort did he buy?

Let x be the number of apples and y the number of oranges: then $\dfrac{x}{6}$ and $\dfrac{y}{4}$ will express the number of pence which they cost, which is equal to $5s.$ or $60d.$: therefore,

$$\frac{x}{6} + \frac{y}{4} = 60 \ldots \ldots \ldots \ldots (1).$$

Again, $\frac{2x}{3}$ apples were sold for $\frac{1}{6} \times \frac{2x}{3}$ or $\frac{x}{9}$ pence, and $\frac{y}{2}$ oranges for $\frac{1}{4} \times \frac{y}{2}$ or $\frac{y}{8}$ pence, which both together amounted to $3s.$ or $36d.$: consequently,

$$\frac{x}{9} + \frac{y}{8} = 36 \ldots \ldots \ldots \ldots (2).$$

If we clear equations (1) and (2) of fractions, we get

$$\left. \begin{array}{l} 2x + 3y = 720 \\ 8x + 9y = 2592 \end{array} \right\}.$$

Eliminating y, we get

$$6x + 9y = 2160$$
$$8x + 9y = 2592$$
$$\overline{ 2x = 432}$$
$$x = 216$$

Also, since $2x + 3y = 432 + 3y = 720$, we get

$$3y = 288,$$
and $\quad y = 96.$

(4) Two porters A and B drink from a cask of beer for 2 hours, after which A falls asleep and B drinks the remainder in 2 hours and 48 minutes: but if B had fallen asleep and A had continued to drink, it would have taken him 4 hours and 40 minutes to finish the cask. In what time would they be able to drink it separately?

Let x and y represent the numbers of hours it would take A and B respectively to finish the cask: then $\frac{1}{x}$ and $\frac{1}{y}$ represent the respective portions of the entire cask which they respectively drink in one hour: consequently the quantity remaining after 2 hours joint drinking is $1 - \frac{2}{x} - \frac{2}{y}$: and if this be divided by $\frac{1}{y}$, it will give the number of hours in which B would drink it alone: consequently, by the conditions of the problem,

$$\left(1 - \frac{2}{x} - \frac{2}{y}\right)y = 2\,\frac{48}{60} = 2\,\frac{4}{5}\ldots\ldots\ldots\ldots(1).$$

$$\left(1 - \frac{2}{x} - \frac{2}{y}\right)x = 4\,\frac{40}{60} = 4\,\frac{2}{3}\ldots\ldots\ldots\ldots(2).$$

Or, reducing,

$$xy - 2y = \frac{24x}{5} \left.\right|\ldots\ldots\ldots\ldots(3).$$

$$xy - 2x = \frac{20y}{3} \left.\right|\ldots\ldots\ldots\ldots(4).$$

Subtracting these equations from each other, we get

$$2x - 2y = \frac{24x}{5} - \frac{20y}{3}\ldots\ldots\ldots(5),$$

or $\qquad\qquad 30x - 30y = 72x - 100y,$

or $\qquad\qquad 42x = 70y,$

or $\qquad\qquad y = \dfrac{3x}{5}.$

If we substitute this value of y in either of the equations (3) and (4), we get $x = 10$, and therefore $y = 6$.

This is an example of a pair of simultaneous equations different in its form from any of those which we have considered in Art. 406: they are strictly speaking quadratic equations, but if we replace y by $\frac{3x}{5}$ in equations (3) and (4), we find the equations,

$$\frac{3x^2}{5} - \frac{6x}{5} = \frac{24x}{5},$$

$$\frac{3x^2}{5} - 2x = 4x,$$

which are easily reducible to identity with each other and in both of which x is a factor of every term: we therefore divide them severally by x, and we get the simple equations

$$\frac{3x}{5} - \frac{6}{5} = \frac{24}{5} \left.\right\}$$
$$\frac{3x}{5} - 2 = 4 \left.\right\}$$

from both of which the value of x may be determined.

(5) Bought different kinds of cloth for £6. 10s. at 10s. and 12s. per yard: but if the cost per yard of each kind of cloth had been exactly equal to the number of yards purchased, the cost would have amounted to £3. 14s. only. How many yards of each kind were purchased?

Let x and y represent the numbers of yards purchased at 12s. and 10s. respectively: then

$$12x + 10y = 130 \dots\dots\dots\dots(1).$$

Again, the cost of x yards at x shillings a yard is $x \times x$ or x^2, and the cost of y yards at y shillings a yard is y^2: consequently,

$$x^2 + y^2 = 74 \dots\dots\dots\dots(2).$$

Solve the first equation (1) with respect to y, giving us $y = 13 - \dfrac{6x}{5}$, and substitute this value of y in the second equation (2), and we get

$$x^2 + 169 - \frac{156x}{5} + \frac{36x^2}{25} = 74.$$

This equation, reduced in the ordinary manner, becomes

$$\frac{780}{61}x - x^2 = \frac{2375}{61}.$$

If we subtract both its members from $\left(\dfrac{390}{61}\right)^2$, we get

$$\frac{152100}{3721} - \frac{780}{61}x + x^2 = \frac{7225}{3721}.$$

Extracting the square root of both sides, we get

$$\frac{390}{61} - x = \frac{85}{61} \quad \text{and} \quad x = 5,$$

or $\quad x - \dfrac{390}{61} = \dfrac{85}{61} \quad$ and $\quad x = \dfrac{475}{61}.$

The value of y is $= 7$, if $x = 5$: or $y = \dfrac{223}{61}$ if $x = \dfrac{475}{61}$: but the conditions of the problem obviously require that x and y should be whole numbers, and therefore those fractional values of x and y must be rejected, unless it be supposed that the problem was formed with a view to comprehend fractional as well as entire numbers or multiples of yards*.

* The following problems are of a similar kind:

(1) A person engages at play with a gamester of superior skill, upon condition of receiving 5s. for every game he wins, and paying 2s. for every game he loses: at the end of a certain number of games he has won 20s.: but if he had received only 4s. for every game he won and had paid 3s. for every game he lost, he would have lost 5s.: how many games did he win and how many did he lose?

Let x and y represent the numbers of games he won and lost respectively: the equations are

$$5x - 2y = 20, \brace 3y - 4x = 5,$$

and $x = 10, \quad y = 15.$

(2) What fraction is that which is equal to $\frac{1}{2}$ or to $\frac{1}{3}$ according as its numerator and denominator are both of them increased or both of them diminished by 2?

If the numerator be denoted by x and the denominator by y, the equations will be

$$\frac{x+2}{y+2} = \frac{1}{2} \quad \text{and} \quad \frac{x-2}{y-2} = \frac{1}{3}:$$

and the fraction is $\frac{6}{14}$.

(3) A and B can do a piece of work in 6 days: A and C can do it in 9 days, and A, B, C can do 8 times the same work in 45 days: in what times can they do it separately?

Let x, y and z represent the numbers of days in which A, B and C respectively can do their work: the equations are

$$\frac{1}{x} + \frac{1}{y} = \frac{1}{6},$$

$$\frac{1}{x} + \frac{1}{z} = \frac{1}{9},$$

$$\frac{1}{x} + \frac{1}{y} + \frac{1}{z} = \frac{8}{45};$$

$\therefore \quad x = 10, \quad y = 15, \quad \text{and} \quad z = 90.$

(4) There is a number consisting of two digits, whose product is equal to twice their sum: but if the digits be inverted, the number will exceed the sum of its digits by 56: what is the number?

Let x be the highest and y the lowest digit, the equations are

$$xy = 2x + 2y,$$

$$10y + x = x + y + 54;$$

$\therefore \quad x = 3 \quad \text{and} \quad y - 6.$

416.   In the solution of the preceding problems we have
generally used the word number in its largest sense, as signifying fractional as well as whole numbers, and we have considered the solution of problems as practicable and possible,
when the unknown numbers sought for were comprehended in
this extended meaning of the term: many cases however will
present themselves in which the term *number* must be understood in its most limited sense, as signifying whole numbers
only, and where the occurrence of fractions or incommensurate
numbers would be altogether incompatible with the declared
conditions of the problem: thus, if the problem proposed, "to
find a number, in the series of natural numbers, the double of
whose square should exceed three times the number itself by 5,"
we should find that the only value of x in the corresponding
equation

$$2 x^2 - 3 x = 5,$$

would be $\frac{5}{2}$, which is a fraction and not one of the series of
natural numbers, and that consequently the problem is impossible in the precise sense in which it was proposed. Again,
if the problem proposed "to find a number consisting of two
digits, which, when divided by the sum of its digits, gives a
quotient greater by 2 than its first digit; but if its digits were
inverted and the resulting number divided by a number greater
by unity than the sum of its digits, the quotient is greater by
2 than the one obtained before," we should find, upon representing the two digits in their order by x and y, that the
corresponding values of x and y would be 2 and 4, $\frac{14}{133}$ and $\frac{100}{133}$
respectively, the second of which must be rejected, as not
being included in the meaning of the word number as limited
to the expression of one of the nine digits.

417.   The discrepancies, such as those just noticed, between
the results of algebraical and other operations and the strict
interpretation which they must sometimes receive in order to
answer the conditions of a problem, will be confined in Arithmetical Algebra, whenever the results are possible and therefore
obtained, to our enlarged use of the word number: in Symbolical Algebra, however, when operations become practicable,
under all circumstances, by the independent use of signs of

affection, which must be interpreted with a mixed reference to the general conditions which they are required to fulfil and the specific nature of the magnitudes or symbols to which they are prefixed, we shall perpetually meet with results which are foreign to the problem in whose solution they originate, and which are incapable of any interpretation with immediate reference to it: thus we shall find a symbolical result in the solution of those simple equations which we have characterized as impossible, inasmuch as they require the performance of an operation which is not possible in arithmetic, (Art. 380): and in all quadratic equations we shall find two roots or values of the unknown symbol, not only in those cases which we have considered to be unambiguous, but likewise in those which are arithmetically impossible, (Art. 386): but it must be kept in mind, that we are not thus enabled to extend the range of the arithmetical solution, or to obtain any results which will answer the arithmetical conditions of the problem, in a proper arithmetical sense, which are not equally obtainable by the more limited methods which we have pursued in this chapter.

CHAPTER VI.

ON ARITHMETICAL, GEOMETRICAL AND HARMONICAL PROGRESSIONS OR SERIES.

418. A SERIES of numbers, consisting of any number of terms, which continually increase or diminish by equal differences, is termed an *Arithmetical Series* or *Progression*. Thus, the series of natural numbers 1, 2, 3, 4, 5, 6, 7, 8, 9, 10, 11, &c. forms an Arithmetical Progression, since they continually increase by unity: and the same series of numbers in an inverted order 11, 10, 9, 8, 7, 6, 5, 4, 3, 2, 1, forms equally an Arithmetical Progression, because they continually diminish by the same number.

419. The number, by which the successive terms of an Arithmetical Series is increased or diminished, is called their *common difference;* and it will follow that if the first term, the common difference and the character of the series, whether increasing or decreasing, be known, we may form any number of its successive terms. Thus, if the first term of an *increasing* arithmetical series be 4 and if the common difference be 3, we readily form the series 4, 7, 10, 13, 16, 19, 22, &c.: and if the first term of a *decreasing* arithmetical series be 30 and the common difference be 4, the series will be 30, 26, 22, 18, 14, 10, 6, 2: it will not be possible to continue it farther than the last term 2, since we cannot subtract a greater number (4) from a less (2)*.

420. If we assume a to represent the first term, and b the common difference, of an arithmetical series, the series itself, if increasing, will be represented by

$$\begin{array}{cccccc} (1) & (2) & (3) & (4) & (5) & (6) \\ a, & a+b, & a+2b, & a+3b, & a+4b, & a+5b, & \&c. \end{array}$$

---

* In Symbolical Algebra, this operation is possible and the Series may be continued indefinitely, the succeeding terms being -2, -6, -8, &c.: the same remark applies to all decreasing series.

and if decreasing by

$$\overset{(1)}{a,} \quad \overset{(2)}{a-b,} \quad \overset{(3)}{a-2b,} \quad \overset{(4)}{a-3b,} \quad \overset{(5)}{a-4b,} \quad \overset{(6)}{a-5b,} \text{ &c.}$$

We have placed the numbers (1), (2), (3), (4), (5), (6), &c. above the successive terms to designate their position with reference to the first, and it will be evident both from inspection and from the least consideration of the successive formation of these terms, that the coefficient of the multiple of the *common difference* which is added to or subtracted from, the first term, in order to form any assigned term of the series, will be less by unity than the number which denominates the position of the term : thus, in the third term this coefficient is 2, in the sixth term it is 5, and in the nth term, it will be $n-1$: if, therefore, the whole number of terms in the series be denoted by n, the last term of the first series will be represented by $a+(n-1)\,b$, and of the second series by $a-(n-1)\,b$.

Expression of the nth term.

421. The usual mode of representing an entire series of n terms is, to write down the first, second and as many more terms at the beginning of the series, as are sufficient to explain the law of its formation, and also its last term, interposing between them a series of dots to indicate the intermediate and deficient terms : thus, an increasing arithmetic series whose first term is a, common difference b, and the number of whose terms is n, would be written thus,

Mode of representing a series of n terms.

$$a + (a+b) + \ldots\ldots\ldots\ldots\{a+(n-1)\,b\},$$

$$\text{or} \quad a + (a+b) + (a+2b) + \ldots\ldots\{a+(n-1)\,b\} ;$$

two terms of the beginning of the series being sufficient to indicate the law of its formation, when the character of the series is known, and three of them being generally sufficient in other cases when the nature of the series, whether it is arithmetical or not, is not previously known : thus, the series of n natural numbers, beginning from 1, would be represented by

$$1 + 2 + \ldots\ldots\ldots\ldots\ldots n,$$

and the reverse series by

$$n + (n-1) + \ldots\ldots\ldots\ldots\ldots 1 :$$

the series of n odd numbers beginning from 1, would be represented by

$$1 + 3 + \ldots\ldots\ldots\ldots\ldots(2n-1),$$

and of n even numbers, beginning from 2, by

$$2 + 4 + \ldots\ldots\ldots\ldots\ldots 2n :$$

In a similar manner, the continued product of n natural numbers beginning from 1 would be represented by

$$1 \times 2 \times \ldots\ldots\ldots\ldots\ldots\ldots n,$$

$$\text{or} \quad 1 \cdot 2 \ldots\ldots\ldots\ldots\ldots\ldots n;$$

or, if taken, in a reverse order, by

$$n(n-1)\ldots\ldots\ldots\ldots\ldots 2 \times 1,$$

$$\text{or} \quad n(n-1) \ldots\ldots\ldots\ldots\ldots 1.$$

These modes of representing a series of terms, which follow a law which is either previously expressed, or which is required to be inferred from the examination of a *sufficient* number of its terms and *no more*, are not only extremely convenient, but absolutely necessary, in all general reasonings concerning the summation and properties of such series.

422. If the several terms of an arithmetical series be added together, we may represent their sum by s, and it will be easy to investigate a simple rule by which such a sum (s) may be determined by a shorter process than the aggregation of all its terms, and more particularly so, if the number of those terms be considerable: for it is evident that the sum of an arithmetical series will be the same, when the same series of terms are written in a direct and a reverse order, and therefore we have $\quad$ *Investigation of a rule for finding the sum of an arithmetic series.*

$$s = \quad a \quad + \quad (a+b) \quad + \quad (a+2b) \quad + \ldots\{a+(n-1)b\}. \ (1),$$

$$s = \{a+(n-1)b\}+\{a+(n-2)b\}+\{a+(n-3)b\}+\ldots\ldots a \ldots\ldots(2);$$

where the first and last terms of the first series, the second and last term but one, the third and last term but two, the fourth and last term but three, and so on, are written severally underneath each other in the two series: consequently, if we add the two series (1) and (2) together, term by term, we shall get

$$2s = \{2a+(n-1)b\} + \{2a+(n-1)b\} + \ldots\{2a+(n-1)b\},$$

which is a series of n identical terms, each equal to $2a+(n-1)b$, or to the sum of the first and last terms of the original series (1): it is therefore evident, that the sum of these n equal terms will be equal to n times one of them, or that

$$2s = \{2a+(n-1)b\}\,n,$$

and therefore

$$s = \{2a+(n-1)b\}\frac{n}{2}, \ldots\ldots\ldots\ldots(3).$$

If the series was decreasing, we should find in a similar manner

$$s = \{2a - (n-1)b\}\frac{n}{2} \dots\dots\dots\dots(4),$$

where $2a - (n-1)b$, is the sum of a and of $a - (n-1)b$, the first and last terms of the series.

423. It will follow therefore that the sum of an arithmetic series is in all cases *equal to the product of half the number of its terms into the sum of its first and last terms: or that it is equal to the product of half the number of its terms into the sum or difference of twice the first term and of the product of the common difference and of the number of terms less one, according as the series is increasing or decreasing.*

424. The following are examples:

(1)   To find the sum of the first 20 odd numbers.

In this case $a = 1$, $b = 2$, $n = 20$, and therefore

$$s = 10(2 + 19 \times 2)$$
$$= 10 \times 40 = 400 = (20)^2.$$

The sum is therefore equal to the square of (20), the number of terms: and if the number of terms was n, the sum would be equal to n^2.

(2)   To find the sum of the first 20 even numbers.

In this case $a = 2$, $b = 2$, $n = 20$, and

$$s = 10(4 + 19 \times 2) = 10 \times 42 = 420.$$

If n be the number of terms of this series, the sum

$$= \frac{n}{2}\{4 + 2(n-1)\} = \frac{n}{2}(2n + 2) = n(n+1) = n^2 + n.$$

(3)   To find the sum of 58 terms of the series

$$28 + 35 + 42 + \dots$$

In this case $a = 28$, $b = 7$ and $n = 58$: therefore,

$$s = 29(56 + 57 \times 7)$$
$$= 29 \times 455 = 13195.$$

(4)   To find the sum of 13 terms of the series

$$67 + 64 + 61 + \dots$$

In this case $a = 67$, $b = 3$, $n = 13$, and the series is decreasing: therefore,

$$s = \frac{13}{2}\,(134 - 12 \times 3)$$

$$= \frac{13}{2}\,(98) = 13 \times 49$$

$$= 637.$$

425. If we replace, in the formulæ,

$$s = \{2\,a + (n-1)\,b\}\,\frac{n}{2} \ldots \ldots \ldots (3),$$

or $\quad s = \{2\,a - (n-1)\,b\}\,\frac{n}{2} \ldots \ldots \ldots (4),$

Given three of the four quantities, the sum, first term, common difference and number of terms, to find the fourth.

any three of the four symbols *a, b, n,* and *s* by specific numbers, we shall form an equation, from which the value of the fourth symbol may be found: thus, if the fourth symbol required be *s* or the sum of the series, the formulæ (3) and (4) constitute the solution of the equation with respect to *s*, (Art. 406, Note), and its value is therefore given by them, as in the preceding examples, upon the substitution of the numerical values of the symbols which the formula involves: but if any one of the three symbols *a, b,* or *n* be unknown, the equation furnished by the formulæ (3) and (4), will require to be *solved* with respect to this symbol before its value can be assigned: the following are examples.

426. (1) The sum of an increasing arithmetical series *Examples.* is 154, the common difference 4, and the number of terms 7: to find the first term of the series.

In this case, we replace, in formula (3), *s* by 154, *b* by 4, and *n* by 7: we thus get the equation

$$154 = (2\,a + 6 \times 4)\,\frac{7}{2}$$

$$= 7\,a + 84:$$

consequently, $\qquad 7\,a = 154 - 84 = 70,$

$$a = 10.$$

The first term of the series is therefore 10, and the series is

$$10 + 14 + 18 + \&\text{c.}$$

(2) The sum of a decreasing arithmetical series is $\dfrac{105}{2}$, the first term 5, and the number of terms 21: to find the common difference.

Replacing, in the formula (4), s by $\dfrac{105}{2}$, a by 5, and n by 21, we get

$$\frac{105}{2} = (10 - 20b)\frac{21}{2}$$
$$= 105 - 210\,b.$$

Therefore

$$210b = 105 - \frac{105}{2}$$
$$= \frac{105}{2},$$
$$b = \frac{105}{420} = \frac{1}{4}.$$

The series is therefore

$$5, \quad 4\tfrac{3}{4}, \quad 4\tfrac{1}{2}, \quad 4\tfrac{1}{4}, \quad 4, \quad \&c. \dots$$

the last term being 0.

(3) The sum of an *increasing* arithmetical series is 147, the first term is 7, and the common difference 7: required the number of its terms.

In this case we replace, in formula (3), s by 147, a by 7, and b by 7: we thus get

$$147 = \{14 + 7(n-1)\}\frac{n}{2}$$
$$= (7n + 7)\frac{n}{2}$$
$$= \frac{7n^2}{2} + \frac{7n}{2}.$$

Therefore $n^2 + n = 42.$

Completing the square, we get

$$n^2 + n + \frac{1}{4} = \frac{169}{4}.$$
$$n + \frac{1}{2} = \frac{13}{2},$$
$$n = 6,$$

which is the number of terms of the series.

(4) The sum of a *decreasing* arithmetical series is 36: the first term is 12 and the common difference 2: required the number of its terms.

In this case, we replace, in formula (4), *s* by 36, *a* by 12, and *b* by 2: we thus get

$$36 = \{24 - 2(n-1)\} \frac{n}{2}$$

$$= (26 - 2n) \frac{n}{2}$$

$$= 13n - n^2.$$

Consequently,

$$\frac{169}{4} - 13n + n^2 = \frac{169}{4} - 36 = \frac{25}{4},$$

$$\frac{13}{2} - n = \frac{5}{2}, \quad \text{and} \quad n = 4,$$

$$\text{or} \quad n - \frac{13}{2} = \frac{5}{2}, \quad \text{and} \quad n = 9.$$

It is the *least* of these values only which is strictly applicable to the problem proposed, the four terms of the series being

$$12, \quad 10, \quad 8, \quad 6,$$

whose sum is equal to 36.

But this series cannot be extended to 9 terms without the introduction of negative terms, and consequently the second value of *n*, in the quadratic equation to which the problem leads, must be rejected: it follows therefore that the arithmetical solution of the problem is *not* ambiguous*.

* The complete series of 9 terms, which *Symbolical* Algebra would furnish, is

$$12, 10, 8, 6, 4, 2, 0, -2, -4,$$

the algebraical sum of whose terms is equal to 36, equally with the sum of the four first terms 12, 10, 8, 6: it remains to explain the paradox of the occurrence of a real and integral value of one of the roots of the equation, which is not applicable to the problem in which that equation originates.

The same equation, whose two roots we are considering, would present itself likewise in the solution of the following problem:

" To find a number, which multiplied into the excess of 13 above it, shall give a product equal to 36."

There are two numbers (if there be one) which will equally answer the conditions of this problem, which is obviously identical with the following:

" To

A geometric series defined.

427. A geometric series is one where each succeeding term is the same multiple of the preceding, the word multiple being taken in its largest sense*: thus if a, b, c, d, e, &c.

"To find two numbers whose sum shall be 13, and whose product shall be 36."

The enquiry, directed by the problem considered in the text, leads to the solution of the same problem, namely, "to find a number n such, that the product of n and $2a - (n-1)b$, or of n and $2a + b - bn$ shall be equal to $2s$": or what is the same thing, "to find n so that the product of n and $\dfrac{2a+b}{b} - n$ shall be equal to $\dfrac{2s}{b}$". To this problem, if there be one answer, there must be two: and each of these answers would equally denote the number of terms of the decreasing arithmetical series, if two series could possibly be formed in arithmetic, which had the same first term, the same common difference and the same sum, but not the same number of terms: it is the impossibility of satisfying this last condition which restricts the answer required to the least of the two numbers which satisfy the equation to which the problem leads; but, in Symbolical Algebra, both the answers are possible, inasmuch as two such decreasing series can be formed, which have the same first term, the same common difference, but not the same number of terms.

* A geometric series may be otherwise defined to mean a series whose successive terms bear the same ratio to each other: thus, if a, b, c, d, e, &c. represent the successive terms of such a series, then the ratios $\dfrac{a}{b}, \dfrac{b}{c}, \dfrac{c}{d}, \dfrac{d}{e}$ &c. are severally equal to each other, and consequently their inverse ratios $\dfrac{b}{a}, \dfrac{c}{b}, \dfrac{d}{c}, \dfrac{e}{d}$ &c. are likewise equal to each other, (Art. 291): if we call r the value of this *inverse* ratio, we have

$$\frac{b}{a} = r, \quad \frac{c}{b} = r, \quad \frac{d}{c} = r, \quad \frac{e}{d} = r \ \text{&c.}$$

and therefore
$$b = ar,$$
$$c = br = ar^2,$$
$$d = er = ar^3,$$
$$e = dr = ar^4 \ \text{&c.,}$$

which evidently gives the same relation of the terms as results from the more simple definition which is given in the text.

It is evident, likewise, that the terms of such a series are in continued proportion (Art. 288), since
$$a : b :: b : c :: c : d :: d : e \ \text{&c.}$$
and therefore whatever properties we have shewn to characterize such continued proportionals, will belong likewise to the successive terms of a geometric series.

The phrases *arithmetical progression* and *geometric progression*, have reference to an essential distinction between *arithmetic proportion* and *geometric proportion*, which modern mathematicians have not retained: four numbers were said

be the successive terms of such a series, and if r be the common multiplier which connects them successively with each other, we shall find

$$b = ar.$$

$$c = br = ar^2, \text{ replacing } b \text{ by } ar.$$

$$d = cr = ar^3, \ldots\ldots c \text{ by } ar^2.$$

$$e = dr = ar^4, \ldots\ldots d \text{ by } ar^3.$$

$$\ldots\ldots\ldots\ldots$$

It will follow therefore that a geometric series, as thus defined, will be correctly represented by

$$a + ar + ar^2 + ar^3 + ar^4 + \&c.$$

where a is the first term and r the common multiplier.

428. If the first term a and the common multiplier or common ratio r of a geometric series be given, the series corresponding may be immediately formed and written down to any extent, as follows:

$$\overset{(1)}{a} + \overset{(2)}{ar} + \overset{(3)}{ar^2} + \overset{(4)}{ar^3} + \overset{(5)}{ar^4} + \overset{(6)}{ar^5} + \overset{(7)}{ar^6} + \&c.$$

The first term and common ratio or multiplier of a geometric series being given, the series may be continued to any orders.

If we place the numbers 1, 2, 3, 4, 5, 6, &c. above the several terms, to designate their positions in the series, we shall readily see that the index of the power of r which is involved in each term, will be less by unity than the number which denominates the position of the term: thus the 6th term is ar^5, the 7th term ar^6, and the nth term will be ar^{n-1}: a series of n terms therefore may be represented, in conformity with the principles of notation explained and exemplified in Art. 421, by

$$a + ar + \ldots\ldots ar^{n-1}:$$

to be in *arithmetic proportion*, when the difference of the first and second was equal to the difference of the third and fourth: whilst four numbers were in geometric proportion, when the quotient of the first divided by the second was equal to the quotient of the third divided by the fourth, or when they satisfied the conditions of the common geometric definition of proportion: again, three numbers were said to be in *continued arithmetic* proportion, when the difference of the first and second was equal to the difference of the second and third: and a continued series of numbers in continued arithmetical proportion, constituted an *arithmetical progression*, in the same manner that a continued series of numbers in continued geometric proportion constituted a *geometric progression*.

for the two first terms of the series, its character being known, will furnish us with a and with r, and will therefore enable us to form the succeeding terms of the series, and the last term will shew the extent to which the series is carried.

429. An abbreviated expression for the sum of n terms of a geometric series may be found in the following manner: calling its sum or the result of the aggregation of all its terms s, we put

$$s = a + ar + \ldots\ldots ar^{n-1} \ldots\ldots (1),$$

and multiplying both sides of this equation by r, we get

$$rs = ar + ar^2 + \ldots\ldots ar^{n-1} + ar^n \ldots (2).$$

The sum of n terms of the series (1) will be greater or less than the sum of n terms of the series (2), according as r is greater or less than 1: in the first case, we subtract the series (2) from the series (1), and we thus get

$$rs - s = ar^n - a *,$$

$$\text{or} \quad (r-1)s = a(r^n - 1),$$

$$\text{or} \quad s = \frac{a(r^n - 1)}{r - 1} \ldots\ldots (3):$$

and in the second case, we subtract the series (2) from the series (1), which gives us

$$s - rs = a - ar^n,$$

$$\text{or} \quad s(1 - r) = a(1 - r^n),$$

$$\text{or} \quad s = \frac{a(1 - r^n)}{1 - r} \ldots\ldots (4). †$$

430. The formulæ

$$s = \frac{a(r^n - 1)}{r - 1} \ldots\ldots (3),$$

$$\text{and} \quad s = \frac{a(1 - r^n)}{1 - r} \ldots\ldots (4),$$

---

* For if we subtract the two series from each other, term by term, the first term (a) of the first series (1) and the last term (ar^n) of the last series (2) will alone remain, all the others being common to both series, and therefore disappearing by the subtraction of one series from the other.

† In Symbolical Algebra, the second of these formulæ is deducible from the first and conversely.

are immediately applicable to the summation of geometric series:
for if such a series

$$a + ar + ar^2 + \&\text{c.}$$

be given, the first term is a, and we divide the second term
by the first in order to find r: we then replace a, r and n
in the formulæ (3) or (4) by their proper numerical values,
and thus determine the value of s.

The following are examples:

(1) To find the sum of 10 terms of the series

$$1 + 2 + 2^2 + 2^3 + \ldots$$

In this case $a = 1$, $r = 2$ and $n = 10$: therefore, by formula (3),

$$s = \frac{1 \times (2^{10} - 1)}{2 - 1} = 1023.$$

(2) To find the sum of 12 terms of the series

$$2 + 6 + 18 + 54 + \&\text{c.}$$

In this case $a = 2$, $r = \frac{6}{2} = 3$ and $n = 12$: consequently, by
formula (3),

$$s = \frac{2(3^{12} - 1)}{3 - 1} = 3^{12} - 1$$

$$= 531440.$$

(3) To find the sum of 10 terms of the series

$$1 + \frac{1}{2} + \frac{1}{4} + \frac{1}{8} + \&\text{c.}$$

In this case $a = 1$, $r = \dfrac{\frac{1}{2}}{1} = \frac{1}{2}$ and $n = 10$: therefore, by formula (4),

$$s = \frac{\left(1 - \frac{1}{2^{10}}\right)}{1 - \frac{1}{2}} = \frac{2^{10} - 1}{2^9}$$

$$= \frac{1023}{512},$$

which differs from twice the first term by $\frac{1}{512}$.

(4)   To find the sum of 14 terms of the series

$$4 + \frac{8}{3} + \frac{16}{9} + \frac{32}{27} + \&c.$$

In this case $a = 4$, $r = \frac{8}{3 \times 4} = \frac{2}{3}$ and $n = 14$: therefore, by the formula (4), we get

$$s = \frac{4\left(1 - \frac{2^{14}}{3^{14}}\right)}{1 - \frac{2}{3}} = 12\left(1 - \frac{2^{14}}{3^{14}}\right)$$

$$= \frac{12 \times 4766585}{4782969} = \frac{19066340}{1594323}.$$

Given three of the four quantities involved in the expression for the sum of a geometric series, to find the fourth.

431.   In the equation, which expresses the sum of a geometric series, there are four quantities involved, which are the sum of the series (s), the first term (a), the common multiplier or ratio (r), the number of terms (n), and any three of these quantities being given, the fourth may be found by the solution of the equation. The formulæ (3) and (4) furnish the solution of the equation with respect to s, and no difficulty presents itself in the solution of the same equation with respect to a: but this equation becomes one of n dimensions with respect to r, and is what is called a *transcendental* equation with respect to n, and in neither of these cases is its solution practicable (if n exceeds 2 in the first case), by the principles of arithmetical algebra alone: we are reminded, not only in this case, but in many other parts of the theory both of arithmetical and geometrical series and their summation, of the limits which are opposed to our progress, when deprived of the aid of the principles of symbolical algebra.

Quotient of a divided by $1 - r$.

432.   If we divide a by $1 - r$, the process and its result will assume the following form: (Art. 87)

$$1 - r\,)\; a\;(a + ar + ar^2 + ar^3 + \ldots$$
$$\underline{a - ar}$$
$$ar$$
$$\underline{ar - ar^2}$$
$$ar^2$$
$$\underline{ar^2 - ar^3}$$
$$ar^3$$

The quotient

$$a + ar + ar^2 + \ldots$$

is the geometric series whose first term is a and whose common multiplier or ratio is r; and inasmuch as the remainder can never disappear (Art. 87), the process, and therefore the series whose terms it generates, may be indefinitely continued: and inasmuch as the nth remainder is ar^n, and therefore grows less and less (r being less than 1) the greater n is*, it is evident that the longer the process is continued, the more nearly does the series produced approximate in value to the true quotient of a divided by $1 - r$ or to the true value of the fraction $\dfrac{a}{1-r}$ (Arts. 166, 167, 168): it is from these considerations, that we are enabled to conclude that $\dfrac{a}{1-r}$ is the *limit* to which the sum of the series

$$a + ar + ar^2 + \ldots$$

continually approximates more and more nearly, the further it is continued, and which it actually *equals*, when this series is supposed to be continued indefinitely †.

It is in this sense that we speak of the sums of indefinite series, meaning in every case the *limit* to which the actual aggregate of an *assignable* number of terms will approximate nearer and nearer the greater that number is. (Art. 166.)

Limit of the sum of an indefinite series.

---

* Thus, if $r = \dfrac{1}{2}$, $r^2 = \dfrac{1}{4}$, $r^3 = \dfrac{1}{8}$, $r^{10} = \dfrac{1}{1024}$ and so on: if $r = .9$, $r^2 = .81$, $r^3 = .729$, $r^4 = .6561$, $r^{10} = .3486379401$: and it may be easily shewn, that if r be less than 1, a power of r and therefore a value of ar^n may be always found, which is less than any assigned number however small.

† The same remark applies to the series

$$a - ar + ar^2 - ar^3 + \&c \ldots$$

which originates in the division of a by $1 + r$, and which for the same reason we may consider, when indefinitely continued, as equal to the fraction

$$\frac{a}{1+r}.$$

433. (1) Thus the sum of the indefinite series

$$1 + \frac{1}{2} + \frac{1}{4} + \frac{1}{8} + \ldots$$

is $= \dfrac{1}{1 - \dfrac{1}{2}} = 2$, or is equal to twice the first term.

(2) The sum of the indefinite series

$$1 + \frac{1}{3} + \frac{1}{9} + \frac{1}{27} + \&c.$$

is $= \dfrac{1}{1 - \dfrac{1}{3}} = \dfrac{3}{2}$.

(3) The sum of the indefinite series

$$1 + \frac{4}{5} + \frac{16}{25} + \ldots$$

is $= \dfrac{1}{1 - \dfrac{4}{5}} = 5$.

(4) The sum of the indefinite series

$$3 + \frac{1}{2} + \frac{1}{12} + \&c.$$

is $= \dfrac{3}{1 - \dfrac{1}{6}} = \dfrac{18}{5}$.

(5) The value of the circulating decimal

$$.333\ldots$$

is $= \dfrac{\dfrac{3}{10}}{1 - \dfrac{1}{10}} = \dfrac{3}{9} = \dfrac{1}{3}$*.

* Many examples have been given in Chap. II. Arts. 162–168, of the summation of circulating decimals, or of their conversion into equivalent fractions upon principles precisely similar to those stated in the text.

434. Numbers, whose *reciprocals* form an arithmetical progression are said to be in *harmonical proportion* or to form an *harmonical progression:* thus the numbers 2, 3 and 6 are in *harmonical proportion*, since their reciprocals $\frac{1}{2}$, $\frac{1}{3}$ and $\frac{1}{6}$ form an *arithmetical progression:* the same is the case with the numbers 3, 4 and 6: and also with the numbers 4, 5, $\frac{20}{3}$, 10, 20.

Definition of numbers in harmonical progression.

435. The knowledge of the two first terms of such a series will enable us easily to determine all the rest: thus if a and b be the two first terms of such a series, and if we represent the third term by x, then their reciprocals $\frac{1}{a}$, $\frac{1}{b}$ and $\frac{1}{x}$ being in arithmetical progression, we must have

Given the two first terms of such a series, to form the other terms.

$$\frac{1}{a} - \frac{1}{b} = \frac{1}{b} - \frac{1}{x}*,$$

or

$$\frac{1}{x} = \frac{2}{b} - \frac{1}{a} = \frac{2a-b}{ab},$$

and therefore

$$x = \frac{ab}{2a-b}.$$

It will follow therefore that the formation of an additional term in such a series, whether originally consisting of two or of a greater number of terms, will always be *possible*, when twice the *first* or *penultimate* term is greater than the *second* or *ultimate* term: in all other cases, the additional term will be either *infinite*, when $2a = b$, or *negative*, when $2a$ is less than b, and therefore such as cannot be formed without the aid of the principles of Symbolical Algebra.

436. Thus if the two first terms be 4 and 5, the third term will be $= \frac{4 \times 5}{2 \times 4 - 5} = \frac{20}{3}$: the second and third terms

Examples.

---

* If a be greater than b, then

$$\frac{1}{b} - \frac{1}{a} = \frac{1}{x} - \frac{1}{b} \quad \text{and} \quad x = \frac{ab}{2a-b},$$

the same expression as in the text.

being 5 and $\frac{20}{3}$, the fourth term will be $\dfrac{5 \times \frac{20}{3}}{2 \times 5 - \frac{20}{3}} = \dfrac{100}{10} = 10$:

the third and fourth terms being $\frac{20}{3}$ and 10, the fifth term

will be $\dfrac{\frac{20}{3} \times 10}{2 \times \frac{20}{3} - 10} = 20$: but the series is incapable of being

continued further, inasmuch as the next or sixth term, would be, in conformity with the formula, Art. 435,

$$\frac{20 \times 10}{2 \times 10 - 20} = \frac{200}{0},$$

which is the symbol, as we shall afterwards see, of an infinite number.

Given the two first terms of an harmonic series to find the nth term.

437. More generally, if the two first terms a and b of an harmonic series were given, and if it was required to find an expression for the nth term of the series, we should observe that the series formed by the inverted terms

$$\frac{1}{a}, \quad \frac{1}{b}, \quad \&c.$$

is an arithmetic series (Art. 434), whose first term is $\frac{1}{a}$ and whose common difference is $\frac{1}{a} - \frac{1}{b}$ (a being less than b), and therefore its nth term (Art. 420), would be

$$\frac{1}{a} - (n-1)\left(\frac{1}{a} - \frac{1}{b}\right) *$$

$$= \frac{1}{a} - \frac{(n-1)}{a} + \frac{(n-1)}{b}$$

$$= \frac{b - (n-1)b + (n-1)a}{ab}$$

---

* For if the first term of a decreasing arithmetic series be a' and its common difference b', its nth term is $a' - (n-1)b'$ (Art. 420): and if we replace a' by

$$\frac{1}{a} \text{ and } b' \text{ by } \frac{1}{a} - \frac{1}{b},$$

we get the expression in the text.

$$= \frac{(n-1)a - (n-2)b}{ab}:$$

it follows, therefore, that the *reciprocal* of this expression, or

$$\frac{ab}{(n-1)\,a - (n-2)\,b},$$

is the expression for the nth term of the harmonic series, and will continue to be possible as long as $(n-1)\,a$ is greater than $(n-2)\,b$. Thus if a be 5 and b be 4, the tenth term of the corresponding harmonic series, will be

$$\frac{4 \times 5}{9 \times 5 - 8 \times 4} = \frac{20}{13}:$$

and it is obvious that the harmonic series may be continued indefinitely whenever the first term is greater than the second and in no other case*.

438. If there be three terms a, b and c, which are in harmonical progression, then

An harmonical series otherwise defined.

$$\frac{1}{a} - \frac{1}{b} = \frac{1}{b} - \frac{1}{c},$$

$$\text{or } \frac{b - a}{ab} = \frac{c - b}{bc},$$

$$\text{or } \frac{b - a}{a} = \frac{c - b}{c}:$$

it will follow, therefore, by resolving this equation into a proportion, that

$$a : c :: b - a : c - b;$$

or in other words, *if three numbers a, b and c be in harmonic proportion, then the first of them will bear to the third the same ratio, which the difference of the first and second bears to the difference of the second and third.* This is the common definition of numbers in harmonic progression, by which we may very easily deduce as a proposition, the property of such numbers, (Art. 434), which we have employed as the foundation of the preceding investigations†.

---

* It is not possible to find any simple abbreviated expression for the sum of a series of terms in harmonical progression, as in the case of arithmetical (Art. 422), and geometrical (Art. 429) series: such a sum can only be found by the aggregation of all its terms.

† For if

$$a : c :: b - a : c - b,$$

we get

Problems connected with arithmetical and geometrical progressions.

439. Many problems may be proposed which are connected with arithmetical, geometrical and harmonical series and their properties: thus if two numbers be given, it may be proposed to assign an intermediate number x, so that the three numbers a, x and b may be in arithmetic, geometric or harmonical progression.

Arithmetic and geometric means.

The arithmetic mean will be found, by observing that if a, x and b are in arithmetic progression, then

$$x - a = b - x,$$

$$\text{or} \quad 2x = a + b,$$

$$\text{or} \quad x = \frac{a + b}{2},$$

the arithmetic mean required, and which is equal to half the sum of the extremes.

we get $\qquad ac - ab = bc - ac :$

and dividing both members of this equation by abc, we find

$$\frac{1}{b} - \frac{1}{c} = \frac{1}{a} - \frac{1}{b},$$

which is the property which we have assumed, (Art. 434), as defining numbers in harmonical progression.

The term *harmonical* has been applied to such numbers, from their relation to those subdivisions of the monochord, which furnish harmonic sounds: for the numbers of vibrations of stretched strings will be inversely as their lengths, and consequently, if a monochord be divided into lengths whose reciprocals are any assigned numbers, the numbers of their vibrations and therefore the *pitches* of the sounds severally produced by them, will be proportional to those numbers : thus, if the lengths of two strings be represented by 1 and $\frac{1}{2}$, the pitches will be as 1 and 2, and the second will be the *octave* of the first, producing a *unison*, the most perfect of all concords : if their lengths be represented by $\frac{1}{2}$ and $\frac{1}{3}$ the numbers of their vibrations will be as the numbers 2 and 3, producing a perfect concord, which is called the *fifth* : if these lengths be as

$$\frac{1}{3} \text{ and } \frac{1}{4}, \ \frac{1}{4} \text{ and } \frac{1}{5}, \ \frac{1}{5} \text{ and } \frac{1}{6}, \ \frac{1}{3} \text{ and } \frac{1}{5}, \ \frac{1}{5} \text{ and } \frac{1}{8},$$

the corresponding numbers of vibrations will be as the numbers 3 and 4, 4 and 5, 5 and 6, 3 and 5, 5 and 8, producing concords which are severally denominated a *fourth*, a *major third*, a *minor third*, a *major sixth*, and a *minor sixth*: no prime numbers, higher than 5, enter into the expression of the ratios of any numbers of vibrations which are found to produce concords in music.

The succession of numbers which form many harmonic progressions, attracted the particular attention of the Platonists in their researches after the mystical and other properties of numbers, as involving the numerical ratios which express the most

Again, the corresponding geometric mean y between a and b will be determined by observing that if a, y and b are in geometric progression, then

$$\frac{y}{a} = \frac{b}{y},$$

or $\quad y^2 = ab,$

or $\quad y = \sqrt{ab},$

the geometric mean required, and which is equal to the square root of the product of the extremes.

Lastly, an harmonical mean z between a and b will be determined, by observing that

$$\frac{1}{a} - \frac{1}{z} = \frac{1}{z} - \frac{1}{b},$$

or $\quad \dfrac{2}{z} = \dfrac{1}{a} + \dfrac{1}{b} = \dfrac{a+b}{ab};$

and therefore $\quad z = \dfrac{2ab}{a+b}$ *,

the harmonical mean required.

most perfect concords in music : thus, the harmonic numbers 2, 3 and 6, form the ratios $\frac{2}{3}$, $\frac{2}{6}$ or $\frac{1}{3}$, $\frac{3}{6}$ or $\frac{1}{2}$, which express the *fifth*, the *twelfth*, and the *octave*, which are the most perfect· concords in music : the harmonic numbers 3, 4, 6 express the ratios $\frac{3}{4}$, $\frac{4}{6}$ or $\frac{2}{3}$, $\frac{3}{6}$ or $\frac{1}{2}$, or the fourth or *diatesseron*, the *fifth* or *diapente*, the *octave* or *diapason* : and it was not only observed, but made the foundation of important theories, that the *sum*, (Art. 268), of the two first of these ratios or $\frac{3}{4} \times \frac{2}{3}$ was equal to the last.

If the harmonic mean be sought for between the terms of the ratio $\frac{1}{2}$ of the fundamental note to its octave, it will be found to be $\frac{4}{3}$, which is the *diatesseron* or *fourth* : whilst the corresponding harmonic mean between the terms of the ratio, $\frac{1}{3}$, of the fundamental note to its *twelfth*, will be $\frac{3}{2}$, or the *fifth* : these and other properties of harmonic means made them as much the objects of attention to the Platonic philosophers, as the mystical and other properties which they sought for and discovered in arithmetical and geometrical means.

 * Thus, an arithmetic mean between 4 and 16 is $\frac{4+16}{2}$ or 10: a geometric mean between the same numbers is $\sqrt{4 \times 16} = \sqrt{64} = 8$: whilst the corresponding harmonical mean is $\frac{2 \times 4 \times 16}{4+16} = \frac{128}{20} = 6.4$; the first is always greater than the second, and the second than the third, unless the extremes are equal to each other.

Represen-
tation of
unknown
numbers
in arithme-
tic and
geometric
progres-
sion.

440. If it be required to represent three or four unknown numbers which are in arithmetic progression, it is very often convenient to denote the mean term in the first case by x and the two extremes by $x-y$ and $x+y$, and in the second case, to denote the two mean terms by $x-y$ and $x+y$, and the two extremes by $x-3y$ and $x+3y$; the common difference in the first case being denoted by y and in the second by $2y$. Thus, in the solution of the following problem, "to find a number of three digits, forming a decreasing arithmetic series, whose sum is 12, and the sum of whose squares is 56," we represent the three digits by $x+y$, x and $x-y$ respectively, and immediately form the equations

$$(x+y) + x + (x-y) = 12 \ldots \ldots \ldots (1)$$

$$(x+y)^2 + x^2 + (x-y)^2 = 56 \ldots \ldots \ldots (2).$$

The first equation becomes,

$$3x = 12, \text{ or } x = 4:$$

and the second equation is

$$x^2 + 2xy + y^2 + x^2 + x^2 - 2xy + y^2 = 56,$$

$$\text{or } 3x^2 + 2y^2 = 56,$$

which becomes, by replacing x by 4,

$$48 + 2y^2 = 56,$$

$$\text{or } 2y^2 = 8,$$

$$\text{or } y^2 = 4,$$

$$\text{or } y = 2.$$

The digits are therefore 6, 4 and 2 and the number is 642 *.

Again, if it was required "to find four numbers in arithmetic progression whose sum is equal to 22, and the product of whose extremes is less than the product of their means by 18," we

---

* If we had represented the first of these numbers by x and the common difference by y, the equations would have been

$$x + x - y + x - 2y = 12 \ldots \ldots \ldots \ldots (1),$$

$$x^2 + (x-y)^2 + (x-2y)^2 = 56 \ldots \ldots \ldots \ldots (2),$$

which would not admit of an equally simple solution with those which are given in the text.

should represent the numbers by $x - 3y$, $x - y$, $x + y$, and $x + 3y$ respectively, and thence form the equations

$$\left.\begin{array}{l} x - 3y + x - y + x + y + x + 3y = 22, \\ (x + y)(x - y) - (x + 3y)(x - 3y) = 18, \end{array}\right\}$$

$$\left.\begin{array}{l} \text{or} \quad 4x = 22, \text{ or } x = \dfrac{11}{2}, \\ x^2 - y^2 - (x^2 - 9y^2) = 18, \end{array}\right\}$$

$$\text{or } 8y^2 = 18,$$

$$\text{or } y^2 = \frac{9}{4},$$

$$\text{or } y = \frac{3}{2}:$$

we thus find $x - 3y = \dfrac{11}{2} - \dfrac{9}{2} = 1$,

$$x - y = \frac{11}{2} - \frac{3}{2} = 4, \quad x + y = \frac{11}{2} + \frac{3}{2} = 7,$$

$$\text{and } x + 3y = \frac{11}{2} + \frac{9}{2} = 10,$$

which are the numbers required*.

In a similar manner we may represent three unknown numbers in geometric progression by $\dfrac{x}{y}$, x and xy, the mean term being x and the common ratio or multiplier y: thus if it was proposed "to find three numbers in geometric progression whose sum is 13, and the product of whose extremes is equal to 9," we should denote them by $\dfrac{x}{y}$, x and xy respectively, and then form the equations

$$\left.\begin{array}{l} \dfrac{x}{y} + x + xy = 13 \\ x^2 = 9 \end{array}\right\}.$$

---

* If the first of these numbers had been denoted by x and their common difference by y, we should have got the equations

$$x + x + y + x + 2y + x + 3y = 22,$$
$$x(x + 3y) - (x + y)(x + 2y) = 18,$$

which are not equally simple with those given in the text.

We thus at once get $x = 3$, and replacing x by 3 in the first equation, we find

$$\frac{3}{y} + 3 + 3y = 13,$$

$$\frac{3}{y} + 3y = 10,$$

$$\frac{1}{y} + y = \frac{10}{3},$$

$$1 + y^2 = \frac{10y}{3},$$

or $\frac{10y}{3} - y^2 = 1,$

or $\frac{25}{9} - \frac{10y}{3} + y^2 = \frac{25}{9} - 1 = \frac{16}{9},$

$$\frac{5}{3} - y = \frac{4}{3}, \text{ or } y = \frac{1}{3},$$

or $y - \frac{5}{3} = \frac{4}{3}, \text{ or } y = 3.$

It is obvious that $y = 3$, or $y = \frac{1}{3}$ will equally answer the conditions of the problem, and that the numbers are 1, 3 and 9.

CHAPTER VII.

THEORY OF COMBINATIONS AND PERMUTATIONS.

441. THE different orders, in which any quantities or letters Permutations defined. which represent them, may be arranged, are called their Permutations. Thus the permutations of the two things or letters a and b, taken both together, are ab and ba, a occupying the first place in one and b in the other: the permutations of the three things or letters a, b and c, taken all together, are abc, acb, bac, bca, cab and cba: whilst the permutations of the same three letters, when taken two and two together only, are ab, ba, ac, ca, bc and cb.

In thus expressing the permutations of ab or of abc, by writing the letters which form them consecutively as in the operation of multiplication, we designate their order of succession only, and not the products which are usually denoted by symbols placed in this manner without the interposition of any signs between them.

442. In investigating the expressions for the numbers of permutations of n different things, when taken two and two, three Great convenience, in general investigations, of employing the same letter, with subscript numbers. and three, four and four, ... r and r together, it will be found to be extremely convenient to denote them by the same letter a with different and successive *subscript* numbers, such as a_1, a_2, a_3, a_4, a_5, ... a_n, where the numbers *subscribed* will not only serve to distinguish the different symbols (and therefore the things which they represent) from each other, but will determine likewise their order of succession in the series.

443. We shall now proceed to determine the expressions Number of permutations of n things. for the number of *permutations* of n different things or letters, when taken one and one, two and two, three and three, ... r and r together, when r is any whole number less than n.

P P

Taken separately or one by one.

The number of permutations of n letters or things taken separately, or one by one, is evidently equal to the number of letters or to n.

Two and two together.

The number of permutations of n things taken two and two together, is $n(n-1)$.

For a_1 may be placed successively before a_2, $a_3, \ldots a_n$, and thus form $(n-1)$ permutations taken two and two together: a_2 may be placed successively before a_1, a_3, $a_4, \ldots a_n$, and thus form $(n-1)$ permutations two and two together, which are different from the former: and the same thing may be equally done with $a_3, a_4, \ldots a_n$, and there will therefore be $(n-1)$ permutations two and two together corresponding to the successive series of permutations headed by each letter, which are different from each other and from all the others: it will follow therefore that the whole number of such permutations will be n times the number $(n-1)$ of them comprehended in each series, and will consequently be equal to $n(n-1)$.

Three and three together.

444. The number of permutations of n things taken three and three together, is equal to $n(n-1)(n-2)$.

For a_1 may be placed successively before the $(n-1)(n-2)$ permutations two and two*, which can be formed by the $n-1$ letters a_2, $a_3, \ldots a_n$, thus making $(n-1)(n-2)$ permutations three and three together, in each of which a_1 occupies the first place: and it is obvious that the same thing may be done with all the other letters a_2, $a_3, \ldots a_n$, forming, with those first formed, altogether n times $(n-1)(n-2)$ permutations or $n(n-1)(n-2)$ permutations taken three and three together.

Four and four together.

445. By a similar process, we should be able to shew that the number of permutations of n things, taken four and four together, would be expressed by the formula

$$n(n-1)(n-2)(n-3),$$

where there are as many factors (which are the natural numbers descending from n) as there are letters in each permutation.

---

* For the number of permutations of n letters is equal to $n(n-1)$, or if expressed in words, it is equal to the *product of the number of letters and of that number diminished by unity* : if therefore the number of letters be $n-1$ instead of n, this number diminished by unity will be $n-2$, and their product will be $(n-1)(n-2)$, which is therefore the expression for the number of permutations of $(n-1)$ letters taken two and two together.

446. Let us now suppose that the same law prevails in the expression of the number of permutations of n things taken $(r-1)$ and $(r-1)$ together, which would therefore be

$$n(n-1)\ldots(n-r+2)*:$$

it may be easily proved that it must prevail likewise for the expression of the number of permutations of n things taken r and r together, which will be therefore

$$n(n-1)\ldots(n-r+2)(n-r+1).$$

For a_1 may be placed successively before each permutation of $(r-1)$ of the $(n-1)$ letters $a_2, a_3, \ldots a_n$, forming

$$(n-1)(n-2)\ldots(n-r+1)\dagger$$

permutations, in each of which a_1 will occupy the first place; and it is obvious that the same thing may be equally done with all the other letters $a_2, a_3, \ldots a_n$, forming, with those first formed, altogether n times as many permutations as those in which a_1 occupies the first place or n times $(n-1)(n-2)\ldots(n-r+1)$ permutations, which is equal to

$$n(n-1)(n-2)\ldots(n-r+1).$$

It is thus proved that if the assumed law for the formation of the expression for the number of permutations of n things be true when they are taken $r-1$ and $r-1$ together, that it is necessarily true likewise for the next superior number, or when they are taken r and r together: but we have proved this law to prevail in the expressions for the number of permutations of n things taken two and two, three and three together: it is therefore true, by the theorem just demonstrated, when they

---

* For the number subtracted from n in each term of the descending series of natural numbers, n, $n-1$, $n-2$, &c. is less by unity than the number which denominates the position of the term, and therefore in the last or $(r-1)^{\text{th}}$ term it is $r-2$, and the term itself is $n-r+2$.

† For if the number of permutations of n things taken $(r-1)$ and $(r-1)$ together be expressed by

$$n(n-1)\ldots\ldots\ldots(n-r+2),$$

it will be merely necessary to replace n by $n-1$ in this expression, in order to get the corresponding number of permutations of $(n-1)$ things taken $(r-1)$ and $(r-1)$ together: such is the expression given in the text.

are taken four and four together: and if true when they are taken four and four together, it is true likewise when they are taken five and five together, and so on successively for any number of them, not greater than n, which may be taken together.

447. We have given the demonstration of the general formula in the last Article, with great detail, not merely on account of the importance of the formula itself, but as presenting a very complete example of the application of the *principle* of *demonstrative induction* in mathematical reasoning and which we shall have very frequently occasion to employ. The principle itself may be stated generally as follows. A law or formula is proved to be true for two or more successive numbers, which present such a connection with each other, as to authorize the hypothetical assumption of its truth for all numbers whatsoever: we then convert our *hypothesis* into a *proof*, by demonstrating that if the law be true for any assigned number whatsoever, such as $r-1$, it is *necessarily* true for the next superior number r: we are thus enabled to connect the particular cases which we have demonstrated, as the foundation of our assumption, step by step, with all those which follow, until we have ascended to the general formula, where the number, whose different and successive values are considered, is denoted by a general symbol.

448. We have denominated this principle of reasoning, which is quite complete and satisfactory, *demonstrative induction*, to distinguish it from that less conclusive and less certain species of *induction* which prevails in physical and other sciences, by which facts may be classified and general laws may be suspected, though not demonstrated, to prevail: in such cases we can rarely indicate the dependence of the particular facts upon each other, and much less demonstrate that the existence or truth of the law for *any case whatsoever which may be assigned* will determine its existence or truth for the case which immediately succeeds to it, and consequently for all cases whatever which can be proposed: unless this relation of dependence of all successive cases can be shewn to exist, or unless it can be shewn to be independent of their position in a series of them, generalizations which are formed by induction should be considered as hypotheses only, which must await

the confirmation of more complete investigations, or which must be established by the aid of other principles of reasoning*.

449. We shall now proceed to examine some of the consequences deducible from the formula demonstrated in Art. 442.

If we suppose $r = n$, or if we suppose *that each permutation comprehends all the* n *letters* a_1, $a_2 \ldots a_n$, the formula under consideration will become

$$n \, (n-1) \ldots \ldots 2 \times 1,$$

or, if written in a contrary order,

$$1 \times 2 \ldots \ldots \ldots (n-1) \, n,$$

which is the product of all the natural numbers as far as n: the following are examples of its application.

Number of permutations of n things taken all together.

(1) Required the number of changes which can be rung upon 8 bells.

Examples.

This number, which is equal to all the variations in their order of succession, in which the 8 bells can be sounded, is equal to

$$1 \times 2 \times 3 \times 4 \times 5 \times 6 \times 7 \times 8 = 40320.$$

(2) What is the number of different arrangements which can be made of 12 persons at a dinner table?

This number $= 1 \times 2 \times \ldots \ldots 12 = 479001600.$

450. A case which frequently presents itself for consideration, is the determination of the number of permutations of n things, when any assigned number of them become identical with each other, or when different classes of them become so.

Number of permutations when different classes of letters become identical.

Thus, let it be required to find an expression for the number of permutations of n things, r of which are identical with each other.

---

* Fermat asserted that the formula $2^n + 1$ is always a prime number, and the examination of every case from $n = 1$ to $n = 31$, would appear to confirm the truth of this conclusion: but Euler shewed however that $2^{32} + 1$ was a composite number. Again, the formula

$$x^2 + x + 41,$$

gives prime numbers for all values of x from 1 to 39: it would be a false induction to conclude from thence, that the same formula would give prime numbers in all cases, for it obviously fails to do so, when $x = 40$ or $x = 41$: such examples, of the danger of making erroneous inductions, are very common in the theory of numbers.

The expression for the number of permutations of n things taken all together, supposing them all different from each other (Art. 449) is

$$n\,(n-1)\ldots 2 \cdot 1:$$

if r of these quantities become identical, the permutations which arise from their interchange with each other, or from their *particular* permutations, which are $1 \cdot 2 \ldots r$ in number, *for any assigned position of the other letters*, are reduced to one: the number of permutations, therefore, when all the letters are different from each other, is $1 \cdot 2 \ldots r$ times as great as when r of them become identical: or in other words,

$$\frac{n\,(n-1)\ldots 2 \cdot 1}{1 \cdot 2 \ldots r},$$

is the expression for the number of permutations under the circumstances supposed.

If, in addition to r quantities which become identical, there are s others, which though different from the former, are still identical with each other, then there are $1 \cdot 2 \ldots s$ permutations corresponding to their interchange with each other, which are reduced to one, for any given position of the other quantities: the expression for the number of permutations, under these circumstances, becomes

$$\frac{n\,(n-1)\ldots 2 \cdot 1}{1 \cdot 2 \ldots r \times 1 \cdot 2 \ldots s}.$$

The same reasoning may obviously be applied equally to any number of classes of letters or things, which become identical with each other, and consequently if, of n quantities, r_1 are of one kind, r_2 of another, r_3 of a third, and so on, as far as r_m of the mth class, then their whole number of the permutations will be expressed by

$$\frac{n\,(n-1)\ldots\ldots 2 \cdot 1}{1 \cdot 2 \ldots r_1 \times 1 \cdot 2 \ldots r_2 \times 1 \cdot 2 \ldots r_3 \times \ldots \times 1 \cdot 2 \ldots r_m}.$$

451. It may be useful to illustrate these formulæ by a few examples.

(1) To find the number of permutations (p) of the letters in the word *Algebra*.

In this case $n = 7$, and the letter a appears twice: consequently

$$p = \frac{7 \cdot 6 \cdot 5 \cdot 4 \cdot 3 \cdot 2 \cdot 1}{1 \cdot 2} = 2520.$$

(2) To find the number of permutations of the letters in the word *perseverance.*

In this case $n = 12$, and the letter e appears four times, and r twice: therefore

$$p = \frac{12 \cdot 11 \cdot 10 \cdot 9 \cdot 8 \cdot 7 \cdot 6 \cdot 5 \cdot 4 \cdot 3 \cdot 2 \cdot 1}{1 \cdot 2 \cdot 3 \cdot 4 \times 1 \cdot 2} = 9979200.$$

(3) To find the number of permutations of the letters of the product $a^3 b^5 c^2$ written at full length.

In this case $n = 10$, and the letter a appears *three* times, b *five* times, and c *twice;* therefore the number of permutations (p)

$$= \frac{10 \cdot 9 \cdot 8 \cdot 7 \cdot 6 \cdot 5 \cdot 4 \cdot 3 \cdot 2 \cdot 1}{1 \cdot 2 \cdot 3 \times 1 \cdot 2 \cdot 3 \cdot 4 \cdot 5 \times 1 \cdot 2} = 2520.$$

(4) To find the number of permutations of the letters in the expressions $a^{m-1} b$, $a^{m-2} b^2$, $a^{m-3} b^3$, and $a^{m-r} b^r$ respectively;

$$(p) \text{ in } a^{m-1} b = \frac{m (m - 1) \ldots 2 \cdot 1}{1 \cdot 2 \ldots \ldots (m - 1)} = m.$$

$$(p) \text{ in } a^{m-2} b^2 = \frac{m (m - 1) (m - 2) \ldots 2 \cdot 1}{1 \cdot 2 \times 1 \cdot 2 \ldots (m - 2)} = \frac{m (m - 1)}{1 \cdot 2},$$

striking out the $(m - 2)$ last factors, from the numerator and denominator, which are severally identical with each other:

$$(p) \text{ in } a^{m-3} b^3 = \frac{m (m - 1) (m - 2) (m - 3) \ldots 2 \cdot 1}{1 \cdot 2 \cdot 3 \times 1 \cdot 2 \ldots (m - 3)}$$

$$= \frac{m (m - 1) (m - 2)}{1 \cdot 2 \cdot 3}$$

$$(p) \text{ in } a^{m-r} b^r = \frac{m (m - 1) \ldots (m - r + 1) (m - r) \ldots 2 \cdot 1}{1 \cdot 2 \ldots r \times 1 \cdot 2 \ldots (m - r)}$$

$$= \frac{m (m - 1) \ldots (m - r + 1)}{1 \cdot 2 \ldots r}.$$

striking out the $(m - r)$ last factors of the numerator and denominator.

These expressions are remarkable, inasmuch as they will be found to be severally the expressions for the number of *combinations* of n things, taken *one* and *one, two* and *two, three* and *three,* and r and r together.

Combinations: their meaning. **452.** By the *combinations* of different letters or quantities, we mean the different collections which can be made of any assigned number of them, without reference to the order of their arrangement.

Thus, ab, ac and bc are the only different combinations of the three letters a, b, c, taken two and two together, which form *six* different permutations: there is only *one* combination of the same three letters, taken *all* together, though they form *six* different permutations, (Art. 441).

Number of combinations. **453.** We shall now proceed to determine the number of combinations of n things, taken r and r together, where r is less than n.

The number of combinations of n things, taken separately or one and one together, is clearly n.

Taken two and two together. The number of combinations of n things, taken two and two together, is $\dfrac{n(n-1)}{1.2}$.

For the number of permutations of n things, ta en two and two together, is $n(n-1)$, (Art. 443); and there are two permutations (ab, ba) corresponding to one combination: the number of combinations will be found, therefore, by dividing the number of permutations by 2 or by 1.2.

Three and three together. **454.** The number of combinations of n things, taken three and three together, is $\dfrac{n(n-1)(n-2)}{1.2.3}$.

For the number of permutations of n things, taken three and three together, is $n(n-1)(n-2)$, (Art. 444), and there are $1.2.3$ permutations for one combination of three things: the number of combinations will be therefore found by dividing the number of permutations by $1.2.3$.

Taken r and r together. **455.** The number of combinations of n things, taken r and r together, is $\dfrac{n(n-1)\dots(n-r+1)}{1.2\dots r}$.

For the number of permutations of n things, taken r and r together, is $n(n-1)\dots(n-r+1)$; and there are $1.2\dots r$ permutations corresponding to each combination of r things:

the number of combinations of n things, therefore, taken r and r together, will be found by dividing the number of their corresponding permutations by $1.2...r$.

456. There are some properties of these expressions which are attended with very important consequences and which we shall now proceed to point out.

In the first place, the number of combinations of n things, taken r and r together, is the same as the number of combinations of n things, taken $n-r$ and $n-r$ together.

For the number of combinations of n things, taken r and r together, is

$$\frac{n(n-1).....(n-r+1)}{1.2 \ ..... \ r} \ ...... \ (\alpha).$$

The number of combinations of n things taken r and r together, the same as when taken $n-r$ and $n-r$ together.

The number of combinations of n things, taken $n-r$ and $n-r$ together, will be expressed by putting $n-r$ in the place of r in the preceding expression (α), when the last term of its numerator becomes $n-(n-r)+1$ or $r+1$, the last term of the denominator $n-r$, and the expression itself

$$\frac{n(n-1).....(r+1)}{1.2 \ .....(n-r)} \ ...... \ (\beta).$$

The same expression (β), somewhat differently written, though identical in signification, is

$$\frac{n(n-1)....(n-r+1)(n-r)....(r+1)}{1.2 \ .... \ r \ . \ (r+1)....(n-r)};$$

where the last terms of the numerator and denominator of (α), and the first and last additional terms introduced into the numerator and denominator of (α) in order to obtain (β), are written down: we thus see that all those additional terms are common both to the numerator and denominator, and that consequently the first expression (α) is equal to the second (β): or, in other words, the number of combinations of n things, taken r and r together, is equal to the number of combinations of n things, taken $(n-r)$ and $(n-r)$ together.

457. The same conclusion may be otherwise and more simply obtained as follows: if we take the n quantities $a_1, a_2,...a_n$, and form any one combination of r of these quantities, those

Second proof.

which remain will form a corresponding and *supplementary* combination of $(n-r)$ quantities: it follows, therefore, that no combination can exist without its *supplement*, and that consequently they must be equal in number.

458. If we further consider the expression (a) for the number of combinations of n things taken r and r together, and examine its successive values for successive values of r, it will obviously continue to increase, until the additional term successively introduced into the numerator becomes equal to or less than the corresponding additional term introduced into the denominator: now the rth term of the numerator is $n-r+1$, and the corresponding term in the denominator is r: if these be equal to each other, we have $n-r+1=r$, and consequently $r = \dfrac{n+1}{2}$: and since r is necessarily a whole number, n must, in this case, be necessarily an odd number: there is, therefore, in this case, the *same* number, and also the *greatest* number, of combinations, when they are taken $\dfrac{n-1}{2}$ together and $\dfrac{n+1}{2}$ together, such combinations being *supplementary* to each other.

If n be an even number, the greatest number of combinations takes place when they are taken $\dfrac{n}{2}$ together: for in this case, $n-r+1$ becomes $n-\dfrac{n}{2}+1$ or $\dfrac{n}{2}+1$, which is greater than the corresponding value of r or $\dfrac{n}{2}$; whilst the next succeeding value of $n-r+1$, which is $\dfrac{n}{2}$, is less than the corresponding value of r, or of the last term of the denominator. which is $\dfrac{n}{2}+1$.

459. There are few subjects which admit of more varied or instructive illustrations than the Theory of Combinations: for such problems, for the most part, resolve themselves, with very slight preparatory adaptation, into problems for the calculation of chances and probabilities, and consequently almost immediately spring from them. It is for this reason that we shall devote the remaining Articles of this Chapter to such a statement of the first principles of the Doctrine of Chances, as may be requisite to shew its connection with the Theory

of Combinations, and as may enable a student to solve a very extensive class of questions, which are intimately connected with the ordinary business of life.

460. The term *chance*, in popular language, has various Popular meanings of the word Chance. meanings attached to it, whether primitive or derived, though it is not always very easy, nor in this instance very important, to distinguish one from the other: it sometimes means an *event*, whose occurrence is uncertain, whether under the influence or not, of determined or determinable laws: on other occasions, it is used to express the *cause* which influences the happening of an event: and sometimes it is used as the expression of our opinion of the intensity of the cause which determines or influences a possible event, whether it be according to expectation or the contrary.

461. It is in this latter sense that it approaches most nearly Its mathematical meaning. to its mathematical meaning, where it is used as synonymous with *probability;* and the *chance* of the happening, or the *probability* of the happening, of an event or its contrary, is measured, and *therefore defined,* by the ratio which exists between the number of events which *must* happen, or of cases which *must* exist, and the whole number of events which both *must* and *may* happen, or of cases which both *must* and *may* exist, *and which are all of them similarly circumstanced.*

462. This ratio may be expressed by means of a fraction, Mode of expressing it. whose numerator is the number of favourable events or cases, and whose denominator is the number of *all* the events or cases, whether favourable or unfavourable: for all ratios are expressed and measured by means of fractions, whose numerators are the antecedents and whose denominators are the consequents of the ratios. Art. 263.

Thus, if *a* expresses the number of favourable events or cases, and *b* the number of those which are unfavourable, the *chance* of the favourable event or of the required case existing, is expressed by

$$\frac{a}{a+b};$$

whilst the *chance* of an unfavourable event or of the required case not existing, is expressed by

$$\frac{b}{a+b}.$$

Certainty represented by unity.

463. From such a mode of representation, it will follow that *certainty*, which supposes all the events or cases favourable, in the first case, when $b = 0$, or all of them unfavourable, in the second case, when $a = 0$, will be expressed by 1: the ratio, therefore, of the *chance* to *certainty*, or of the degree or probability (as it is sometimes expressed) to certainty, will be the ratio which the fraction, by which it is denoted, bears to unity, or the ratio of its numerator to its denominator.

Odds for or against.

464. The ratio of the chance of success to that of failure, or the ratio of the *odds for or against*, as expressed in popular language, will be that of a to b, or of b to a, which are the numerators of the fractions by which the respective chances are denoted.

Absolute and moral chances.

465. Chances generally may be separated into two great classes, as *absolute* and *moral*: the first are those, where the numerator and denominator of the fractions by which they are expressed, admit of absolute determination: the second are those, where the numerator and denominator, one or both of them, admit not of absolute determination, but are inferred, approxi-

Absolute and moral certainties.

mately at least, from experiment or observation: the *certainties* also, in which these different classes of *chances* may be said to terminate, as the limit of their different values, may be distinguished from each other, in a similar manner, as *absolute* and *moral*.

466. The chances considered in the following problems, belong chiefly to the first of these classes, and their determination requires no principle which is foreign to the theory of combinations: in most cases, however, moral chances are convertible, as far as their estimation is concerned, into absolute chances; and a few examples will be given, in order to shew the nature of the reasoning which is employed for this purpose.

The following are examples of the representation of simple chances:

Simple chances: of throwing an ace with one die.

(1) To find the chance of throwing an ace with a single die.

There is only one face, which *can be* uppermost, or there is only one throw, the occurrence of which is *favourable*, though there are six which are equally likely to be so, five of which are necessarily *unfavourable*: the chance, therefore, that this face is the *ace*, is $\frac{1}{6}$.

(2) The chance that this face is not the *ace*, is $\frac{5}{6}$: for there are five out of six equally possible cases, which are favourable to this hypothesis.

Of not throwing an ace.

(3) The chance that the face thrown is either an ace or a deuce, is $\frac{2}{6}$ or $\frac{1}{3}$: for there are here two favourable cases out of six which are equally likely to happen: the chance of failure, or that it is neither an ace nor a deuce, is $\frac{4}{6}$ or $\frac{2}{3}$.

Of throwing an ace or deuce.

(4) If the die had been a regular tetrahedron, whose faces were marked with the numbers 1, 2, 3, 4, the chance of its *resting upon* an ace would be $\frac{1}{4}$; the chance of its not doing so, would be $\frac{3}{4}$.

Of throwing an ace with a tetrahedral die.

(5) The chance of drawing the ace of spades from a pack of 52 cards, is $\frac{1}{52}$: the chance of drawing any one of the four aces, is $\frac{4}{52}$ or $\frac{1}{13}$: for there are four favourable cases out of fifty-two which are both favourable and unfavourable, and all of them are equally likely to happen.

Of drawing an ace or specified card from a pack of cards.

(6) The chance that the 14th of November of any year not assigned, falls upon a Friday, is $\frac{1}{7}$: for this is one of seven successive days, one of which, and one only, must be a Friday: and it cannot fall upon a determinate day, since neither 365 nor 366 are multiples of 7, and therefore different and successive years begin upon different days of the week.

That a given day of a given month in a year not given, is a given day of the week.

(7) If 14 white and 6 black balls be thrown into an urn, the chance of drawing a white ball out of it, at one trial, is $\frac{14}{20}$: the chance of failing, or of drawing a black ball, is $\frac{6}{20}$.

Of drawing a white or a black ball from an urn containing a given number of both.

Chances of
success and
failure sup-
plemental
to each
other.

467. In the preceding and in all other cases, the chances of success and failure of the *same* event are *supplemental* to each other, their sum being equal to 1, which is the measure and representative of *certainty*: the knowledge of one, therefore, necessarily determines the other.

Compound
chances.

468. The following examples of Compound Chances are introductory to the first elements of their general theory, which will follow.

Chance of
throwing
an ace
twice with
one die.

(1) To find the chance of throwing an ace, twice in succession, with a single die.

There are six cases, which are equally likely to occur at the first throw, and the same number at the second: these may be combined or permuted together in 6×6 or 36 different ways, which are equally likely to happen, and only *one* of them is favourable: the chance is, therefore, $\frac{1}{36}$.

With two
dice.

(2) The chance of throwing *two aces* at one *contemporaneous* throw with two dice, is equally $\frac{1}{36}$: for the succession of time makes no difference whatever in the number of favourable and unfavourable permutations.

Of throw-
ing an ace
and deuce.

(3) The chance of throwing an *ace* at the first throw, and a *deuce* at the second, is also $\frac{1}{36}$: for there is only one favourable permutation out of 36.

(4) The chance of throwing an *ace* at one throw, and a *deuce* at the other, *without reference to their order of succession*, is $\frac{1}{18}$: for in this case there are two permutations forming one combination (1, 2 and 2, 1), which are favourable to the hypothesis made, and two *only*, out of the whole 36.

Proposition
respecting
compound
chances.

469. The chance of an event contingent upon other events, is the continued product of the chances of the separate events.

Let the several chances be

$$\frac{a_1}{a_1 + b_1}, \quad \frac{a_2}{a_2 + b_2}, \quad \frac{a_3}{a_3 + b_3}, \cdots \frac{a_n}{a_n + b_n},$$

where a_1, a_2, a_3,...a_n represent the numbers of cases which are favourable, and b_1, b_2, b_3,...b_n the numbers of cases which are unfavourable, to the particular hypothesis made in each separate event, whether of success or failure.

We will consider, in the first instance, the chance which is dependent upon the two separate chances

For two chances.

$$\frac{a_1}{a_1 + b_1} \quad \text{and} \quad \frac{a_2}{a_2 + b_2}.$$

Every case in $a_1 + b_1$ may be combined with every case in $a_2 + b_2$, and thus form $(a_1 + b_1)(a_2 + b_2)$ combinations of cases, which are equally likely to happen.

The favourable cases in the first (a_1) may be combined severally with the favourable cases in the second (a_2), and thus form $a_1 a_2$ combinations of cases favourable to the compound event.

The compound chance is denoted, therefore, by

$$\frac{a_1 a_2}{(a_1 + b_1)(a_2 + b_2)},$$

which is the product of the separate chances.

Let us now pass to the consideration of the chance of the event contingent upon three other events, whose respective chances are

For three chances.

$$\frac{a_1}{a_1 + b_1}, \quad \frac{a_2}{a_2 + b_2}, \quad \frac{a_3}{a_3 + b_3}.$$

The several combinations of all the cases in the two first chances, which are, by the last case, $(a_1 + b_1)(a_2 + b_2)$ in number, may be severally combined with the $a_3 + b_3$ different cases, both favourable and unfavourable, of the third chance, and thus form $(a_1 + b_1)(a_2 + b_2)(a_3 + b_3)$ combinations which are equally likely to happen.

The favourable cases in the two first chances, which are $a_1 a_2$ in number, may be combined severally with the a_3 favourable cases of the third chance, and thus form $a_1 a_2 a_3$ cases which are favourable to the compound event.

The chance, therefore, of the compound event, is

$$\frac{a_1 a_2 a_3}{(a_1 + b_1)(a_2 + b_2)(a_3 + b_3)},$$

which is the product of the simple chances.

For any
number of
them.

If we now consider any number (n) of chances,

$$\frac{a_1}{a_1 + b_1}, \quad \frac{a_2}{a_2 + b_2}, \quad \frac{a_3}{a_3 + b_3}, \cdots \frac{a_n}{a_n + b_n},$$

and assume the law expressed in the enunciation of the proposition as true for $(n-1)$ of them, it may be proved to be true for n of them (Art. 446): for the chance of the event contingent upon the $(n-1)$ first events being

$$\frac{a_1 a_2 \ldots a_{n-1}}{(a_1 + b_1)(a_2 + b_2)\ldots(a_{n-1} + b_{n-1})},$$

all the combinations of favourable and unfavourable cases in its denominator, may be severally combined with the $a_n + b_n$ favourable and unfavourable cases in the nth chance, and thus produce

$$(a_1 + b_1)(a_2 + b_2)\ldots(a_n + b_n)$$

favourable and unfavourable cases, for the compound event, which are equally likely to happen.

In a similar manner the $a_1 a_2 \ldots a_{n-1}$ favourable cases of the first $(n-1)$ chances, may be severally combined with the a_n favourable cases of the nth chance, and thus produce $a_1 a_2 \ldots a_n$ favourable cases for the compound event, which are equally likely to happen: the compound chance is, therefore, denoted by

$$\frac{a_1 a_2 \ldots a_n}{(a_1 + b_1)(a_2 + b_2)\ldots(a_n + b_n)},$$

which is the product of all the simple chances.

It follows, therefore, that the law which has been proved to be true for two and three chances, is necessarily true for four, five, and so on, as far as any number of separate chances whatever. (Art. 447.)

Its great
import-
ance.

This is a most important proposition in the Doctrine of Chances, and makes the calculation of the chance of any compound event dependent upon the separate and simple chances of the several events, in their assigned order, upon which it is dependent.

Before we proceed to the consideration of some other important propositions which are intimately connected with it, we will illustrate its application by a few examples.

470. To find the chance of throwing an ace in the first *only* of two successive throws.

The first simple chance is $\frac{1}{6}$.

The second simple chance is $\frac{5}{6}$: for an ace must *not* be thrown the second time, and there are five *favourable** cases for its failure.

The compound chance is therefore, $\frac{1}{6} \times \frac{5}{6} = \frac{5}{36}$.

471. What is the chance of drawing the four aces from a pack of cards, in four successive trials?

The first simple chance is $\frac{4}{52}$.

The second simple chance is $\frac{3}{51}$.

For if an ace be drawn the first time, there remain only 3 aces and 51 cards.

The third simple chance is $\frac{2}{50}$.

For if two aces be drawn the two first times, there remain only 2 aces and 50 cards.

The fourth simple chance is $\frac{1}{49}$.

For if three aces be drawn the three first times, there remain only 1 ace and 49 cards.

The compound chance required is therefore

$$\frac{4 \cdot 3 \cdot 2 \cdot 1}{52 \cdot 51 \cdot 50 \cdot 49} = \frac{1}{270725}.$$

---

* It must be kept in mind, that the favourable cases are those which satisfy the particular hypothesis made for each event or trial: it is an ace in the first throw and any other point in the second.

472. What is the chance of winning two games at whist (or of any other game where there are only two equal chances for winning or losing) in succession?

The first simple chance is $\frac{1}{2}$.

The second simple chance is $\frac{1}{2}$.

For the event of the first game does not influence the chance of the second.

The compound chance is, therefore,

$$\frac{1}{2} \times \frac{1}{2} = \frac{1}{4}.$$

The chance of not winning two games in succession, (which is supplemental to the other) is, therefore, $\frac{3}{4}$.

The odds against winning two games in succession, are 3 to 1.

The chance of winning three games in succession is $\frac{1}{8}$, being the product of the three simple chances $\frac{1}{2}$, $\frac{1}{2}$ and $\frac{1}{2}$.

The chance of winning the two first games and losing the third, or of winning the first, losing the second and winning the third, or of losing the first and winning the second and third, is in each case $\frac{1}{8}$, inasmuch as the simple chances are $\frac{1}{2}$, $\frac{1}{2}$ and $\frac{1}{2}$, the same as in the first instance.

The chance of winning two games out of three, without reference to their order of succession, is $\frac{3}{8}$, the sum of the chances of each separate event, which equally answer the conditions of the question.

The chance of losing the two first games and winning the third, or of losing the first, winning the second and losing the third, or of winning the first and losing the second and third, is in each case $\frac{1}{8}$, inasmuch as the three simple chances are $\frac{1}{2}$, $\frac{1}{2}$ and $\frac{1}{2}$.

The chance of losing two games in succession, without reference to their order of succession, is $\frac{3}{8}$, the sum of the chances of the three events, which equally answer the conditions of the question.

The chance of losing three games in succession is $\frac{1}{8}$, the product of the three simple chances $\frac{1}{2}$, $\frac{1}{2}$ and $\frac{1}{2}$. *Or losing three in succession.*

473. In all cases of successive trials, where the number of favourable (a) and unfavourable cases (b) for each event remains the same, the chance of the required event happening n times in succession is expressed by *For repeated trials where the number of favourable and unfavourable cases remains the same.*

$$\frac{a^n}{(a+b)^n}.$$

For this is the expression for the continued product of each separate chance $\frac{a}{a+b}$ repeated n times. (Art. 469.)

The chance of the required event happening $(n-1)$ times and failing once, *in a specified order*, is $\frac{a^{n-1}b}{(a+b)^n}$: for the $(n-1)$ separate chances of success are expressed severally by $\frac{a}{a+b}$, and the single chance of failure is expressed by $\frac{b}{a+b}$.

The chance of the required event happening $(n-1)$ times and failing once, *without reference to the order of the events*, is expressed by $\frac{na^{n-1}b}{(a+b)^n}$: for there are n different ways in which the conditions of the problem may be equally satisfied, and the chance of its happening in each of these ways is expressed by $\frac{a^{n-1}b}{(a+b)^n}$, and therefore the whole chance is expressed by their sum or by $\frac{na^{n-1}b}{(a+b)^n}$.

The chance of the required event happening $(n-2)$ times and failing twice, *in a specified order*, is expressed by $\dfrac{a^{n-2}b^2}{(a+b)^n}$: for the $(n-2)$ first chances are severally expressed by $\dfrac{a}{a+b}$ and the two last by $\dfrac{b}{a+b}$, and therefore the compound chance is expressed by their continued product, which is $\dfrac{a^{n-2}b^2}{(a+b)^n}$.

The chance of the required event happening $(n-2)$ times and failing twice, *without reference to their order of succession*, is expressed by $\dfrac{n(n-1)}{2} \cdot \dfrac{a^{n-2}b^2}{(a+b)^n}$: for there are $\dfrac{n(n-1)}{2}$ different combinations of $(n-2)$ and 2 events (Art. 456), the probability of each of which is $\dfrac{a^{n-2}b^2}{(a+b)^n}$, and their sum or the joint probability is therefore expressed by $\dfrac{n(n-1)}{1 \cdot 2} \cdot \dfrac{a^{n-2}b^2}{(a+b)^n}$.

Generally, the chance of the required event happening $(n-r)$ times and failing r times, *in a specified order*, is expressed by $\dfrac{a^{n-r}b^r}{(a+b)^n}$: for the $(n-r)$ separate chances of success are represented severally by $\dfrac{a}{a+b}$ and the separate chances of failure by $\dfrac{b}{a+b}$, and therefore the compound chance is represented by their continued product or by $\dfrac{a^{n-r}b^r}{(a+b)^n}$.

The chance of the required event happening $(n-r)$ times and failing r times, *without reference to their order of succession*, is expressed by $\dfrac{n(n-1)\ldots(n-r+1)}{1 \cdot 2 \ldots r} \cdot \dfrac{a^{n-r}b^r}{(a+b)^n}$.

For this condition may be satisfied by any combination of $(n-r)$ and r events, which are $\dfrac{n(n-1)\ldots(n-r+1)}{1 \cdot 2 \ldots r}$ (Art. 456) in number, and each of these combinations of events is equally likely to happen: and as the chance of each separate combination of these events is $\dfrac{a^{n-r}b^r}{(a+b)^r}$, the sum of these chances, which is the chance required to be determined, will be expressed by $\dfrac{n(n-1)\ldots(n-r+1)}{1\,.\,2\ldots r}\cdot\dfrac{a^{n-r}b^r}{(a+b)^n}$.

The chance of the required event happening *at least* $(n-r)$ times and failing *at most* r times, *without reference to their order of succession*, will be expressed by

$$\dfrac{a^n + na^{n-1}b + \dfrac{n(n-1)}{1\,.\,2}a^{n-2}b^2 + \ldots\ldots \dfrac{n(n-1)\ldots\ldots(n-r+1)}{1\quad.\quad2\quad\ldots\quad r}a^{n-r}b^r}{(a+b)^n}.$$

For the condition of the problem will be satisfied by the happening of the event n times, or by its happening $(n-1)$ times and failing once, or by its happening $(n-2)$ times and failing twice, and so on, as far as its happening $(n-r)$ times and failing r times, and in every case *without reference to their order of succession;* and consequently the entire chance will be expressed by the sum of those separate chances, and therefore by the formula we have given above.

474. The following examples will serve to illustrate the application of these formulæ. Examples.

(1) In the game of *cross* and *pile* (*heads* and *tails*), what is the chance that *cross* will come up three times exactly in seven trials?

In each trial, either *cross* or *pile* may equally happen.

Consequently $a=1$, $b=1$, $n=7$ and $r=4$: the chance, therefore,

$$=\dfrac{7\,.\,6\,.\,5\,.\,4}{1\,.\,2\,.\,3\,.\,4}\cdot\dfrac{a^3b^4}{(a+b)^7}=\dfrac{7\,.\,6\,.\,5\,.\,4}{1\,.\,2\,.\,3\,.\,4}\cdot\dfrac{1}{2^7}=\dfrac{35}{128}.$$

The chance that *cross* will come up three times at least, is

$$\dfrac{a^7 + 7a^6b + \dfrac{7\,.\,6}{1\,.\,2}a^5b^2 + \dfrac{7\,.\,6\,.\,5}{1\,.\,2\,.\,3}a^4b^3 + \dfrac{7\,.\,6\,.\,5\,.\,4}{1\,.\,2\,.\,3\,.\,4}a^3b^4}{(a+b)^7}$$

$$=\dfrac{1+7+21+35+35}{2^7}=\dfrac{99}{128}.$$

(2) In five throws with a single die, to find the chance of throwing two aces *only* in the two last throws.

In this case, the order of the successive events is specified: and since $a = 1$, $b = 5$, $n = 5$ and $r = 3$, the chance is

$$\frac{a^2 b^3}{(a+b)^5} = \frac{125}{7776}.$$

The chance that an ace is thrown twice only in five trials, without reference to their order of succession, is

$$\frac{5 \cdot 4 \cdot 3}{1 \cdot 2 \cdot 3} \cdot \frac{a^2 b^3}{(a+b)^5} = \frac{1250}{7776}.$$

The chance that an ace is thrown at least twice in any five trials, is

$$\frac{a^5 + 5 a^4 b + 10 a^3 b^2 + 10 a^2 b^3}{(a+b)^5} = \frac{1526}{7776}.$$

(3) Two persons, A and B, whose skill is in the proportion of 4 to 3, play at bowls together: what is the chance that A will at least win 6 games out of 7?

Meaning of the term *skill*.

By A's *skill*, in this and other cases, as far at least as the purposes of calculation are concerned, we mean the ratio of the number of cases or events which are favourable to A, to the whole number of them, whether favourable or unfavourable: and the *relative* skill of A to B would be defined by the ratio of the numbers of cases or events, which were respectively favourable to A and to B: if this ratio be constant and invariable, the term *skill* may be used as equivalent to *chance* for all purposes of calculation: if this ratio be not constant, and admits only of determination within small limits, its *approximate* value must be used as if it were constant and the *moral* chance considered equivalent to the absolute chance which this approximate value would express: in other words, skill in its *ultimate* application must be *assumed* to depend upon fixed and invariable causes*.

---

* There are not many games of pure skill, and in most cases the influence of skill compared with that of chance, can only be calculated from their combined effects: thus the natural chances of a game should enable A to win five games out of six: but the influence of superior skill is found by experience to enable him to win six games out of seven: then the value of A's skill (estimated absolutely) is $\frac{6}{7} - \frac{5}{6} = \frac{36-35}{42} = \frac{1}{42}$, or is such as would enable him to win 1 game out of 42, by its influence alone.

It is not often, however, that such a separation of the effects of chance and skill is either required or practicable, as we commonly observe their combined

These considerations bring the present problem under the general formula given above (Art. 473), where $a = 4$, $b = 3$, $n = 7$, $r = 1$: the chance is, therefore,

$$= \frac{a^7 + 7\,a^6 b}{(a + b)^7} = \frac{102400}{823543}.$$

(4) There is a lottery, consisting of a great number of tickets, where the prizes are to the blanks in the ratio of 1 to 7: what is the chance of taking at least three prizes in five trials?

In this case, we may consider the relation of the prizes to the blanks as not sensibly affected by the tickets which are drawn, inasmuch as they bear a very small ratio to the whole number: in other words, we may consider the problem as one of repeated trials, where the simple chances are the same.

We have, therefore, $a = 1$, $b = 7$, $n = 5$ and $r = 2$, and consequently the chance

$$= \frac{a^5 + 5\,a^4 b + 10\,a^3 b^2}{(a + b)^5}$$

effect in the results of repeated trials, and form our estimate accordingly: for there exists a *popular assurance*, independent of any refined mathematical reasoning, that the actual results of repeated trials will be proportional to the combined influence of chance and skill, and the *intensity* of this assurance increases rapidly with the increase of the number of trials.

Thus, if A should win from B 40 games out of 70, it would be probable that A's skill was to B's as 4 to 3, or (in case chance was combined with skill) that the cases in favour of A and B respectively were in that proportion: but if A should win 400 games out of 700, this *assurance* could be much increased, and still more so, if A should win 4000 games out of 7000.

It is not our present object to enquire into the mathematical limits of error of such determinations, an investigation of great difficulty, and requiring the application of some of the most refined artifices of analysis: it is sufficient for us to assert, what such investigations would establish, that the ratio of the numbers of events in favour of A or of B, would *approximate* to the ratio of the chances in favour of each.

In most cases, the mathematical assurance will increase much more rapidly than the popular assurance: if an ace is thrown 10 times successively with a single die, it is extremely probable that the die is loaded: but if an ace is thrown 20 times successively, the mathematical probability of the truth of this hypothesis is increased in the proportion of 6^{10} to 6^{20}, or as 1 to 60466176, a ratio with which the popular assurance can keep no pace.

$$= \frac{1 + 35 + 490}{8^5} = \frac{526}{32768}$$

$$= \frac{3}{187} \text{ nearly.}$$

475. It frequently happens, that there are more than two ways in which an event may happen: thus, if an urn contain assigned numbers of black, white and red balls, and the chance of drawing a ball of an assigned colour is required: or, if there be more than two players at a game, who have equal or different chances of winning: and similarly for other cases. The theory of combinations, which enabled us to represent and to estimate all the chances by which assigned events might happen, when there were two possible species of events in each simple chance, would be found equally serviceable and almost equally easy of application, when there are a greater number of them.

476. The following are miscellaneous problems, admitting of solution by the aid of the theory of combinations and those general principles of chances which we have already had occasion to make use of.

(1) In the French lottery there are 90 numbers, 5 of which are drawn at a time: what is the chance that two and two *only* of five specified numbers will be drawn?

The whole number of quinary combinations, which are equally likely to be drawn, is

$$\frac{90.89.88.87.86}{1.2.3.4.5} \ \ldots\ldots (\alpha).$$

The number of ternary combinations of 85 numbers which contain neither of the specified numbers, is

$$\frac{85.84.83}{1.2.3} \ \ldots\ldots\ldots(\beta).$$

The number of binary combinations of 5 numbers (any of which may come up), is

$$\frac{5.4}{1.2} \ \ldots\ldots\ldots (\gamma).$$

The whole number of favourable quinary combinations is

$$\frac{85.84.83}{1.2.3} \times \frac{5.4}{1.2} \ldots \ldots (\delta):$$

for any one binary combination in (γ) may be joined with any one ternary combination in (β).

The chance, or $\frac{(\delta)}{(\alpha)}$, therefore, is,

$$\frac{85.84.83}{1.2.3} \times \frac{5.4}{1.2} \times \frac{1.2.3.4.5}{90.89.88.87.86} = \frac{1}{48} \text{ nearly.}$$

(α) The chance that two, at *least*, of five numbers, would be drawn, which is the sum of the separate chances that five, four, three and two of them will be severally drawn, is, therefore,

$$\frac{\left\{1 + \dfrac{85}{1} \times \dfrac{5.4.3.2}{1.2.3.4} + \dfrac{85.84}{1.2} \times \dfrac{5.4.3}{1.2.3} + \dfrac{85.84.83}{1.2.3} \times \dfrac{5.4}{1.2}\right\} \times 1.2.3.4.5}{90.89.88.87.86}$$

$$= \frac{31025}{1031796} = \frac{1}{42} \text{ nearly.}$$

(β) The chance that two specified numbers will be drawn (an *amb* or *bine*, in the lottery phrase) is

$$\frac{85.84.83}{1.2.3} \times \frac{1.2.3.4.5}{90.89.88.87.86} = \frac{1}{448} \text{ nearly.}$$

(γ) The three last problems, and all others relating to this species of lottery, will be the same, whether we suppose the five numbers to be drawn at once or successively one by one.

For the combinations, upon which the chances depend, will be precisely the same in both cases.

(2) To find the chance, in the game of whist, of the dealer and his partner having the four honours.

There are two cases to be considered: first, when the dealer turns up an honour: secondly, when he does not turn up an honour.

In both cases, the dealer and his partner have 25 cards out of the remaining 51, which may be any one of

$$\frac{51 \cdot 50 \ldots 27}{1 \cdot 2 \ldots 25} \ldots \ldots \ldots (\alpha)$$

different combinations.

The number of these combinations, which contain the three honours, will be the same as the number of combinations of 48 cards, taken 22 and 22 together, which is

$$\frac{48 \cdot 47 \ldots 27}{1 \cdot 2 \ldots 22} \ldots \ldots \ldots (\beta).$$

If the first supposition be true, the chance of the remaining three honours being found with the dealer and his partner, is

$$= \frac{(\beta)}{(\alpha)} = \frac{25 \cdot 24 \cdot 23}{51 \cdot 50 \cdot 49} = \frac{92}{833}.$$

The chance of an honour being turned up by the dealer, is $\frac{4}{13}$.

The compound chance of these two events is, therefore,

$$\frac{92}{833} \times \frac{4}{13} = \gamma.$$

If an honour is not turned up, which is the second supposition, the chance of the four honours being found with the dealer and his partner, is

$$\frac{25 \cdot 24 \cdot 23 \cdot 22}{51 \cdot 50 \cdot 49 \cdot 48} = \frac{253}{4998}.$$

The chance that an honour is not turned up, or that the second supposition is true, is $\frac{9}{13}$.

The compound chance of these two events is

$$\frac{253}{4998} \times \frac{9}{13} \ldots \ldots \ldots (\delta).$$

The entire chance, that the dealer and his partner have the four honours in one way or the other, is, therefore,

$$= \gamma + \delta = \frac{92}{833} \times \frac{4}{13} + \frac{253}{4998} \times \frac{9}{13}$$

$$= \frac{115}{1666} \text{ or } \frac{2}{29} \text{ nearly.}$$

The chance of the two other partners having the four honours, will be found to be $\frac{69}{1666}$, or $\frac{1}{24}$ nearly.

(3) If we draw four cards out of a whole pack, what is the chance that one of them will be a heart, another a diamond, the third a club, and the fourth a spade?

The whole number of quaternary combinations is

$$\frac{52.51.50.49}{1.2.3.4}.$$

Every one of the 13 hearts may be combined with every one of the 13 diamonds, and these binary combinations with every one of the 13 clubs, and these ternary combinations with every one of the 13 spades, and thus form $13 \times 13 \times 13 \times 13$ or 13^4 quaternary combinations, which are alone favourable to the hypothesis made.

The chance, therefore, is

$$\frac{13^4 \times 1.2.3.4}{52.51.50.49} = \frac{2197}{20825} = \frac{2}{19} \text{ nearly.}$$

(4) If an urn contain 26 balls, of which 5 are white, 6 black, 7 red and 8 blue: what is the chance of drawing, when 10 are drawn at a time, 2 white, 3 black and 4 red balls?

The whole number of denary combinations is

$$\frac{26.25\ldots\ldots17}{1.2\ \ldots\ 10}.$$

The number of binary combinations of 5 white balls

$$= \frac{5.4}{1.2} = 10\ldots\ldots\ldots\ldots(\lambda_1).$$

The number of ternary combinations of 6 black balls

$$= \frac{6.5.4}{1.2.3} = 20\ldots\ldots\ldots(\lambda_2).$$

The number of quaternary combinations of 7 red balls

$$= \frac{7 \cdot 6 \cdot 5 \cdot 4}{1 \cdot 2 \cdot 3 \cdot 4} = 35 \ldots \ldots (\lambda_3).$$

The number of blue balls (taken one by one)

$$= 8 \ldots \ldots \ldots \ldots \ldots (\lambda_4).$$

The whole number of denary combinations which answer the conditions of the question $= \lambda_1 \lambda_2 \lambda_3 \lambda_4$: and the chance is, therefore,

$$= \frac{10 \times 20 \times 35 \times 8 \times 1 \times 2 \ldots 10}{26 \times 25 \ldots \ldots \ldots \ldots 17}$$

$$= \frac{11200}{1062347} = \frac{7}{664} \text{ nearly.}$$

CHAPTER VIII.

ON THE FORMATION OF BINOMIAL PRODUCTS AND POWERS.

477. THE products of binomial and other factors, whose terms possess no peculiar or assigned relation to each other, may be easily formed, in all cases, by the general rule which is given for that purpose (Art. 61): but there are some laws which are found to prevail in the formation of the products of binomial factors which have the same first term, and more particularly in the products or powers of binomial factors which are identical with each other, which not only furnish most rapid and convenient rules for the performance of the operation of multiplication and involution in such cases, but either constitute or lead to, the most important theorems both in Arithmetical and Symbolical Algebra.

Important laws which are found to prevail in the formation of binomial products and powers.

478. We will begin with the formation of the product of two binomial factors $x + a$ and $x + b$*, which have the same first term x: the process exhibited at full length, will stand as follows:

Products of two binomial factors which have the same first term.

$$x + a$$
$$x + b$$

$$x^2 + a x$$
$$+ b x + a b$$

$$x^2 + (a + b) x + a b$$

The terms of this product are arranged according to the powers of the letter x, and consequently the terms $a x$ and $b x$, both involving the simple power of x, are *like* terms (Art. 28),

---

* See Examples 1, 2, 3, 4, Art. 69.

and are therefore, when added together, collected into the single term $(a + b)x$: it consequently appears that *the coefficient of* x, *in the second term, is the sum of the second terms of the binomial factors* x + a *and* x + b, *and that the last term is their product**.

479. Let it now be required to form the product of three binomial factors $x + a$, $x + b$ and $x + c$, which have the same first term x: if we multiply the product

$$x^2 + (a + b)x + ab$$

of the two first factors $x + a$ and $x + b$ (Art. 478.) into the third factor $x + c$, the process will stand as follows:

$$x^2 + (a + b)x + ab$$
$$x + c$$

$$\overline{x^3 + (a + b)x^2 + abx}$$
$$+ cx^2 + (a + b)cx + abc$$

$$\overline{x^3 + (a + b + c)x^2 + (ab + ac + bc)x + abc.}$$

This result is arranged according to the powers of the letter x, and consequently $(a + b)x^2$ and cx^2, being *like* terms, make, when added together, the single term $(a + b + c)x^2$†: in a similar manner, the like terms abx and $(a + b)cx$, make, when added together, the single term $(ab + ac + bc)x$‡: it appears therefore that *the coefficient* (a + b + c) *of the second term of this product is the sum of the second terms of the several binomial factors: that the coefficient of the third term or* ab + ac + bc, *is the sum of all their products two and two, and that the last term is their continued product.*

---

* The product of $x - a$ and $x - b$ will be found to be $x^2 - (a + b)x + ab$, differing from the former in the sign of the second term only, which is negative: the product of $x + a$ and $x - b$ is $x^2 + (a - b)x - ab$, and that of $x - a$ and $x + b$ is $x^2 - (a - b)x - ab$.

† For the sum of their coefficients, $(a + b)$ and c, is $a + b + c$.

‡ For the sum of their coefficients ab and $(a + b)c$, or ab and $ac + bc$ (for $(a + b)c = ac + bc$, Art. 45) is $ab + ac + bc$: by putting this sum under the form $ab + ac + bc$ instead of $ab + (a + b)c$, we make its symmetrical composition, in terms of a, b and c, not only more manifest to the eye, but also more easily expressible in ordinary language.

480. If we should multiply the product given in the last Article by an additional factor $x + d$, we should find for the result

$$x^4 + (a + b + c + d)x^3 + (ab + ac + ad + bc + bd + cd)x^2$$
$$+ (abc + abd + acd + bcd)x + abcd,$$

which is arranged according to the descending powers of x, and in which *the coefficient of the second term is the sum of the second terms of the four binomial factors, the coefficient of the third term is the sum of all their products two and two, the coefficient of the fourth term is the sum of all their products three and three, and the last term is their continued product.*

481. The law of formation of the products of such binomial factors is now sufficiently manifest, and we are authorized therefore to assume *hypothetically* that the same law will prevail in the formation of the product of (n) such factors: and it may be easily demonstrated that if it be true for $(n - 1)$ such factors, it must necessarily be true for a number of them expressed by the next superior number n. (Art. 447.)

482. For let us suppose the $(n - 1)$ first factors to be expressed by $x + a_1,\ x + a_2, \ldots x + a_{n-1}$*, and their product by

$$x^{n-1} + p_1 x^{n-2} + p_2 x^{n-3} + \ldots p_{n-1} \ldots\ldots\ldots (1),$$

where the coefficients p_1, p_2, $p_3, \ldots$ of the descending powers of x, are respectively the sum of all the second terms of the several binomial factors, the sum of all their products two and two†, the sum of all their products three and three, and so on, the last term p_{n-1} being their continued product. If we now suppose this *assumed* product of $(n - 1\cdot)$ binomial factors

---

* In denoting a series of quantities, where both their number and order of succession are required to be expressed, we adopt this notation, in preference to $x + a$, $x + b$, $x + c$, $x + d$, &c. where the successive letters of the alphabet are employed to denote the successive second terms of the binomial factors.

† By all the products two and two, we mean all those which can be formed by every possible combination of the letters a_1, a_2, and a_{n-1}, taken two and two together: the same remark applies to the products three and three together, four and four together, &c.

to be multiplied by an additional factor $x + a_n$, the process will stand as follows:

$$x^{n-1} + p_1 x^{n-2} + p_2 x^{n-3} + \ldots p_{n-1}$$

$$x + a_n$$

$$x^n + p_1 x^{n-1} + p_2 x^{n-2} + \ldots p_{n-1} x$$
$$a_n x^{n-1} + p_1 a_n x^{n-2} + \ldots p_{n-2} a_n x + p_{n-1} a_n$$

$$x^n + (p_1 + a_n) x^{n-1} + (p_2 + p_1 a_n) x^{n-2} + \ldots (p_{n-1} + p_{n-2} a_n) x + p_{n-1} a_n$$

or $\quad x^n + q_1 x^{n-1} + q_2 x^{n-2} + \ldots q_{n-1} x + q_n,$

representing $p_1 + a_n$ by q_1, $p_2 + p_1 a_n$ by q_2, and so on: it remains to determine the law of composition of the coefficients of the final product in terms of $a_1, a_2, \ldots a_n$.

In the first place,

$$q_1 = p_1 + a_n = a_1 + a_2 + \ldots a_n,$$

or is equal to the sum of the second terms of *all* the binomial factors, since p_1 is, by the hypothesis, the sum of the second terms of all the $(n-1)$ binomial factors in the first product.

Again, $\qquad q_2 = p_2 + p_1 a_n,$

where p_2 is, by hypothesis, the sum of all the products, two and two which can be formed of the first $(n-1)$ quantities $a_1, a_2, \ldots a_{n-1}$, and where p_1 is their sum: therefore $p_1 a_n$ is the sum of all the additional products, two and two, which can be formed by the new quantity a_n combined with all the others $a_1, a_2, \ldots a_{n-1}$: it follows therefore that q_2 is the sum of all the products two and two which can be formed by the second terms of the n binomial factors, or by the n quantities $a_1, a_2, \ldots a_n$.

Again, $\qquad q_3 = p_3 + p_2 a_n,$

where p_3 is the sum of all the products three and three, and p_2 the sum of all the products two and two, which can be formed of the $(n-1)$ letters $a_1, a_2, \ldots$ and a_{n-1}: consequently $p_2 a_n$ will express the sum of all the products three and three which can be formed of the n letters $a_1, a_2, \ldots a_n$, in which a_n appears as a factor: and therefore q_3 must necessarily express the sum of all the products three and three which can be formed of the n letters $a_1, a_2, \ldots a_n$.

It is obvious that the same reasoning may be applied, in the same manner, to the succeeding coefficients q_4, q_5, ... q_n, so that the law which has been assumed to prevail for $(n-1)$ binomial factors, having the same first term, must prevail likewise when the number of such factors is increased by unity: but this law has been proved to prevail, when the number of factors is 2, 3 and 4: it is therefore necessarily true for 5: and if for 5, it is necessarily true for 6, and so on successively for any number of factors whatever.

483. If the binomial factors were $x - a_1$, $x - a_2$, $x - a_3$, ... $x - a_n$, whose second terms a_1, a_2, ... a_n are severally subtracted from the first, their product would be expressed by

$$x^n - q_1 x^{n-1} + q_2 x^{n-2} - q_3 x^{n-3} + q_4 x^{n-4} - \&c.$$

When the second terms of the binomial factors are negative.

where the coefficients q_1, q_2, q_3, &c. are the same as in the last Article, but the terms are alternately negative and positive, beginning with the second*.

484. The following are examples: *Examples.*

(1) $(x+3)(x+5) = x^2 + 8x + 15$,

     where $8 = 3 + 5$ and $15 = 3 \times 5$ ... (Art. 478).

---

* If it was required to express the product of a series of mixed binomial factors, such as $x + a_1$, $x - a_2$, $x - a_3$, $x + a_4$, &c. where some of the second terms are positive and others negative, the coefficients q_1, q_2, ... q_n would severally express the same series of combinations of the letters a_1, a_2, ... a_n, but those combinations would be negative or positive according as an odd or an even number of letters, preceded by negative signs, entered into each product: thus, the product of $x + a$, $x - b$ and $x + c$, would be

$$x^3 + (a - b + c)x^2 - (ab - ac + bc)x - abc:$$

the product of $x + a$, $x - b$ and $x - c$, would be

$$x^3 + (a - b - c)x^2 - (ab + ac - bc)x + abc:$$

the product of $x - a$, $x - b$, $x + c$ and $x - d$, would be

$$x^4 - (a + b - c + d)x^3 + (ab - ac + ad - bc + bd - cd)x^2$$
$$+ (abc - abd + acd + bcd)x - abcd:$$

the formation however of such products, as included in the general theorem, given in Article 482, will be easily understood in Symbolical Algebra, where symbols are considered, at pleasure, as negative or positive, *per se*, and not in virtue merely of the sign of the operation, whether of subtraction or addition, which precedes them.

(2) $(x-10)(x-12) = x^2 - 22x + 120$, (Art. 478. Note)

where $22 = 10 + 12$ and $120 = 10 \times 12$.

(3) $(x+3)(x+5)(x+7) = x^3 + 15x^2 + 1x + 105$,

(Art. 479), where $15 = 3 + 5 + 7$,

$$71 = 3 \times 5 + 3 \times 7 + 5 \times 7,$$

$$105 = 3 \times 5 \times 7.$$

(4) $(x-1)(x-2)(x-3) = x^3 - 6x^2 + 11x - 6$,

where $6 = 1 + 2 + 3$,

$$11 = 1 \times 2 + 1 \times 3 + 2 \times 3,$$

$$6 = 1 \times 2 \times 3.$$

(5) $(x+2)(x+6)(x+10)(x+14)$

$$= x^4 + 32x^3 + 344x^2 + 1408x + 1680,$$

where $32 = 2 + 6 + 10 + 14$,

$344 = 2 \times 6 + 2 \times 10 + 2 \times 14 + 6 \times 10 + 6 \times 14 + 10 \times 14$*,

$1408 = 2 \times 6 \times 10 + 2 \times 6 \times 14 + 2 \times 10 \times 14 + 6 \times 10 \times 14$,

$1680 = 2 \times 6 \times 10 \times 14$,   (Art. 486).

(6) $(x-3)(x-5)(x-7)(x-9) = x^4 - 24x^3 + 206x^2 - 754x + 945$,

where $24 = 3 + 5 + 7 + 9$,

$206 = 3 \times 5 + 3 \times 7 + 3 \times 9 + 5 \times 7 + 5 \times 9 + 7 \times 9$,

$754 = 3 \times 5 \times 7 + 3 \times 5 \times 9 + 3 \times 7 \times 9 + 5 \times 7 \times 9$,

$945 = 3 \times 5 \times 7 \times 9$.

The theorem in Art. 482, is the foundation of the theory of equations,

485. The theorem given in Art. 482, whose use in the easy and expeditious formation of binomial products we have just exemplified, assumes a character of much greater importance when viewed, as it will hereafter be in Symbolical Algebra, as the basis of the whole Theory of Equations: it requires likewise a very slight modification of its form in order to furnish the law of the formation of binomial powers, which under the name of the *binomial*

---

* In forming all the products two and two, three and three, which the numbers 2, 6, 10 and 14 can form, it is convenient to combine them successively, in their proper order of succession, as written down in the several factors: we thus form the combinations 2 and 6, 2 and 10, 2 and 14, 6 and 10, 6 and 14, 10 and 14, and in that order, so that there is no danger of omissions.

theorem, will be found to be incomparably the most important of all the theorems which are to be found in the science of Algebra: we shall now proceed to explain the mode in which it is deduced.

and leads also to the binomial theorem.

486. If we suppose the binomial factors $x + a_1,$ $x + a_2, \ldots$ $x + a_n$ to become severally equal to each other and to $x + a,$ their continued product will become equal to $(x + a)^n$: it remains to consider what change the expression

The binomial theorem deduced.

$$x^n + q_1 x^{n-1} + q_2 x^{n-2} + \ldots q_n$$

for the continued product of n unequal binomial factors, with the same first term x, will undergo, when they thus become equal to each other and to $x + a$.

The first term will be x^n as before.

The coefficient q_1 of the second term will be equal to na: for q_1 is the sum of the quantities $a_1,$ $a_2, \ldots a_n$, which are n in number, and will therefore be equal to na, when they become equal to each other and to a.

The coefficient of the third term or q_2 will be equal to $\dfrac{n(n-1)}{1 . 2} a^2$: for q_2 is the sum of all the products two and two of $a_1, a_2, \ldots a_n$, which are $\dfrac{n(n-1)}{1 . 2}$* in number; and each of these products will become equal to a^2, when $a_1,$ $a_2,$ $a_3,$ &c. become equal to each other and to a.

The coefficient of the third term or q_3 will be equal to $\dfrac{n(n-1)(n-2)}{1 . 2 . 3} a^3$: for q_3 is the sum of the products three and three of $a_1,$ $a_2, \ldots a_n$, which are $\dfrac{n(n-1)(n-2)}{1 . 2 . 3}$† in number; and each of these products will become equal to a^3, when $a_1,$ $a_2, \ldots a_n$ become equal to each other and to a.

* For the number of combinations of n things, taken two and two together, is $\dfrac{n(n-1)}{1 . 2}$, (Art. 453.)

† For $\dfrac{n(n-1)(n-2)}{1 . 2 . 3}$ is the number of different combinations of n things taken three and three together, (Art. 454.)

More generally the rth coefficient q_r of the $(r+1)^{\text{th}}$ term, will be equal to $\dfrac{n(n-1)\ldots(n-r+1)}{1\,.\,2\ldots r}\,a^r$: for q_r is equal to the sum of all the products, taken r and r together, of $a_1,\ a_2,\ldots a_n$, which are $\dfrac{n(n-1)\ldots(n-r+1)}{1\,.\,2\ldots r}*$ in number: and each of these products becomes equal to a^r, when $a_1,\ a_2,\ldots a_r$ become equal to each other and to a. We conclude therefore that

$$(x+a)^n = x^n + n a x^{n-1} + \frac{n(n-1)}{1\,.\,2}\,a^2 x^{n-2}$$

$$+ \ldots \frac{n(n-1)\ldots(n-r+1)}{1\,.\,2\ldots r}\,a^r x^{n-r} + \&\text{c.}$$

Great distinction in principle and in form between the theorems for binomial products and binomial powers.

487. It appears, therefore, that the law of formation of any assigned power of a binomial, such as $(x+a)^n$, may be expressed *explicitly* by means of symbols, without requiring the aid of any verbal statement: in this respect consequently the binomial series is altogether distinguished from the expression for the continued product

$$(x+a_1)(x+a_2)\ldots(x+a_n),$$

where the composition of the coefficients q_1, q_2, q_r, &c. is not expressible *explicitly* in symbols, but requires to be stated in words. It is this great and essential difference between the form of expression of these two theorems, which gives to the second of them, though in other respects included in the first and therefore less general than it, its peculiar value and importance in Algebra: and whilst one theorem can only furnish the complete symbolical expression for the product, when the specific number of its binomial factors is given, the other will equally give us the complete series for the power of a binomial, whether the index is a specific and digital number or expressed by a general symbol.

Composition of the terms of the series for $(x+a)^n$.

488. An examination of the several terms of the binomial series will shew that they consist generally of two portions, one dependent upon the index of the power only, and the

---

* For $\dfrac{n(n-1)\ldots(n-r+1)}{1\,.\,2\ldots r}$ is the number of combinations of n things taken r and r together, (Art. 455).

other upon the two symbols which form the binomial. The first of these portions, in the second, third, fourth,... and $(r+1)^{th}$ terms, will be the expression for the number of combinations of n things taken one and one, two and two, three and three, ... r and r together, and will consequently be the same in the $(r+1)^{th}$ and $(n-r+1)^{th}$ terms, or in the terms which are equidistant from the two extremes, the whole number of terms being equal to $n+1$ *: whilst the second portion of the several terms will present a series of powers of x decreasing by unity and of powers of a increasing by unity, the first being x^n and the last a^n, and the sum of their indices in all other terms will be equal to n or to the index of the binomial: they will form therefore a geometric series of $(n+1)$ terms, of which the common ratio (Art. 427) or multiplier is $\dfrac{a}{x}$.

489. If the index n be an even number, the number $(n+1)$ of the terms of the series for $(x+a)^n$ will be odd, and the middle term, whose coefficient is the greatest†, will be the $\left(\dfrac{n}{2}+1\right)^{th}$ term of the series and will be expressed by

Middle term or terms.

$$\frac{n(n-1)\ldots\left(\dfrac{n}{2}+1\right)}{1.2\ \ldots\ldots\ \dfrac{n}{2}}\,a^{\frac{n}{2}}x^{\frac{n}{2}}:$$

but if the index n be an odd number, the number of terms $(n+1)$ of the series will be even and the two middle terms will be the $\left(\dfrac{n+1}{2}\right)^{th}$ and $\left(\dfrac{n+3}{2}\right)^{th}$, which are expressed respectively by

* The number of terms involving the n successive descending powers of x, the first being x^n, will be n, to which if we add the last term or a^n, their number will be $(n+1)$: and since the numerical coefficient (or the first portion of each term as distinguished from the second) of the $(r+1)^{th}$ term is the number of combinations of n things taken r and r together, and the numerical coefficient of the $(n-r+1)^{th}$ is the number of combinations of n things, taken $n-r$ and $n-r$ together, these coefficients are therefore equal to each other, in conformity with the proposition which has been demonstrated in Art. 456.

† For the greatest number of combinations of n things, when n is an even number, is when they are taken $\dfrac{n}{2}$ and $\dfrac{n}{2}$ together, Art. 457.

$$\frac{n(n-1)\dots\left(\frac{n+3}{2}\right)}{1\,.\,2\,\dots\,\left(\frac{n-1}{2}\right)}\,a^{\frac{n-1}{2}}\,x^{\frac{n+1}{2}},$$

$$\text{and } \frac{n(n-1)\dots\left(\frac{n+3}{2}\right)\left(\frac{n+1}{2}\right)}{1\,.\,2\,\dots\dots\,\left(\frac{n-1}{2}\right)\left(\frac{n+1}{2}\right)}\,a^{\frac{n+1}{2}}\,x^{\frac{n-1}{2}},$$

whose coefficients are obviously equal to each other. These co-efficients are likewise the two greatest of the series. (Art. 457.)

The sum of the numerical coefficients of the series for $(x+a)^n$ is 2^n.

490. If we suppose the binomial to be $a+x$ instead of $x+a$, the terms of the resulting series will be reversed, and we shall find

$$(a+x)^n = a^n + na^{n-1}x + n\frac{(n-1)}{1\,.\,2}\,a^{n-2}x^2 + \&c.\dots$$

replacing a by x and x by a in every term of the series for $(x+a)^n$ (Art. 486): if we further replace a by 1, the several powers of a will be likewise replaced by 1 in every term, and therefore

$$(1+x)^n = 1 + nx + \frac{n(n-1)}{1\,.\,2}\,x^2 + \&c.\dots;$$

if we further replace x by 1 we shall get

$$(1+1)^n = 1 + n + \frac{n(n-1)}{1\,.\,2} + \&c.$$

where the terms of the series will be the numerical coefficients of $(1+x)^n$ or $(a+x)^n$ only; and since $(1+1)^n = 2^n$, it follows that 2^n will be equal to their sum.

The series for $(x-a)^n$.

491. The series for $(x-a)^n$ is

$$x^n - na^{n-1}x + \frac{n(n-1)}{1\,.\,2}\,a^{n-2}x^2 - \&c.\dots\,^*$$

---

* For the binomial product $(x-a_1)(x-a_2)\dots(x-a_n)$ differs from that of $(x+a_1)(x+a_2)\dots(x+a_n)$ in the signs of the alternate terms *only*, beginning with the second (Art. 483): and it is obvious therefore, from Art. 486, that the corresponding series for $(x+a)^n$ and $(x-a)^n$ will differ from each other in a similar manner.

which differs from that for $(x+a)^n$ in the signs of the alternate terms, beginning with the second, which are all negative: if we replace a by x, and x by a, we shall also get

$$(a-x)^n = a^n - na^{n-1}x + \frac{n(n-1)}{1 \cdot 2} a^{n-2}x^2 + \&c. \ldots$$

If we now make $a = 1$, we shall get

$$(1-x)^n = 1 - nx + \frac{n(n-1)}{1 \cdot 2} x^2 - \&c. \ldots$$

If we further suppose $x = 1$, we get

$$(1-1)^n = 0 = 1 - n + \frac{n(n-1)}{1 \cdot 2} - \frac{n(n-1)(n-2)}{1 \cdot 2 \cdot 3} + \&c. \ldots$$

it follows, therefore, that the difference of the sums of the numerical coefficients of the odd and even terms is equal to zero, and that they are consequently equal to each other*.

The sum of the numerical coefficients of the odd terms of $(1+x)^n$ is equal to the sum of the numerical coefficients of the even terms.

492. The following are examples of the application of the binomial theorem to the formation of the powers of binomials.

Examples of the formation of powers of binomials.

(1) $(x+a)^3 = x^3 + 3ax^2 + 3a^2x + a^3$.

(2) $(x+a)^4 = x^4 + 4ax^3 + 6a^2x^2 + 4a^3x + a^4$.

(3) $(x+a)^5 = x^5 + 5ax^4 + 10a^2x^3 + 10a^3x^2 + 5a^4x + a^5$.

(4) $(a+x)^6 = a^6 + 6a^5x + 15a^4x^2 + 20a^3x^3 + 15a^2x^4$
$\qquad + 6ax^5 + x^6$.

(5) $(a-x)^7 = a^7 - 7a^6x + 21a^5x^2 - 35a^4x^3 + 35a^3x^4$
$\qquad - 21a^2x^5 + 7ax^6 - x^7$.

(6) $(a-x)^{10} = a^{10} - 10a^9x + 45a^8x^2 - 120a^7x^3 + 210a^6x^4 - 252a^5x^5$
$\qquad + 210a^4x^6 - 120a^3x^7 + 45a^2x^8 - 10ax^9 + x^{10}$.

* The sum of the coefficients of the even terms will express the number of the odd combinations of n things, taken one and one, three and three, five and five, and so on together: whilst the sum of the coefficients of the odd terms, *omitting the first*, will express the number of the even combinations of n things taken two and two, four and four, six and six, and so on, together: it follows, therefore, that the number of odd combinations of any number of things will exceed the corresponding number of even combinations, by the first coefficient of the series or by unity.

(7)   The middle term of $(a + x)^{12}$ is

$$\frac{12 \times 11 \times 10 \times 9 \times 8 \times 7}{1 \times 2 \times 3 \times 4 \times 5 \times 6} \; a^6 x^6 \text{ or } 924 a^6 x^6.$$

(8)   The two middle terms of $(a + x)^{13}$ are
$$1716 a^7 x^6 \text{ and } 1716 a^6 x^7.$$

(9)   The tenth term of $(a + x)^{21}$ is $293930 a^{12} x^9$.

(10) $(a^2 - ax)^8 = a^{16} - 8 a^{15} x + 28 a^{14} x^2 - 56 a^{13} x^3$
$$+ 70 a^{12} x^4 - 56 a^{11} x^5 + 28 a^{10} x^6 - 8 a^9 x^7 + a^8 x^8.$$

In this example, the terms of the binomial or a^2 and ax may be replaced in the first instance by any two other symbols, such as c and d, and when the series for $(c - d)^8$ is formed, we replace c and d by a^2 and ax respectively in all its terms.

(11) $\left(\dfrac{1}{2} x - 2 y \right)^7 = \dfrac{x^7}{128} - \dfrac{7 x^6 y}{32} + \dfrac{21 x^5 y^2}{8} - \dfrac{35 x^4 y^3}{2}$
$$+ 70 x^3 y^4 - 168 x^2 y^5 + 224 x y^6 - 128 y^7.$$

We shall have occasion, in Symbolical Algebra, to resume at some length the consideration of the *binomial theorem* when the index is not a whole number and when the series itself is indefinitely continued.

CHAPTER IX.

ON THE SOLUTION, IN WHOLE NUMBERS, OF INDETERMINATE EQUATIONS OF THE FIRST DEGREE.

493. An equation is indeterminate, as we have already seen (Art. 405. Note), when it involves more unknown symbols than one: and a system of simultaneous equations is reducible to a single indeterminate equation, when the number of unknown symbols exceeds the number of equations which involve them (Art. 402): under such circumstances, we can only express *explicitly* one unknown symbol in terms of the others, whose value is therefore dependent upon them.

494. Thus the equation

$$3x + 7y = 61$$

becomes, when solved with respect to x, (Art. 405. Note),

$$x = \frac{61 - 7y}{3};$$

and it is obvious that if any value whatever be assigned to y between 0 and $\frac{61}{7}$, which are its limits, we shall be enabled to determine corresponding and possible values of x: thus if

$$y = 1, \quad \text{we find} \quad x = 18,$$

$$y = 2, \quad \ldots\ldots \quad x = \frac{47}{3},$$

$$y = 3, \quad \ldots\ldots \quad x = \frac{40}{3},$$

$$y = 4, \quad \ldots\ldots \quad x = 11,$$

$$y = 5, \quad \ldots\ldots \quad x = \frac{26}{3},$$

U U

$$y = 6, \quad \ldots\ldots \quad x = \frac{19}{3},$$

$$y = 7, \quad \ldots\ldots \quad x = 4,$$

$$y = 8, \quad \ldots\ldots \quad x = \frac{5}{3}.$$

Corresponding values which are whole numbers.

495. If, however, the conditions of the problem proposed had been such as to restrict the use of the word *number* (Art. 416.) to mean *whole numbers* only, *excluding fractions altogether,* we should find only three pairs of values of x and y, which would answer the requisite conditions: these are

$$y = 1, \qquad x = 18,$$
$$y = 4, \qquad x = 11,$$
$$y = 7, \qquad x = 4.$$

Problems in which the word *number* means whole numbers only.

496. There are many problems, leading to indeterminate equations, in which the values of the unknown symbols, which they involve, are thus restricted to denote whole numbers only: of this kind are the following.

(1) To find a number such, that five times the first digit added to six times the second shall be equal to 50.

If x and y be the two digits, the conditions of the problem lead immediately to the equation

$$5x + 6y = 50.$$

There is only one pair of integral values or *digits*, namely, $x = 4$ and $y = 5$, which satisfy this equation, which ceases therefore to be indeterminate when viewed with reference to the problem proposed.

(2) To find a number, which divided by 7 shall leave a remainder 6 and which divided by 10 shall leave a remainder 7.

If we call x the quotient of this number when divided by 7, and y its quotient when divided by 10, and if we further denote the number itself by n, we shall get

$$n = 7x + 6 = 10y + 7,$$

and therefore

$$7x - 10y = 1:$$

it is obvious that x and y, or the quotients of the divisions, are necessarily whole numbers.

The successive pairs of integral values of x and y, and the corresponding values of n, will be found to be as follows:

$$x = 3, \quad y = 2, \quad n = 27,$$
$$x = 13, \quad y = 9, \quad n = 97,$$
$$x = 23, \quad y = 16, \quad n = 167,$$
$$x = 33, \quad y = 23, \quad n = 237,$$
$$x = 43, \quad y = 30, \quad n = 307,$$
$$\ldots\ldots \quad \ldots\ldots \quad \ldots\ldots$$

We thus find that the values of x increase by 10 (the coefficient of y), and the values of y increase by 7 (the coefficient of n), and that the series of them is unlimited: the corresponding series of numbers 27, 97, 167, 237, 307, &c. will be severally found to answer the conditions of the problem.

497. There are only two different forms of indeterminate equations of the first degree, when completely reduced, (Art. 394.), which are

$$ax - by = c \ldots\ldots\ldots\ldots (1),$$
$$ax + by = c \ldots\ldots\ldots\ldots (2),$$

where a, b and c are whole numbers: we may further suppose that a, b and c have no common measure: for if such a common measure exists, we may simplify the equation by dividing all its terms by it: if, however, a be not prime to b, in the equation thus reduced, its solution will be impossible in whole numbers: for since a and b, x and y are whole numbers, c, which is either the sum or difference of ax and by, must be divisible by any common measure of a and b, (Art. 101.), which is contrary to the hypothesis which has been made.

498. A particular solution of either of the equations, (Art. 196.),

$$ax - by = 1 \ldots\ldots (1),$$
$$\text{or} \quad by - ax = 1 \ldots\ldots (2),$$

will immediately lead to the general solution of the equations

$$ax - by = c \ldots\ldots (3),$$
$$\text{and} \quad ax + by = c \ldots\ldots (4).$$

There are only two forms of indetermi-nate equations of the first degree which in-volve two unknown symbols.

A particular solution of the equation $ax-by=1$ or $by-ax=1$, will lead to the general solution of the equations $ax-by=c$ or $ax+by=c$.

For if p and q be particular values of x and y, which are found to satisfy the equations (1) or (2), we shall find in the first instance

$$ap - bq = 1 \ldots\ldots(5),$$

and in the second

$$bq - ap = 1^* \ldots\ldots(6).$$

If we multiply the equations (5) and (6) by c, we get

$$acp - bcq = c \ldots\ldots(7),$$
$$bcq - acp = c \ldots\ldots(8).$$

If we add and subtract abm, or the product of the coefficients of x and y and of an *indeterminate number* m, to and from, the first member of the equations (7) and (8), we get

$$acp - bcq + abm - abm = c \ldots\ldots(9),$$
$$bcq - acp + abm - abm = c \ldots\ldots(10).$$

The first equation (9) may be put under any one of the three following equivalent forms:

$$a(cp + bm) - b(cq + am) = c \ldots\ldots(11),$$
$$a(cp - bm) - b(cq - am) = c\dagger \ldots\ldots(12),$$

* It may be proper to observe that the second of these solutions (6) is immediately derivable from the first: for if

$$ap - bq = 1,$$

we get, by adding and subtracting the product of a and b,

$$ap - bq + ab - ab = 1,$$
$$\text{or} \quad (ab - bq) - (ab - ap) = 1,$$
$$\text{or} \quad b\{a - q\} - a(b - p) = 1:$$

it follows, therefore, that if

$$ap - bq = 1,$$
$$\text{and} \quad bq' - ap' = 1,$$

then $q' = a - q$ and $p' = b - p$ and conversely,

$$q = a - q' \text{ and } p = b - p'.$$

† The two forms (11) and (12) may be reduced to one, if written thus;

$$a(cp \pm bm) - b(cy \pm am) = c,$$

it being understood that the two upper or the two lower signs are to be taken simultaneously.

$$a(cp - bm) + b(am - cq) = c^* \ldots \ldots (13).$$

The second equation (10) may be put under either of the two following equivalent forms:

$$a(bm - cp) - b(am - cq) = c \ldots \ldots (14),$$
$$a(bm - cp) + b(cq - am) = c \dagger \ldots \ldots (15).$$

If we compare the equation

$$ax - by = c \ldots \ldots (3)$$

with the three forms (11), (12) and (14), and if we suppose them to coincide, or to be identical, with each other, we shall find

$$x = cp + bm \quad \text{and} \quad y = cq + am,$$
$$\text{or} \quad x = cp - bm \quad \text{and} \quad y = cq - am\ddagger,$$

when p and q satisfy the equation

$$ap - bq = 1 \ldots \ldots (1) ;$$

and also $\quad x = bm - cp \quad$ and $\quad y = am - cq,$

when p and q satisfy the equation

$$bq - ap = 1 \ldots \ldots (2).$$

* For if the brackets be removed in each of the forms (11), (12), (13), they will become

$$acp + abm - bcq - abm = c \ \ldots\ldots\ (11.)$$
$$acp - abm - bcq + abm = c \ \ldots\ldots\ (12.)$$
$$acp - abm + abm - bcq = c \ \ldots\ldots\ (13.)$$

which merely differ from each other and from equation (9) in the order in which the terms succeed each other.

† For if the brackets be removed in each of the forms (14) and (15), they will become

$$abm - acp - abm + bcq = c \ \ldots\ldots\ (14.)$$
$$abm - acp + bcq - abm = c \ \ldots\ldots\ (15.)$$

which merely differ from each other and from the equation (10), in the order in which the terms succeed each other.

‡ Or they may be included under the single form

$$x = cp \pm bm \quad \text{and} \quad y = cq \pm am.$$

Again, if we compare the equation
$$ax + by = c \ldots \ldots (4)$$
with the two forms (13) and (15), we shall find
$$x = cp - bm \quad \text{and} \quad y = am - cq,$$
when p and q satisfy the equation
$$ap - bq = 1 \ldots \ldots (1),$$
and also $\qquad x = bm - cp \quad$ and $\quad y = cq - am,$
when p and q satisfy the equation
$$bq - ap = 1 \ldots \ldots (2).$$

499. The following are examples:

(1) Let $x = 3$ and $y = 2$ furnish a particular solution of the equation
$$9x - 13y = 1,$$
and let it be required to find its general solution.

Since
$$9 \times 3 - 13 \times 2 = 1,$$
by adding and subtracting $9 \times 13m$, we find
$$9 \times 3 - 13 \times 2 + 9 \times 13m - 13 \times 9m = 1,$$
$$\text{or} \quad 9\,(13m + 3) - 13\,(9m + 2) = 1:$$
consequently, comparing this equation with
$$9x - 13y = 1,$$
we get $\qquad x = 13m + 3 \quad$ and $\quad y = 9m + 2,$
where m may be any term in the series
$$0, \quad 1, \quad 2, \quad 3, \quad 4, \quad \&\text{c.}$$

If $\quad m = 0, \qquad$ we get $x = 3 \qquad$ and $y = 2,$

$\qquad m = 1, \qquad \ldots \ldots \quad x = 16 \qquad$ and $y = 11,$

$\qquad m = 2, \qquad \ldots \ldots \quad x = 29 \qquad$ and $y = 20,$

$\qquad m = 3, \qquad \ldots \ldots \quad x = 42 \qquad$ and $y = 29,$

$\qquad m = 10, \qquad \ldots \ldots \quad x = 133 \qquad$ and $y = 92,$

$\qquad m = 2000, \quad \ldots \ldots \quad x = 26003$ and $y = 18002.$

. . . .

(2) With the same data, let it be required to find the solution of the equation

$$9x - 13y = 20.$$

Since
$$9 \times 3 - 13 \times 2 = 1.$$

we get, by multiplying both sides of the equation by 20,

$$9 \times 60 - 13 \times 40 = 20 :$$

adding and subtracting $9 \times 13m$, we get

$$9 \times 60 - 13 \times 40 + 9 \times 13m - 9 \times 13m = 20,$$

$$\text{or} \quad 9(60 \pm 13m) - 13(40 \pm 9m) = 20.$$

If the upper sign be taken, m may be any term whatsoever of the series

$$0, \quad 1, \quad 2, \ldots \ldots \text{in infinitum};$$

but if the lower sign be taken, m cannot exceed the number 4*.

Comparing the equation

$$9(60 \pm 13m) - 13(40 \pm 9m) = 20$$

with the proposed equation

$$9x - 13y = 20,$$

we find
$$x = 60 \pm 13m \quad \text{and} \quad y = 40 \pm 9m,$$

the two upper or the two lower signs being taken simultaneously.

With the upper sign, if

$m = 0,$	$x = 60$	and $y = 40,$
$m = 1,$	$x = 73$	and $y = 49,$
$m = 2,$	$x = 86$	and $y = 58,$
$m = 100,$	$x = 1360$	and $y = 940.$

* For if we make $m = 5$ or any greater number, $40 - 9m$ will involve an impossible operation, or in the language of Symbolical Algebra, would lead to a negative result.

With the lower sign, if

$$m = 0, \quad x = 60 \text{ and } y = 40,$$
$$m = 1, \quad x = 47 \text{ and } y = 31,$$
$$m = 2, \quad x = 34 \text{ and } y = 22,$$
$$m = 3, \quad x = 21 \text{ and } y = 13,$$
$$m = 4, \quad x = 8 \text{ and } y = 4.$$

The last pair of values $x = 8$ and $y = 4$ are the least of those which satisfy the equation

$$9x - 13y = 20.$$

(3) From the same data, let it be required to find the solutions of the equation

$$9x + 13y = 155.$$

Since $\qquad 9 \times 3 - 13 \times 2 = 1,$

we get, by multiplying both sides by 155,

$$9 \times 465 - 13 \times 310 = 155:$$

adding and subtracting $9 \times 13m$, we get

$$9 \times 465 - 13 \times 310 + 9 \times 13m - 9 \times 13m = 155,$$

or $\quad 9(465 - 13m) + 13(9m - 310) = 155.$

Comparing this equation with

$$9x + 13y = 155,$$

we get $\qquad x = 465 - 13m \text{ and } y = 9m - 310.$

It is obvious that m must be a whole number not greater than $\dfrac{465}{13}$ nor less than $\dfrac{310}{9}$, or not greater than 35 nor less than 35: consequently 35 is the only value of x which is admissible, and therefore

$$x = 465 - 13 \times 35 = 10,$$

and $\quad y = 9 \times 35 - 310 = 5.$

(4) If the equation proposed had been

$$9x + 13y = 303,$$

we should have found, in a similar manner,

$$x = 909 - 13m,$$

$$\text{and} \quad y = 9m - 606.$$

Consequently x cannot be greater than 69 (the greatest whole number which does not exceed $\dfrac{909}{13}$), nor be less than 68 (the least whole number which does exceed $\dfrac{606}{9}$): if we take

$$m = 69, \quad \text{we get } x = 12 \quad \text{and } y = 15,$$

$$m = 68, \quad \text{we get } x = 25 \quad \text{and } y = 6.$$

There are, therefore, two integral solutions of the equation proposed, and no more.

(5)   Given a solution ($x = 3$ and $y = 2$) of the equation

$$9x - 13y = 1,$$

to find the general solution of the equation

$$13x - 9y = 17.$$

Since $\qquad 9 \times 3 - 13 \times 2 = 1,$

by multiplying both sides by 17, we get

$$9 \times 51 - 13 \times 34 = 17:$$

adding and subtracting $9 \times 13m$, we find

$$9 \times 51 - 13 \times 34 + 9 \times 13m - 9 \times 13m = 17,$$

$$\text{or} \quad 13(9m - 34) - 9(13m - 51) = 17.$$

Comparing this form with the equation

$$13x - 9y = 17,$$

we get $\qquad x = 9m - 34,$

$$y = 13m - 51,$$

where m may be any term in the series

$$4, \quad 5, \quad 6 \ldots \ldots \textit{in infinitum.}$$

x x

$$\text{If} \quad m = 4, \qquad \text{we get} \quad x = 2 \qquad \text{and} \quad y = 1,$$

$$m = 5, \qquad \ldots \ldots \quad x = 11 \qquad \text{and} \quad y = 14,$$

$$m = 6, \qquad \ldots \ldots \quad x = 20 \qquad \text{and} \quad y = 27,.$$

$$m = 15, \qquad \ldots \ldots \quad x = 101 \qquad \text{and} \quad y = 144.$$

$$\ldots \ldots \qquad \qquad \ldots \ldots \qquad \ldots \ldots \ldots$$

Solution of the equation $ax - by = 1$ **or** $by - ax = 1$.

500. We have given in Art. 196, the method of discovering a particular solution of the equation

$$ax - by = 1,$$

upon which the general solutions of the equations

$$ax - by = c,$$

$$\text{and} \quad ax + by = c,$$

have been shewn to depend.

The rule for this purpose directs us to find a series of fractions converging to $\frac{a}{b}$: then, if $\frac{q}{p}$, or the converging fraction immediately preceding $\frac{a}{b}$, be in an even place, we have

$$ap - bq = 1,$$

where p and q furnish a particular solution of the equation

$$ax - by = 1.$$

But if $\frac{q}{p}$, or the converging fraction immediately preceding $\frac{a}{b}$, be a fraction in an odd place, then

$$bq - ap = 1,$$

where q and p furnish a particular solution of the equation

$$by - ax = 1.$$

In both cases, therefore, we obtain such a particular solution as may be made the basis of the general solution, which is given in Art. 498.

501. The following are examples of the complete solution Examples. of indeterminate equations of the first degree involving two unknown symbols.

(1) Let $23x - 111y = 100$.

Form the series of fractions converging to $\dfrac{23}{111}$.

$$23) \, 111 \, (4$$
$$ 92$$
$$ \overline{19) \, 23 \, (1}$$
$$ 19$$
$$ \overline{4) \, 19 \, (4}$$
$$ 16$$
$$ \overline{3) \, 4 \, (1}$$
$$ 3$$
$$ \overline{1) \, 3 \, (3}$$

Quotients 4, 1, 4, 1, 3.

Converging fractions $\dfrac{1}{4}, \dfrac{1}{5}, \dfrac{5}{24}, \dfrac{6}{29}, \dfrac{23}{111}$.

Therefore $23 \times 29 - 111 \times 6 = 1$,

$23 \times 2900 - 111 \times 600 = 100$,

$23 \times 2900 - 111 \times 600 + 23 \times 111 m - 23 \times 111 \, m = 100$,

$23 \, (2900 + 111 m) - 111 \, (600 + 23 m) = 100$,

or $23 \, (2900 - 111 m) - 111 \, (600 - 23 m) = 100$;

consequently,

$$x = 2900 + 111 \, m, \text{ and } y = 600 + 23 \, m,$$

or $x = 2900 - 111 \, m, \text{ and } y = 600 - 23 \, m.$

The values of m in the first of these forms are any terms whatsoever in the series 0, 1, 2, 3, &c.: in the second form, the greatest value of m is 26, which gives $x = 14$, and $y = 2$, which are the least *integral* values of x and y.

(2)   Let $11x + 13y = 190$.

Form the series of fractions converging to $\frac{11}{13}$:

$$11) \, 13 \, (1$$
$$\underline{11}$$
$$2) \, 11 \, (5$$
$$\underline{10}$$
$$1) \, 2 \, (2$$

Quotients 1, 5, 2.

Converging fractions $\frac{1}{1}$, $\frac{5}{6}$, $\frac{11}{13}$.

Consequently $11 \times 6 - 13 \times 5 = 1$.

Multiplying both sides of this equation by 190, we get

$$11 \times 1140 - 13 \times 950 = 190,$$

or $11 \times 1140 - 13 \times 950 + 11 \times 13\,m - 11 \times 13\,m = 190$,

or $11 \, (1140 - 13\,m) + 13 \, (11\,m - 950) = 190$:

consequently $x = 1140 - 13\,m$, and $y = 11\,m - 950$,

where m must not be greater than $\frac{1146}{13}$ or 87, nor less than $\frac{950}{11}$ or 87: there is therefore only one solution, which is

$$x = 1140 - 13 \times 87 = 9,$$

and $y = 11 \times 87 - 950 = 7$.

(3)   To find two fractions, whose denominators shall be 12 and 29 respectively and whose sum shall be $\frac{655}{328}$.

If the fractions be represented by $\frac{x}{12}$ and $\frac{y}{29}$ respectively, we shall have

$$\frac{x}{12} + \frac{y}{29} = \frac{655}{328},$$

or $29x + 12y = 655$.

Form the series of fractions converging to $\frac{12}{29}$.

$$12 \,) \; 29 \,(\, 2$$
$$\underline{24}$$
$$5 \,) \; 12 \,(\, 2$$
$$\underline{10}$$
$$2 \,) \; 5 \,(\, 2$$
$$\underline{4}$$
$$1 \,) \; 2 \,(\, 2$$

Quotients 2, 2, 2, 2.

Converging fractions $\frac{1}{2}$, $\frac{2}{5}$, $\frac{5}{12}$, $\frac{12}{29}$.

Therefore $29 \times 5 - 12 \times 12 = 1$,

$$29 \times 3275 - 12 \times 7860 = 655 \,;$$

$$29 \, (3275 - 12\,m) + 12 \, (29\,m - 7860) = 655 \,;$$

consequently $x = 3275 - 12\,m$, and $y = 29\,m - 7860$,

and the only value of m is 272 : therefore $x = 11$, and $y = 26$: the fractions required are therefore $\frac{11}{12}$ and $\frac{28}{29}$.

(4) In how many different ways may £100. be paid in guineas and crowns?

Let x be the number of guineas, and y the number of crowns : then the number of shillings in x guineas and in y crowns is $21\,x + 5\,y$, and the conditions of the problem give us

$$21\,x + 5\,y = 2000 :$$

The only fraction converging to $\frac{5}{21}$ will be found to be $\frac{1}{4}$: consequently

$$21 \times 1 - 5 \times 4 = 1 :$$

$$21 \times 2000 - 5 \times 8000 = 2000 \,;$$

$$21 \, (2000 - 5\,m) + 5 \, (21\,m - 8000) = 2000 :$$

therefore $x = 2000 - 5\,m$, and $y = 21\,m - 8000$,

and consequently m cannot be greater than $\dfrac{2000}{5}$ or 400, nor less than $\dfrac{8000}{21}$, or 381: if 0 be excluded from the values of x, the number of the different pairs of values of x and y will be $400 - 381$, or 19: but if 0 be included amongst these values, this number must be increased by unity.

Zero can never be found amongst the values of x or y, unless c or the number on the right-hand side of the equation be completely divisible by one of the coefficients of x and y*.

* The following are additional examples of indeterminate equations of the first degree, involving two unknown symbols and of problems leading to them.

(1) $\qquad\qquad 99x - 100y = 10;$

$\qquad\qquad \therefore x = 100m - 10 \quad \text{and} \quad y = 99m - 10.$

The least values of x and y are 90 and 89 respectively.

(2) $\qquad\qquad 67x - 123y = 44;$

$\qquad\qquad \therefore x = 123m - 484 \quad \text{and} \quad y = 67m - 264.$

The least values of x and y are 8 and 4.

(3) $\qquad\qquad 7x + 23y = 314;$

$\qquad\qquad \therefore x = 3140 - 23m \quad \text{and} \quad y = 7m - 942.$

The values of m are 136 and 135, which give

$$x = 12 \quad \text{and} \quad y = 10, \quad \text{or} \quad x = 35 \quad \text{and} \quad y = 3.$$

(4) To find the least number, which divided by 28 shall leave a remainder 21, and divided by 19 shall leave a remainder 17.

The resulting equation is

$$19x - 28y = 4,$$

which gives 12 and 8 for the least values of x and y: the least number is therefore

$$19x + 17 = 19 \times 12 + 17 = 245.$$

(5) To find two fractions whose denominators are 7 and 9, and whose sum is $\dfrac{110}{63}$.

Let the numerators of the fractions be x and y, and therefore

$$\frac{x}{7} + \frac{y}{9} = \frac{110}{63},$$

$$\text{or} \quad 9x + 7y = 110.$$

To find
the whole
number of
solutions
of the
equation
$ax+by=c$.

502. More generally, if $\frac{q}{p}$ be the converging fraction immediately preceding $\frac{a}{b}$ (Art. 500), then if

$$ap - bq = 1,$$

we get $x = cp - bm$, and $y = am - cg$,

for the general solution of the equation,

$$ax + by = c,$$

where m cannot be greater than $\frac{cp}{b}$ nor less than $\frac{cq}{a}$.

If therefore we make m' the greatest whole number which is *not greater* than $\frac{cp}{b}$, and m'' the greatest whole number, which is *less* than $\frac{cq}{a}$, then $m' - m''$ will express the whole number of the solutions of the equation proposed*.

The only solution is $x = 6$ and $y = 8$: the fractions are therefore

$$\frac{6}{7} \text{ and } \frac{8}{9}.$$

(6) In how many different ways is it possible to pay £100. in half guineas and sovereigns?

Let x be the number of half guineas, and y of sovereigns;

$$21x + 40y = 4000.$$

There are 5 different ways.

If the sum to be paid had been £1000., it might have been paid in 48 different ways.

(7) A party of men and women spend £5. 5s., towards the discharge of which the men pay 3s. 6d. each, and the women 1s. 4d. each: of how many of each did the party consist?

The party consists either of 30 men and no women, or of 22 men and 21 women, or of 14 men and 42 women, or of 6 men and 63 women.

* For if $\frac{cp}{b}$ be a whole number, we make $m' = \frac{cp}{b}$, since there is one solution corresponding to this value of m: and if $\frac{cq}{a}$ be a whole number, we make $m'' = \frac{cq}{a} - 1$, for there is one solution corresponding to $m = \frac{cq}{a}$, and therefore we must subtract from m' a number less by 1 than the integral value of $\frac{cq}{a}$.

503. The expression

$$\frac{cp}{b} - \frac{cq}{a} = c\,\frac{(ap - bq)}{ab} = \frac{c}{ab} \text{ (since } ap - bq = 1),$$

and the greatest whole number which is not greater than $\frac{c}{ab}$ cannot differ from $m' - m''$ by more than 1: thus if $\frac{cp}{b}$ and $\frac{cq}{a}$ be the whole numbers μ and μ', we shall have $m' = \mu'$, and $m'' = \mu'' - 1$,

and therefore $m' - m' = \mu' - \mu'' + 1$:

also if $\frac{cp}{b} = m' + \frac{e}{b}$, and $\frac{cq}{a} = m'' + \frac{e'}{a}$,

then the greatest whole number which is not greater than $\frac{c}{ab}$ will be equal to $m' - m''$ or to $m' - m'' - 1$, according as the first fractional excess or $\frac{e}{b}$ is greater or less than the second fractional excess or $\frac{e'}{a}$.

504. If the indeterminate equation, whose solution in whole numbers is required, involves three unknown symbols, we may transpose one of its terms from one side of the equation to the other, and thus reduce it to an equation of the ordinary form, but where the second member is indeterminate: thus the equation

$$7x - 9y + 4z = 10,$$

may be put under any one of the three forms

$$7x - 9y = 10 - 4z \ldots\ldots\ldots (1),$$
$$7x + 4z = 10 + 9y \ldots\ldots\ldots (2),$$
$$9y - 4z = 7x - 10 \ldots\ldots\ldots (3).$$

If we assign to the unknown symbol on the left hand side of each equation, any such specific value (a whole number) as will not lead to an impossible operation, we shall get a series of indeterminate equations under the ordinary form involving two unknown symbols only and which can be solved by the rules given in the preceding articles.

Thus, if in the first of the forms (1), (2), (3) we make $z = 0$, or 1 or 2, we shall get the three indeterminate equations,

$$7x - 9y = 10,$$
$$7x - 9y = 6,$$
$$7x - 9y = 2,$$

which admit of an indefinite number of solutions included severally under the forms

$$x = 40 \pm 9m, \quad y = 30 \pm 7m, \quad z = 0,$$
$$x = 24 \pm 9m, \quad y = 18 \pm 7m, \quad z = 1,$$
$$x = 8 + 9m, \quad y = 6 + 7m, \quad z = 2.$$

If in the second form (2), we make y successively equal to 0, 1, 2, 3......*in infinitum*, we shall get the equations,

$$7x + 4z = 10 \ldots \ldots \ldots \ldots (a),$$
$$7x + 4z = 19 \ldots \ldots \ldots \ldots (b),$$
$$7x + 4z = 28 \ldots \ldots \ldots \ldots (c),$$
$$7x + 4z = 37 \ldots \ldots \ldots \ldots (d),$$

$$\ldots \ldots \ldots \ldots \ldots \ldots \ldots \ldots$$

of which the first (a) admits of no solution; the second (b) of one solution, which is $x = 1$, $z = 3$, and $y = 1$; the third (c) of two solutions, (Art. 503), which are

$$x = 0, \ z = 7, \text{ and } y = 2, \text{ or } x = 4, \ z = 0, \text{ and } y = 2;$$

the fourth (d) of one solution (Art. 503), which is $x = 3$, $z = 4$, and $y = 3$; and so on for the subsequent equations, which are unlimited in number.

In the third form (3), we may make x successively 2, 3, 4,... *in infinitum*, and the successive equations will be

$$9y - 4z = 4,$$
$$9y - 4z = 11,$$
$$9y - 4z = 18,$$

$$\ldots \ldots \ldots \ldots$$

whose solutions are successively exhibited under the forms

$$y = \; 4 + 4\,m, \quad z = \; 8 + 9\,m, \quad x = 2,$$

$$y = 11 \pm 4\,m, \quad z = 22 \pm 9\,m, \quad x = 3,$$

$$y = 18 \pm 4\,m, \quad z = 36 \pm 9\,m, \quad x = 4.$$

. . . .

Different forms of indeterminate equations with three unknown symbols.

505. Indeterminate equations with three unknown symbols, may present themselves under any one of the three following forms:

$$a\,x - b\,y - c\,z = d \dots \dots \dots (1),$$

$$a\,x + b\,y - c\,z = d \dots \dots \dots (2),$$

$$a\,x + b\,y + c\,z = d \dots \dots \dots (3).$$

The first of these forms involves two terms and the second one, which are preceded by a negative sign, and in both cases the number of their solutions is unlimited (Art. 504.): but in the third form, the solution in whole numbers is sometimes impossible, and in all cases the number of such solutions is limited: it remains to explain the mode of determining the number of possible solutions in the last of these forms, when such solutions exist.

Number of solutions determined when their number is limited.

506. If we transpose one of the three terms $c\,z^*$ from the left to the right hand side of the equation, the equation will become

$$a\,x + b\,y = d - c\,z,$$

and we may suppose z to possess successively every value between zero and the greatest whole number (r) which is not greater than $\dfrac{d}{c}$ †: we shall thus get a series of $(r + 1)$ equations which shall differ from each other in their second members only, which are the successive numbers,

$$d, \; d - c, \; d - 2c, \dots d - rc,$$

----

* Let the term transposed be that whose coefficient is not prime to the other coefficients when such a term exists.

† *Zero* values of x, y and z have been usually excluded from the number of solutions of indeterminate equations: they are included in the subsequent formulæ and examples.

The number of solutions of the equation

$$ax + by = d - cz$$

will be the difference b. ween the greatest whole number (m') which is *not greater than* $\dfrac{(\ldots - cz)\,p}{b}$, and the greatest whole number which is *less than* $\dfrac{(d - cz)\,q}{a}$ (Art 502), where p and q satisfy the equation

$$ap - bq = 1, \quad \text{(Art. 500)}.$$

If we represent the series of values of m' and m'', corresponding to the successive values of z between 0 and r inclusive by $m'_0, m'_1 \ldots m'_r$, and $m_0'', m_1'' \ldots m_r''$, respectively, the whole number of solutions will be expressed by

$$(m_0' - m_0'') + (m_1' - m_1'') + (m_2' - m_2'') + \ldots + (m_r' - m_r'').$$

If we replace m_0' and m_0'', m_1' and $m_1'', \ldots m_r'$ and m_r'' by the fractions or mixed numbers in which they originate, and subtract them from each other, term by term, we shall get the series, (Art. 503),

$$\frac{d}{ab} + \frac{d-c}{ab} + \frac{d-2c}{ab} + \ldots + \frac{d-rc}{ab} \ldots \ldots \ldots (a),$$

whose sum is $\dfrac{(2d - rc)(r+1)}{2ab}$ (Art. 422), or $\dfrac{(d + e)(r+1)}{2ab}$,

if we replace $d - rc$ by e: but this sum includes the fractional excesses of the primitive fractions, and takes no account of the restriction of the values of $m_0'', m_1'', \ldots m_r''$, to those integral values which are next less than their primitive fractions, when those fractions become whole numbers.

The fractional excesses in b successive terms of the series

$$\frac{dp}{b}, \quad \frac{(d-c)p}{b}, \quad \frac{(d-2c)p}{b}, \ldots \ldots \frac{(d-rc)p}{b} \ldots \ldots (\beta)$$

will be, when considered without regard to their order of succession, $\dfrac{1}{b}, \dfrac{2}{b}, \dfrac{3}{b}, \ldots \dfrac{b-1}{b}$ and 0[*], and their sum will be $\dfrac{b(b-1)}{2b}$,

---

[*] For c and p being prime to b, the successive remainders from the division of dp, $(d - c)p$, $(d - 2c)p, \ldots \{d - (b-1)c\}p$, will be different from each other, one

or $\dfrac{b-1}{2}$ (Art. 422): and if there be k complete periods of b terms in the whole number of terms $r+1$, their sum will be $\dfrac{k(b-1)}{2}$: but if $r+1 = kb + b'$, or if b' terms (where b' is less than b) remain, not forming a complete period, we must find their sum (R) by the actual formation and addition of the fractional excesses of the b' first or last terms.

In a similar manner, if $r + 1 = k'a + a'$, the sum of the fractional excesses of the series

$$\frac{dq}{a}, \quad \frac{(d-c)q}{a}, \dots\dots\dots \frac{(d-rc)q}{a} \quad \dots\dots (\gamma),$$

will be expressed by $\dfrac{k'(a-1)}{2} + R'$, where R', is the actual sum of the fractional excesses of the a' first or last terms, which do not form a complete period of a terms.

It will follow, therefore, that the sum of the series (a), or $\dfrac{(d+e)(r+1)}{2ab}$ will be freed from the fractional excesses which are involved in the series (β) and (γ), if it be diminished by the sum $\dfrac{k(b-1)}{2} + R$ of the first series of those excesses, and increased by the sum $\dfrac{k'(a-1)}{2} + R'$ of the second: and that consequently the resulting formula or

$$\frac{(d+e)(r+1)}{2ab} + \frac{k'(a-1)}{2} - \frac{k(b-1)}{2} + R' - R,$$

will express the number of solutions (n) required, if it be augmented by $k' + 1$, or k', according as the remainders of the a'

---

one remainder only being equal to zero: for if the fractional excess be the same in $(d - \mu c)p$ and $(d - \mu'c)p$, we shall get

$$\frac{(d - \mu c)p}{b} = \rho + \frac{\beta}{b} \text{ and } \frac{(d - \mu'c)p}{b} = \rho' + \frac{\beta}{b};$$

and therefore

$$\frac{(d - \mu c)p}{b} - \frac{(d - \mu'c)p}{b} = \frac{(\mu' - \mu)pc}{b} = \rho - \rho',$$

a whole number, which is impossible, since p and c, and therefore pc are prime to c, (Art. 112.), and $\mu' - \mu$ is less than b, and therefore not divisible by it.

last terms of the incomplete period of fractional excesses in the series (γ) include zero or not*.

507. The following are examples: Examples,

(1) To find the number of solutions of the equation

$$5x + 7y + 11z = 224.$$

In this case $d = 224$, $c = 11$, $r = 20$, $e = 4$, $a = 5$, $b = 7$: also $r + 1 = 21 = 3 \times 7$, and $k = 3$, $b' = 0$: also $21 = 4 \times 5 + 1$, and therefore $k' = 4$, and $a' = 1$: consequently

$$\frac{(d + e)(r + 1)}{2ab} = 68\frac{2}{5},$$

$$\frac{k'(a - 1)}{2} = 4 \times 2 = 8,$$

$$\frac{k(b - 1)}{2} = 3 \times 3 = 9,$$

$R = 0$,

$R' =$ the fractional excess of $\dfrac{eq}{a}$, or of $\dfrac{4 \times 2}{5}$ which is $\dfrac{3}{5}$, since $ap - bq = 5 \times 3 - 7 \times 2 = 1$: consequently

$$n = \frac{(d + e)(r + 1)}{2ab} + \frac{k'(a - 1)}{2} - \frac{k(b - 1)}{2} + R' - R + k'$$

$$= 68\frac{2}{5} + 8 - 9 + \frac{3}{5} - 0 + 4$$

$$= 72.$$

If we exclude *zero* values of x, y and z, the number of solutions will be found to be 59: for, with this restriction, we shall find

$r = 19$: the sum of the series (a), its first term being $\dfrac{d - c}{ab}$, is $\dfrac{(d - c + e)(r + 1)}{2ab} = 62$: $k' = 4$, $R' = 0$, and $\dfrac{k'(a - 1)}{2} + R' = 8$; $k = 2$, $R = 3$, and therefore $\dfrac{k(b - 1)}{2} + R = 9$: consequently the number of solutions will be equal to

---

* For m_0'', m_1'', m_2'', ... m_r'' are always less than the fractions in which they originate, and therefore when those fractions become whole numbers, they are less than those whole numbers by 1: there are $k' + 1$ such fractions in one case, and k' such fractions in the other.

$$\frac{(d-c+e)\,(r+1)}{2\,ab} + \frac{k'(a-1)}{2} + R' - \frac{k\,(b-1)}{2} - R - k = 59:$$

for in this case, we subtract k upon the same principle that we added k' in the former.

(2) To find the number of solutions of the equation

$$17\,x + 19\,y + 21\,z = 400.$$

In this case $d = 400$, $c = 21$, $r = 19$, $e = 1$, $a = 17$, $b = 19$: also $r + 1 = 20 = 1 \times 19 + 1 = 1 \times 17 + 3$, and therefore $k = k' = 1$, $a' = 3$, and $b' = 1$.

$$\frac{(d+e)\,(r+1)}{2\,ab} = \frac{4010}{323},$$

$$\frac{k'\,(a-1)}{2} = 8,$$

$$\frac{k\,(b-1)}{2} = 9,$$

$$R = \frac{9}{19},$$

$$R' = \frac{18}{17}:$$

consequently $n = \dfrac{4010}{323} + 8 - 9 - \dfrac{9}{19} + \dfrac{18}{17} + 1$

$$= 13.$$

The solutions are as follows:

$x =$	0	1	2	3	4	10	11	12	13	14	15	5	9
$y =$	10	8	6	4	2	11	9	7	5	3	1	0	13
$z =$	10	11	12	13	14	1	2	3	4	5	6	15	0

Example in which the coefficients are not prime to each other.

(3) To find the number of solutions of the equation

$$12\,x + 15\,y + 20\,z = 1001\ *.$$

* The following are other examples of indeterminate problems of the first degree which involve three or more unknown symbols, and which lead to one or more equations less in number than the symbols involved.

(1) To find the number of solutions of the equation

$$7\,x + 9\,y + 23\,z = 9999,$$

$n = 34634$: but if *zero* values of x, y and z be excluded, then

$$n = 34365.$$

Transposing $20z$, we get

$$12x + 15y = 1001 - 20z,$$

where the coefficients of x and y are *not* prime to each other.

Dividing both sides of the equation by 3 (the greatest common measure of x and y), we get

$$4x + 5y = 333\frac{2}{3} - 6z - \frac{2z}{3} = 333 - 6z - \frac{2(z-1)}{3}:$$

(2) To find the number of solutions of the equation

$$3x + 7y + 17z = 100,$$

$n = 18$: but if *zero* values of x, y and z be excluded, then $n = 10$.

(3) To find three fractions whose denominators are 3, 4 and 5, and whose sum is $\frac{133}{60}$.

If the numerators of the several fractions be x, y and z, then

$$\frac{x}{3} + \frac{y}{4} + \frac{z}{5} = \frac{133}{60};$$

or $\quad 20x + 15y + 12z = 133,$

which is convertible into

$$4x + 3y = 23 - 12u, \quad \text{if} \quad u = \frac{z+1}{5}.$$

The only three fractions are

$$\frac{2}{3}, \quad \frac{3}{4} \quad \text{and} \quad \frac{4}{5}.$$

(4) To find in how many different ways it is possible to pay £1000. in crowns, guineas and moidores or twenty-seven-shilling pieces only,

$$n = 70940.$$

(5) To find the least number, which divided by 13, 17 and 21 respectively, shall leave for remainders 12, 16 and 20.

If n be the number required, we must have

$$n = 13x + 12,$$
$$= 17y + 16,$$
$$= 21z + 20.$$

The solution of the equation

$$13x - 17y = 4,$$

gives 220 for the least number which answers the two first conditions; consequently

$$n = 21z + 20 = 13 \times 17u + 220;$$

for it is obvious that the number sought for must exceed some common multiple of 13 and 17 by 220: we thus find the least value of z to be 220, and therefore

$$n = 4640.$$

This

consequently $z - 1$ is necessarily divisible by 3, and therefore may be replaced by $3z'$: we thus get, putting $3z' + 1$ for z,

$$4x + 5y = 333 - 18z' - 6 - 2z' = 327 - 20z'.$$

Consequently $d = 327$, $r = 16$, $e = 7$, $a = 4$, $b = 5$, $c = 20$,

$$\text{and } \frac{(d + e)\,(r + 1)}{2\,ab} = \frac{334 \times 17}{2 \times 4 \times 5} = \frac{167 \times 17}{4 \times 5}.$$

But since c or 20 is divisible both by 4 and 5, the fractional excesses of the first and second series (β) and (γ), (Art. 506), will be respectively the same in every term : in the first of these series or $\frac{dp}{b}$, $\frac{(d - c)\,p}{b}$, &c., it will be $\frac{3}{5}$ in each, and its sum in 17 terms will be $\frac{51}{5}$: in the second series or $\frac{dq}{a}$, $\frac{(d - c)\,q}{a}$, &c. it will be $\frac{1}{4}$ in each, and its sum in 17 terms will be $\frac{17}{4}$, the number of solutions will therefore be

$$\frac{167 \times 17}{20} - \frac{51}{5} + \frac{17}{4} = \frac{2720}{20} = 136.$$

This is an example of two independent indeterminate equations, with two unknown symbols each, and not of one indeterminate equation with three unknown symbols.

(6) To find the year of the Julian period which corresponds to the 15th year of the Solar Cycle, the 12th of the Lunar Cycle, and the 10th of the Cycle of Indiction.

The Julian Period, so named from its proposer Julius Cæsar Scaliger, is the continued product (7980) of the numbers 28, 19 and 15, which express severally the numbers of years in the Solar and Lunar Cycles and in the Cycle of Indiction: its commencement was fixed for the year 4768 before the birth of Christ.

The number sought for, if divided by 28, 19 and 15 will leave for a remainder 15, 12 and 10 respectively : the least number which will answer the two first conditions is 183 : consequently

$$15z + 10 = 28 \times 19u + 183;$$
$$\text{or } 15z - 532u = 173;$$

we thus find $z = 47$, $u = 1$, and $n = 715$.

CHAPTER X.

ON THE SYMBOLICAL REPRESENTATION AND PROPERTIES OF NUMBERS.

508. THE conventions, upon which arithmetical and algebraical notation are founded, are essentially different from each other, and consequently lead to different rules in those sciences for performing the fundamental operations, and also to very different forms of the results. Thus in one case, the only symbols employed are the nine digits and zero, whilst in the other the symbols are unlimited in number and are only restricted in the generality of their representation by the possibility of the operations in which they are involved: in arithmetical notation, the symbols, when written consecutively, acquire a local value from their position with respect to the place of units, representing a series of *addends* and not a continued product; whilst algebraical symbols similarly placed, without the interposition of signs of operation between them, possess no local value from their position, and express the continued product of the numbers which the consecutive symbols represent. These and other distinctions make it extremely difficult in enquiries relating immediately to the forms of arithmetical notation, to transfer the conclusions of algebra to arithmetic and conversely, except through the medium of ordinary language, and deprive us of many of those advantages which are derived, in other cases, from the use of general symbols.

Essential difference between the conventional notation of numbers in Arithmetic and Algebra.

509. Thus a number expressed by

$$346789,$$

according to the conventions of arithmetical notation " by nine digits and zero, with device of place," would assume the form

Example of the arithmetical and algebraical representation of the same number.

Z Z

$$3 \times 10^5 + 4 \times 10^4 + 6 \times 10^3 + 7 \times 10^2 + 8 \times 10 + 7 \text{ *},$$

if expressed according to the conventions of algebra: and if we further represent the radix of the scale of numeration by r and the successive digits of the number by a_5, a_4, a_3, a_2, a_1, a_0, (using the same symbol with subscript numbers, not only to distinguish them from each other, but also to denote their position with respect to the place of units), then this or any other number, with the same number of places, would be expressed by

$$a_5 r^5 + a_4 r^4 + a_3 r^3 + a_2 r^2 + a_1 r + a_0:$$

General representation of numbers in Algebra. and assuming the same principles of notation, a number generally (of $\{n + 1\}$ places) would be expressed, according to a given scale r, by

$$a_n r^n + a_{n-1} r^{n-1} + \ldots\ldots + a_2 r^2 + a_1 r + a_0,$$

where a_n, $a_{n-1} \ldots\ldots a_2$, a_1, a_0 are the successive digits of the number from the highest digit downwards.

All numbers are capable of representation according to any assigned scale. 510. It is very easy to prove that every number is capable of being thus expressed by means of powers of the radix of the scale of numeration and of a series of digits, whose values are less than the radix, zero included: for if N be a number greater than r, then $N = N_1 r + a_0$, where a_0 is less than r: in a similar manner $N_1 = N_2 r + a_1$, $N_2 = N_3 r + a_2$, ... $N_{n-1} = N_n r + a_{n-1}$, if N_1, N_2, ... N_{n-1} be severally greater and if a_1, a_2, ... a_{n-1} be severally less, than r: if we multiply N_1, N_2, ... N_{n-1} and their equivalent expressions severally by r, r^2, ... r^{n-1} and replace N_n, if less than r by a_n, we shall get

$$N = N_1 r + a_0,$$
$$N_1 r = N_2 r^2 + a_1 r, \text{ for } N_1 = N_2 r + a_1,$$
$$N_2 r^2 = N_3 r^3 + a_2 r^2, \text{ for } N_2 = N_3 r + a_2,$$
$$\ldots\ldots\ldots\ldots\ldots\ldots\ldots\ldots\ldots\ldots\ldots\ldots$$
$$N_{n-2} r^{n-2} = N_{n-1} r^{n-1} + a_{n-2} r^{n-2}, \text{ for } N_{n-2} = N_{n-1} r + a_{n-2},$$
$$N_{n-1} r^{n-1} = a_n r^n + a_{n-1} r^{n-1}, \text{ for } N_{n-1} = a_n r + a_{n-1}.$$

If we add these equals together, obliterating those terms upon each side of the successive equations which are severally identical with each other, we shall get

$$N = a_n r^n + a_{n-1} r^{n-1} + a_{n-2} r^{n-2} + \ldots + a_2 r^2 + a_1 r + a_0.$$

* There are only six symbols employed in one case, and thirty symbols and signs in the other.

511. It will obviously follow from the theorem demonstrated in the last Article, that "if a number N and its successive quotients N_1, N_2, N_3, &c. be divided by r, the successive remainders will be the several digits, from the place of units upwards, in the arithmetical expression of that number in a scale of numeration whose radix is r." The knowledge of this theorem will enable us by a very simple arithmetical operation, to effect the transformation of numbers from one scale of numeration to another. The following are examples.

The rule for the transposition of numbers into different scales.

(1)   To express the number 35 in the *binary* scale.

Example into the binary scale.

$$2)\,35$$
$$2)\,17\,,\,1$$
$$2)\,8\,,\,1$$
$$2)\,4\,,\,0$$
$$2)\,2\,,\,0$$
$$1\,,\,0$$

The successive remainders 1, 1, 0, 0, 0, 1 are the digits from the place of units upwards, and consequently the number 35, in the binary scale, is expressed by

$$100011*.$$

* In the binary scale, the only digits required are 0 and 1: a system of binary arithmetic, therefore, would require no multiplication table, the operations of multiplication and division resolving themselves immediately into those for addition and subtraction: it was this extraordinary character of simplicity which recommended it to the particular attention of Leibnitz and some contemporary mathematicians. See *Mémoires de l'Académie des Sciences de Paris,* for 1703.

Every significant digit (that in the place of units excepted) in the binary scale, will express a power of 2, whose index is equal to the number which denotes its distance from the place of units: and since every number is capable of expression in the binary scale, it will follow that every number may be formed by the addition of terms in the series 1, 2, 2^2, 2^3, ... 2^n......:

thus $35 = 1 + 2 + 2^5$: and

$1828, \; = 2 + 2^2 + 2^3 + 2^5 \quad 2^8 + 2^9 + 2^{10}$ or

$= 11100100100$

in the binary scale: it follows likewise that a series of weights adapted to the scale 1, 2, 2^2, 2^3, &c. will weigh any weight which is an exact multiple of the primary unit of weight, whether it be 1 lb. or 1 oz. or 1 dwt.

364

Into the ternary scale.

(2) To express the number 365 in the *ternary* scale.

```
3) 365
3) 121 , 2
3) 40 , 1
3) 13 , 1
3) 4 , 1
   1 , 1
```

Therefore 365 is expressed in the ternary scale by

111112.

The digits in this scale are 0, 1 and 2.

From the senary to the quinary scale.

(3) To transpose the number 34510 from the *senary* to the *quinary* scale.

```
5) 34510
5) 4323 , 3
5) 525 , 2
5) 103 , 2
5) 11 , 4
   1 , 2
```

The number 34510 transposed from the senary to the quinary scale is expressed by

124223.

Into the duodenary scale.

(4) To transpose the number 367895 from the *denary* to the *duodenary* scale.

```
12) 367895
12) 30657 , 11
12) 2554 , 9
12) 212 , 10
12) 17 , 8
    1 , 5
```

If we employ the symbols X and X_1 to express the additional digits 10 and 11, which the duodenary scale of notation requires, the number under consideration will be expressed in the duodenary scale by

$$158X9X_1.$$

(5) To transpose the number 367895 from the *denary* to the *vicenary* scale.

$$20) \; 367895$$

$$20) \; 18394 \; , \; 15$$

$$20) \; \text{\tiny...} \; 14$$

$$20) \; 45 \; , \; 19$$

$$2 \; , \; 5$$

If we take X_4, X_5 and X_9 as the digits to represent the remainders 14, 15 and 19, then the number 367895 will be expressed in the *vicenary* scale by

$$25X_9X_4X_5*.$$

---

* The *quinary*, *denary* and *vicenary* scales may be denominated *natural* scales, inasmuch as they have a common origin in the practical methods of numeration which have been more or less followed by all nations, of which so many traces exist or are discoverable, in the etymology and construction of their numeral languages : thus the *quinary* scale of numeration prevails amongst some African tribes, and the *vicenary* scale amongst nearly all the native South American tribes : and it was carried to a considerable extent by the ancient Mexicans and Peruvians. See the article "Arithmetic" in the *Encyclopædia Metropolitana*.

The duodecimal scale, though not a natural scale, presents itself perpetually in the subdivisions of coins, weights, measures and of the other primary concrete units of European nations, and more particularly of their measures of length : thus, if the primary unit be one foot, its subdivisions or inches, lines, &c. proceed by 12 and its powers ; and consequently if the primary units were expressed according to the duodecimal scale, such subordinate units (Art. 205.) would present themselves as successive digits in the same scale, and would be treated therefore by the regular processes which are proper to a system of duodecimal arithmetic : thus, 23 feet 10 inches and 4 lines would be expressed by $1 X_1 : X 4$, transposing 23 into the duodecimal scale, and considering the two last digits X and 4 as duodecimals which are convertible into the equivalent fractions $\frac{10}{12}$ and $\frac{4}{12^2}$: (Art. 201. Note) in a similar manner, 130 feet 9 inches and 11 lines would be expressed by $XX : 9X_1$: and if it was required to determine the area (in square feet, and its duodecimal subdivisions) of the

The remainder from the division of a number by its radix less one is the same as from the division of the sum of its digits by the radix less one.

512. Other properties of numbers, whether in the decimal or any other scale, may be easily deduced from the expression

$$a_n r^n + a_{n-1} r^{n-1} + \ldots \ldots + a_2 r^2 + a_1 r + a_0,$$

which we are now considering: thus if we divide r^n, $r^{n-1}, \ldots r^2$, r by $r - 1$, the remainders will be severally equal to $1*$; and con-

rectangle which would be contained by two sides of the lengths above given, it would be found in the following manner:

$$1X_1 : X4$$
$$XX : 9X_1$$

$$19\ X\ 5\ 8$$
$$1\ 5X\ 9\ 0$$
$$1\ 7\ X7\ 4$$
$$1\ 7X\ \ 7\ 4$$

$$1\ 9\ 8\ \ 1:7\ X_1\ 5\ 8$$

If we reconvert 1981 from the duodecimal to the decimal scale, it will become 3121, and the area required will be equal to 3121 square feet 7 inches 11 lines 5″ and 8‴.

In multiplying or performing any other arithmetical operation in the duodecimal or any other scale of notation, we must take care to *carry* or to *borrow* the radix of the scale whatever it may be, instead of 10 as in the ordinary processes of arithmetic : thus, the first of the partial products in the preceding multiplication is obtained as follows :

"(X_1) or 11 times 4 is $44 = 3 \times 12 + 8$; write down 8 and carry 3: 11 times X or 10 is 110, which becomes, when 3 is added, $113 = 9 \times 12 + 5$; write down 5 and carry 9: 11 times X_1 11 is 121, which becomes, when 9 is added, $130 = 10 \times 12 + 10$: write down X (10) and carry 10: 11 times 1 is 11, which becomes, when 10 is added, $21 = 1 \times 12 + 9$: first write down 9 and then 1 which is carried to the next superior place."

Such processes must, in all cases, when conducted by the mind or expressed in words, be carried on through the medium of our ordinary numeral language which is exclusively adapted to the decimal scale: for neither can the mind be constrained to think in different scales, nor can a corresponding numeral language be invented, in the same manner or with the same facility that digital notations can be adapted to them: it is this incongruity between our associations and numeral language and the scale of notation, different from the decimal, which we are required to use, which constitutes the chief difficulty and embarrassment in the actual performance of arithmetical operations in such scales.

* For if $r - 1 = x$, we get $r = x + 1$, and therefore, by the binomial theorem,
$$(x+1)^n = x^n + n x^{n-1} \ldots \ldots n x + 1,$$
where the last term is 1^n or 1 : and inasmuch as all the terms except the last are multiples of x or of $r - 1$, it follows that the remainder from the division $(x+1)^n$ by x or of r^n by $r - 1$, is equal to 1.

sequently the remainders from the division of $a_n r^n$, $a_{n-1} r^{n-1}$, ... $a_2 r^2$, $a_1 r$ by $r-1$ will be the successive digits a_n, a_{n-1}, ... a_2, a_1, replacing those digits by *zero* which are equal to $r-1$*: it will follow, therefore, that the remainder from the division of N or of

$$a_n r^n + a_{n-1} r^{n-1} + \ldots\ldots + a_2 r^2 + a_1 r + a_0$$

by $r-1$ will be the same as from the division of the sum of its digits or

$$a_n + a_{n-1} + \ldots\ldots + a_2 + a_1 + a_0$$

by $r-1$. It is this proposition which is the basis of the well-known rule for the verification of arithmetical processes by casting out the 9's†.

513. The algebraical representation of numbers, considered in the preceding Articles, is useful in the deduction and demonstration of those properties of numbers which relate to the local values or orders (Art. 146) of their digits: but it affords

The most important properties of numbers are not generally deducible from their algebraical representation according to a given scale.

* For if the remainder from the division of r^n by $r-1$ be 1, the remainder from the division of $a_n r^n$ or a_n, will be a_n times as great, whenever a_n is less than $r-1$ and *zero*, when $a_n = r-1$.

† In the decimal notation 9 corresponds to $r-1$ in the proposition demonstrated in the text. It may be easily shewn, from other considerations, that the remainders from the division of 10, 100, 1000, 100000, &c. by 9 are all equally 1, and that consequently the remainders from the division of the several addends which are expressed by the digits of any number, in their proper places, will be the several digits themselves, if the digit 9, whenever it occurs, be replaced by zero.

If, therefore, the remainders from casting out the 9's from two numbers, N and N' be a and a' respectively, we shall have

$$N = 9m + a \text{ and } N' = 9m' + a':$$

consequently, multiplying them together, we shall find

$$NN' = 81\, mm' + 9am' + 9a'm + aa'$$
$$= 9m'' + aa':$$

it will follow therefore, that the remainder from casting out the 9's from the product NN', should be the same as the remainder from casting out the 9's from the product of a and a': if these remainders are found to be the same, and if the operation has been honestly performed, it is probable (there are eight chances to one in its favour) that the operation is correct: if not, it is certainly wrong.

It is easy to extend this principle to the proof of the corresponding rule for the verification of the operation of division (when there is no remainder), by considering the dividend as the product and the divisor and quotient as its two factors.

us little aid, for reasons which we have mentioned above, in the formation and proof of the rules for the ordinary operations of arithmetic, and is almost entirely useless in investigations of those properties of numbers, which exist independently of the peculiar system of notation by which they are expressed: in all such enquiries, numbers are represented symbolically with reference to their form, character or composition, and not with reference to the digits and radix of the scale by which they are expressed arithmetically.

Numbers may be classed with reference to an assumed modulus.

514.   All numbers may be classed with reference to a given divisor or *modulus m* and the remainder which exists after the operation of division is performed, whether it be zero or any number less than m: thus, if the *modulus m* be contained k times in the number a, with a remainder b, then the relation between a, k, m and b, will be expressed by the equation

$$a = km + b.$$

Properties of prime and composite numbers with reference to moduli which are less than them.

515.   If the number be a *prime* number, its remainders will be different from *zero* for every modulus which is less than a: but if the number be composite, there will be within the same limits of the modulus, as many remainders equal to zero as the number has factors or measures which are different from each other *.

General expressions of odd and even numbers with reference to the modulus 2: also with reference to the modulus 4.

516.   All odd numbers, referred to a modulus 2, will give a remainder 1; and all even numbers, referred to the same modulus, will give a remainder zero: it will follow therefore that the first series of numbers may be expressed by $2k+1$, and the second by $2k$. Also odd numbers may be farther classed, with respect to the modulus 4, according as they furnish a remainder 1 or 3, the first class of numbers being expressed by $4k+1$, and the second by $4k+3$†: whilst even numbers,

---

* For whenever the divisor of a is also a factor of a, the remainder is zero, and in no other case.

Classification of even and odd numbers.

Degrees of parity.

† Numbers of the forms $4k$ and $4k+2$ are called *pariter* and *impariter pares* respectively, whilst those which belong to the two other forms $4k+1$ and $4k+3$ are called *pariter* and *impariter impares*. Even numbers are also sometimes classed according to their *degrees* of *parity*: thus numbers of the forms $2k$, $4k$, $8k$, $16k$,... $2^n k$, where k is an odd number, would be characterized as of the first, second, third, fourth and n^{th} degrees of *parity* respectively.

referred to the same modulus, will be distributed into classes which give remainders 0 and 2 and which are expressed by $4k$ and $4k + 2$ respectively.

517. Numbers, which furnish the same remainder, when referred to the same *modulus*, are said to be *congruous* to each other, whilst those which furnish, under the same circumstances, different remainders, are said to be *incongruous* to each other: it will follow from this definition of the *congruity* of numbers, that a number is always *congruous* to its remainder, with reference to any given modulus: thus, if

$$a = km + b,$$

Numbers considered as congruous or incongruous to other numbers.

a is said to be congruous to b*: thus, 10, 10^2, 10^3, 10^4, &c. are severally congruous to 1, to the modulus 9: for it may be easily shewn that

$$10 = 1 \times 9 + 1,$$
$$10^2 = 11 \times 9 + 1,$$
$$10^3 = 111 \times 9 + 1,$$
$$10^4 = 1111 \times 9 + 1,$$

All powers of 10 are congruous to 1 to the modulus 9.

and so on, for any power of 10 whatsoever.

518. Some of the most important properties of numbers, which are *prime* to each other, have been demonstrated in the second Chapter of this Work: of this kind are the propositions that "if a number p be prime to each of two or more numbers a, b, c, &c. it is prime to their product (Art. 112)": that "if a number p be prime to another number a, then also p is prime

Propositions relating to prime numbers which have been demonstrated in former chapters.

* Gauss has made the *congruity* and *incongruity* of numbers, the foundation of nearly all his researches in the *Disquisitiones Arithmeticæ*: he expresses the congruity of two numbers by the sign $\equiv$: we may thus replace the equation $a = km + b$ by $a \equiv b \pmod{m}$: $10^2 \equiv 1 \pmod{9}$, and $10^n \equiv 1$, $a \times 10^n \equiv a$, to the same modulus: it will very readily follow from this property that

Sign of congruity.

$$a + a_1 \times 10 + a_2 \times 10^2 + \dots a_n \times 10^n \equiv a + a_1 + a_2 + \dots a_n;$$

and that consequently every number, in the decimal scale, is congruous to the sum of its digits, to the modulus 9: this will furnish another demonstration of the proposition given in Art. 512.

In the indeterminate equation

$$ax - by = c,$$

ax is congruous to c, to the modulus b; the equation itself is called a *congruence* of the first degree, and the resolution of the equation is called the resolution of the congruence.

A congruence of the first degree.

to a^n (Art. 117), and also p^m is prime to a^n (Art. 114), where m and n are any whole numbers whatever."

Many other propositions, which were not required for the particular enquiry for which the preceding propositions were introduced, are easily deducible from them, and many others may be added, which are of great importance and interest, whose demonstration will depend upon very simple principles, though it may not always be very easy to deduce them as consequences of any single theorem, or to refer them to any general system of reasoning. Neither the space which is allowed for this Chapter, nor the algebraical knowledge which our readers are supposed to possess, will allow us to push this enquiry to such an extent, as may be requisite to represent even a very slight sketch of the existing state of this department of our knowledge of the theory of numbers: but the following propositions, though they do not present altogether a continuous system of investigations, possess considerable value, and will serve to illustrate some of the methods which must be followed in such cases.

519. PROP. Given the prime factors of a composite number, to find a symbolical form by which it may be represented.

If a, b, c, be the prime factors of a number N, then it may be expressed generally by $a^p b^q c^r$: for if none of the prime factors be contained more than once in the number N, then it may be represented by their continued product abc: but if a be repeated as a factor p times, b, q times and c, r times, then their continued product will be represented by $a^p b^q c^r$, (Art. 41): and similarly, whatever be the number of prime factors, whether repeated or not, which enter into the composition of the number which is required to be represented*.

520. PROP. A composite number can be expressed in one manner only, by means of its prime factors or their powers.

For the same number cannot result from the multiplication of different sets of prime factors, such as a, b, c and α, β, γ, for, if so, $a^p b^q c^r$ and $\alpha^{p'} \beta^{q'} \gamma^{r'}$, which are prime to each other (Art. 518),

---

* Thus, the prime factors of the number 108 are 2 and 3, the first being repeated as a factor *twice* and the second *thrice*: it is therefore represented by $2^2 \times 3^3$: the number 16200 is represented by $2^3 \times 3^4 \times 5^2$: and similarly in other cases.

would be equal to the same number N, which is impossible*: also numbers $a^{p'}b^{q'}c^{r'}$ and $a^p b^q c^r$ are equally prime to any prime numbers different from a, b and c, or to their products: neither can the numbers $a^p b^q c^r$ and $a^{p'}b^{q'}c^{r'}$ be identical with each other, unless $p=p'$, $q=q'$ and $r=r'$; for if possible, let $a^p n = a^{p'} n'$, where a is prime to n and n'; then if p be greater than p', we get $a^{p-p'}n = n'$; and if p be less than p', then $n = n'a^{p'-p}$; and consequently n and n' cannot both of them be prime to a, unless $p = p'$: a similar process will shew that $q = q'$ and $r = r'$: and similarly for any number of such factors.

521. PROB. To find the number of divisors of a composite number, whose composition is given.

To find the number of divisors of a composite number.

Let $N = a^p b^q c^r$: then 1, a, $a^2 \ldots a^p$ are divisors of a^p, and therefore of N, which are $p+1$ in number: 1, b, $b^2 \ldots b^q$ are divisors of b^q, and therefore of N, which are $q+1$ in number: 1, c, $c^2 \ldots c^r$ are divisors of c^r, and therefore of N, which are $r+1$ in number: and so on for all the prime factors of N: it is obvious likewise that every term of the product which arises from multiplying these several series of divisors of N together, will be likewise divisors of N and different from each other; and their number, which is also the number of divisors required, is therefore $(p+1)(q+1)(r+1)$. In this expression, 1 and N† are included amongst the divisors of N.

522. COR. The number of divisors of a composite number $a^p b^q c^r \ldots$ will be an even number, unless p, q, $r \ldots$ are all of them even numbers, and consequently unless it be a perfect square‡.

The number of divisors of all numbers which are not squares is even.

523. PROP. The number of different ways, in which a composite number may be resolved into two factors, is half the number of its divisors.

Expression for the number of ways in which a composite number can be resolved into two prime factors.

* For a, b, c, &c. are severally prime to α, β, γ, &c. and therefore a^p, b^q, c^r, are severally prime to $\alpha^{p'}$, $\beta^{q'}$, $\gamma^{r'}$, and also $a^p b^q c^r$ is prime to $\alpha^{p'}\beta^{q'}\gamma^{r'}$. Art. 518.

† The number of divisors of $2880 = 2^6 \times 3^2 \times 5$ is $7 \times 3 \times 2$ or 42: the number of divisors of $484000 = 2^5 \times 5^3 \times 11^2$ is $6 \times 4 \times 3$ or $= 72$.

‡ The number of divisors of $19600 = 2^4 \times 5^2 \times 7^2 = 5 \times 3 \times 3 = 45$ an odd number: 19600 is the square of $2^2 \times 5 \times 7 = 140$: and generally the square of any number $a^p b^q c^r$ will be $a^{2p} b^{2q} c^{2r}$, where the indices of its several factors are the doubles of those of its roots.

For each pair of such factors will form two divisors of the number: if however the number be a complete square, its square root will form one of two identical factors, and there will be *one pair* of factors corresponding to *one divisor* only: in this case, the number of pairs of factors will be one half of the number of divisors (which is odd) increased by unity[*].

Expression for the sum of the divisors of a composite number.

5.. PROP. The sum of all the divisors of a composite number $a^p b^q c^r$ will be expressed by

$$\frac{a^{p+1} - 1}{a - 1} \times \frac{b^{q+1} - 1}{b - 1} \times \frac{c^{r+1} - 1}{c - 1}.$$

For the sum of these divisors is the sum of the terms of the product formed by the multiplication of the several series

$$1 + a + a^2 + \ldots a^p = \frac{a^{p+1} - 1}{a - 1}, \quad \text{(Art. 429)},$$

$$1 + b + b^2 + \ldots b^q = \frac{b^{q+1} - 1}{b - 1},$$

$$1 + c + c^2 + \ldots c^r = \frac{c^{r+1} - 1}{c - 1},$$

and is therefore equal to the product of their sums which is

$$\frac{a^{p+1} - 1}{a - 1} \times \frac{b^{q+1} - 1}{b - 1} \times \frac{c^{r+1} - 1}{c - 1} \dagger.$$

[*] The number of divisors of the number $99225 = 3^4 \times 5^2 \times 7^2$ is $5 \times 3 \times 3$ or 45: the number of ways in which it is irresolvible into two factors is

$$\frac{45 + 1}{2} = 23,$$

including the two identical factors 315 and 315.

† The sum of the divisors of

$$504 = 2^3 \times 3^2 \times 7 \text{ is } \frac{2^4 - 1}{2 - 1} \times \frac{3^3 - 1}{3 - 1} \times \frac{7^2 - 1}{7 - 1} = \frac{15}{1} \times \frac{26}{2} \times \frac{48}{6} = 15 \times 13 \times 8 = 1560:$$

the sum of the divisors of $6 = 2 \times 3$ is

$$\frac{2^2 - 1}{2 - 1} \times \frac{3^2 - 1}{3 - 1} = 3 \times 4 = 12;$$

A perfect number.

and if we exclude the number itself or 6 from the number of its divisors, their sum will be $12 - 6$ or 6: this is called a *perfect* number, inasmuch as it is equal to the sum of its divisors: in a similar manner the sum of the divisors of 28 or $2^2 \times 7$, excluding 28, is

$$\frac{2^3 - 1}{2 - 1} \times \frac{7^2 - 1}{7 - 1} - 28 = 7 \times 8 - 28 = 28,$$

which is therefore likewise a *perfect* number: the same remark applies to the numbers 496 and 8128.

525. Prob. To find an expression for the number of numbers, which are prime to a given number N, and less than it.

If N be a prime number, all numbers less than N are prime to N, which are $N-1$ or $N\left(1-\dfrac{1}{N}\right)$ in number.

If $N = a^p b^q c^r$, then the number of numbers, not greater than N, which are divisible by a, will be expressed by

$$\frac{N}{a} \quad (1);$$

for all the terms of the series

$$a, 2a, 3a, \ldots\ldots \frac{N}{a} \cdot a,$$

which are $\dfrac{N}{a}$ in number, are divisible by a.

In a similar manner, the number of numbers not greater than N, which are divisible by b, is

$$\frac{N}{b} \quad (2).$$

The number of numbers which are divisible by c and not greater than N, is

$$\frac{N}{c} \quad (3);$$

and similarly, whatever be the number of prime factors of N.

Again, since all multiples of ab are included in both the series (1) and (2), it follows that the number of terms which are common to these series is

$$\frac{N}{ab} \quad (1').$$

The number of terms common to the series (1) and (3) is

$$\frac{N}{ac} \quad (2'),$$

and the number of terms common to the series (2) and (3) is

$$\frac{N}{bc} \quad (3'),$$

and similarly for the terms which are common to any two of a greater number of series (1), (2), (3), (4), &c.

Further, the number of terms which are common to the three series (1′), (2′) and (3′), or which are multiples of abc, is

$$\frac{N}{abc} \quad (1''):$$

for all the terms

$$abc, \; 2\,abc, \; 3\,abc, \; \ldots \frac{N}{abc} \cdot abc,$$

are included in some one of the series (1′), (2′) and (3′), and their number is

$$\frac{N}{abc}.$$

It follows therefore that the whole number of numbers which are less than N and prime to N, will be equal to N, diminished by the number of numbers which are neither greater than N nor prime to it, and is therefore equal to

$$N - \frac{N}{a} - \frac{N}{b} - \frac{N}{c} + \frac{N}{ab} + \frac{N}{ac} + \frac{N}{bc} - \frac{N}{abc}$$

$$= N\left(1 - \frac{1}{a} - \frac{1}{b} - \frac{1}{c} + \frac{1}{ab} + \frac{1}{ac} + \frac{1}{bc} - \frac{1}{abc}\right)$$

$$= N\left(1 - \frac{1}{a}\right)\left(1 - \frac{1}{b}\right)\left(1 - \frac{1}{c}\right), \; \text{(Art. 482)}:$$

and inasmuch as the same principles of reasoning may be extended to 4, 5, or a greater number of prime factors, a similar expression may be easily shewn to apply to express the number of numbers less than N and prime to N, whatever be the number of its prime factors. (Art. 448).

Thus, if $N = 35 = 5 \times 7$, there are $35\left(1 - \frac{1}{5}\right)\left(1 - \frac{1}{7}\right) = (5 - 1)$ $(7 - 1) = 24$ numbers less than 35 and prime to it: if $N = 1225$ $= 5^2 \times 7^2$, there are $1225\left(1 - \frac{1}{5}\right)\left(1 - \frac{1}{7}\right) = 35\,(5 - 1)\,(7 - 1) = 840$ numbers less than 1225 and prime to it: if

$$N = 81000 = 2^3 \times 3^4 \times 5^3,$$

there are

$$2^3 \times 3^4 \times 5^3 \left(1 - \tfrac{1}{2}\right)\left(1 - \tfrac{1}{3}\right)\left(1 - \tfrac{1}{5}\right)$$

$$= 2^2 \times 3^3 \times 5^5 \,(2 - 1)\,(3 - 1)\,(5 - 1) = 21600$$

numbers less than 81000 and prime to it.

526. Prop. In the series of natural numbers beginning from unity, the continued product of r consecutive terms, beginning at any term, is divisible by the continued product of the r first terms of the series.

In other words, the expression

$$\frac{n\,(n+1)\ldots\ldots(n+r-1)}{1 \times 2 \times \ldots\ldots r} \quad \text{(Art. 455.)}$$

is always a whole number, if n be a whole number.

For one of the two first factors of the numerator is of the form $2m$: one of the three first factors is of the form $3m$: one of the four first factors is of the form $4m$: and generally one of the r first factors is of the form rm*: it follows therefore that the numerator is a multiple of all the separate factors of the denominator, and consequently, a complete multiple of all the prime factors which it contains†.

Again, if there be two terms xp and xq, which have a common measure x, where q is greater than p, it will follow that amongst the xq first factors of the numerator and denominator, there are q of them which are multiples of x, and consequently, their continued product will not merely be a multiple of the prime factors which are inferior to xq, but likewise of any power of x, which this portion of the denominator may contain: the same remark will apply to the common measure of any two or more compound factors whatever.

It follows therefore that the numerator is a multiple, not merely of the prime factors of the denominator, but likewise of all its composite factors, and consequently, of their continued product.

---

* For all numbers are of the form $2m$ or $2m+1$ and therefore one of the numbers n and $n+1$ is of the form $2m$; all numbers are of one of the forms $3m$, $3m+1$, $3m+2$, and therefore one of the numbers n, $n+1$, and $n+2$ is of the form $3m$: and similarly for the successive *moduli* 4, 5, ... r.

† For if a number n be divisible by the prime factors a, b, c ..., it is divisible by their product: thus if $n = pa = qb$, where a and b are prime numbers, then $\dfrac{a}{b} = \dfrac{q}{p}$, where q is either equal to a or to a multiple of a, and where p is either equal to b or to a multiple of b: it follows therefore that n is a multiple of ab: and similarly for three or a greater number of prime factors.

To find
the highest
power of a
given prime
number,
which is
a factor
of the con-
tinued pro-
duct of the
natural
numbers,
beginning
from 1.

527. PROB. To find the highest power of a prime number a less than n, which the continued product

$$1 \times 2 \times 3 \times \ldots n$$

contains as a factor.

If we represent the integral parts of the whole or mixed numbers $\dfrac{n}{a}$, $\dfrac{n}{a^2}$, $\dfrac{n}{a^3}$, &c. by $I\left(\dfrac{n}{a}\right)$, $I\left(\dfrac{n}{a^2}\right)$, $I\left(\dfrac{n}{a^3}\right)$, &c., then the index of the factor required is equal to

$$I\left(\frac{n}{a}\right) + I\left(\frac{n}{a^2}\right) + I\left(\frac{n}{a^3}\right) + \&c.$$

For there are $I\left(\dfrac{n}{a}\right)$ factors not greater than n,

$$a, \ 2a, \ 3a, \ \ldots I\left(\frac{n}{a}\right) \times a$$

which are multiples of a: also$\ldots I\left(\dfrac{n}{a^2}\right)$ factors

$$a^2, \ 2a^2, \ 3a^2, \ \ldots I\left(\frac{n}{a^2}\right) \times a^2,$$

which are multiples of a^2: also $I\left(\dfrac{n}{a^3}\right)$ factors,

$$a^3, \ 2a^3, \ 3a^3, \ \ldots I\left(\frac{n}{a^3}\right) \times a^3,$$

which are multiples of a^3: and so on, until $\dfrac{n}{a^r}$ first becomes less than 1: the sum of all these numbers

$$I\left(\frac{n}{a}\right) + I\left(\frac{n}{a^2}\right) + I\left(\frac{n}{a^3}\right) + \&c.$$

is the index of the highest power of a which is involved as a factor*.

---

* Thus, to find the highest power of 11, which is a factor of
$$1 \times 2 \times 3 \times \ldots\ldots 1000,$$
we get $I\left(\dfrac{1000}{11}\right) = 90,$

$$I\left(\frac{1000}{11^2}\right) = I\left(\frac{90}{11}\right) = 8.$$

The index of the highest power of 11 is therefore 98.

To find the highest power of 2, which is a factor of $1 \times 2 \times 3 \times \ldots 32$.

$$I\left(\frac{32}{2}\right) = 16, \quad I\left(\frac{16}{2}\right) = 8, \quad I\left(\frac{8}{2}\right) = 4, \quad I\left(\frac{4}{2}\right) = 2, \quad I\left(\frac{2}{2}\right) = 1:$$

the highest power of 2, which this product involves, is therefore $2^{16+8+4+2+1} = 2^{31}$.

This process will enable us to express any such product in terms of its prime factors. (Art. 519).

528. Prop. *Fermat's Theorem.* If p be a prime number and if a be not divisible by p, then $a^{p-1} - 1$ is divisible by p.

For, by the binomial theorem (Art. 486), we find

$$(1 + x)^p = 1 + px + \ldots\ldots px^{p-1} + x^p$$
$$= 1 + x^p + mp,$$

since the coefficients of all the terms of the series intermediate to the first and last are divisible by p*, and their sum is therefore a multiple of p: consequently, subtracting $1 + x$ from both sides of this equation, we get

$$(1 + x)^p - (1 + x) = x^p - x + mp,$$

and therefore if $x^p - x$ be divisible by p, $(1 + x)^p - (1 + x)$ is divisible by p: but if $x = 1$, we get $(1 + 1)^p - (1 + 1) = 2^p - 2 = 1^p - 1 + mp = mp$, which is therefore divisible by p: consequently, if $x = 2$, we get $(1 + 2)^p - (1 + 2) = 3^p - 3 = 2^p - 2 + mp$, which is also divisible by p: and in a similar manner it may be shewn that $4^p - 4$, $5^p - 5$, $6^p - 6$, ... $a^p - a$, are severally divisible by p: consequently, $a^p - a = a(a^{p-1} - 1) = mp$: and since p is prime to a, it follows that $a^{p-1} - 1$ is divisible by p. (Art. 112.) †

* For, since p is a prime number, it will follow that the coefficients

$$p, \quad \frac{p(p-1)}{1 \times 2}, \quad \frac{p(p-1)(p-2)}{1 \times 2 \times 3} \quad \text{&c.,}$$

being whole numbers (Art. 526), are also multiples of p: for p is not divisible by any of the factors of the denominator, and it consequently must remain a factor of the numerator, when all the factors of the denominator are obliterated by division.

If p be a composite number, such as $a^\alpha b^\beta c^\gamma \ldots$, the intermediate coefficients are not all of them multiples of p: for if a be the least of the prime factors a, b, c, then the coefficient

$$\frac{p(p-1)\ldots(p-a+1)}{1 \times 2 \ldots a} = \frac{a^{\alpha-1} b^\beta c^\gamma (p-1)\ldots(p-a+1)}{1 \times 2 \times \ldots (a-1)},$$

where none of the factors $p-1$, $p-2$, ... $p-a+1$ are divisible by a; and consequently

$$\frac{a^{\alpha-1} b^\beta c^\gamma (p-1)\ldots(p-a+1)}{1 \times 2 \times \ldots (a-1)}$$

is not a multiple of $a^\alpha b^\beta c^\gamma$ or p.

† Gauss (Disquisitiones Arithmeticæ, Art. 49) has given, after Euler, a proof of this theorem, which he considers to be more conformable, than that in the text, to the proper mode of treating the theory of numbers.

If *p* be prime to *a*, and if *a*^t^ be the least power of *a* which makes *a*^t^ − 1 divisible by *p*, then the remainders from the division of 1, *a*, *a*², ... *a*^t−1^ by *p*, will be all of them different from each other.

529. PROP. If p be prime to a, and if a^t be the *least* power of a, which is of the form $mp + 1$ *, then all the terms of the series

$$a, a^2, \ldots a^{t-1}$$

if divided by p, will leave remainders different from each other and from 1.

For, if possible, let $a^m = rp + a$, and $a^n = r'p + a$, where m and n are both of them less than t: we shall thus get

$$a^n - a^m = (r' - r)\,p,$$
$$\text{or } a^m (a^{n-m} - 1) = (r' - r)\,p,$$

and since p is prime to a^m (Art. 117,) it follows that $a^{n-m} - 1$ is divisible by p, which is impossible, since $n - m$ is less than t, and a^t is the least power of a, which makes $a^t - 1$ divisible by p.

Extension of Fermat's Theorem.

530. PROP. If a^t be the least power of a which is of the form $mp + 1$ when p is a prime number and when a is not divisible by p, then t is either equal to $p - 1$ or to a sub-multiple of $p - 1$.

If *p* be a prime number, and *a* not divisible by *p*, then if *a*^t^ be the least power of *a* which makes *a*^t^ − 1 divisible by *p*, *t* is either equal to *p* − 1, or is a submultiple of it.

For the several terms of the series

$$1, a, a^2, \ldots a^{t-1} \ldots\ldots\ldots (1)$$

will leave remainders when divided by p, which are different from each other (Art. 529), and which are included therefore in the series of numbers

$$1, 2, \ldots p - 1:$$

and if each of these terms be multiplied by a^t, which is of the form $mp + 1$, the remainders from the division of the terms of the series

$$a^t, a^{t+1}, a^{t+2}, \ldots a^{2t-1} \ldots\ldots\ldots (2),$$

will be the same as from the division of the terms of the series (1): and it is obvious that the same results will follow, if the terms of this series be severally multiplied by a^{2t}, a^{3t}, ... a^{rt}, or by any power of a^t: it follows therefore that the remainders from the division of the terms of the series

$$1, a, a^2, \ldots a^{p-2}$$

---

* Or in the language and notation of Gauss, let a^t be *congruous* to 1, to the modulus p, or let $a^t \equiv 1$ (mod. p). Art. 517, Note.

by p will form recurring series of t terms each: and inasmuch as the whole number of them is $p-1$, (for a^{p-1} is the beginning of a new series) it follows that $p-1$ is either equal to t or to $2t$ or to $3t$ or to rt, and consequently, that t is either equal to $p-1$ or to a submultiple of $p-1$.

Thus, if $a=2$ and $p=13$, the first term of the series

Examples.

$$1, 2, 4, 8, 16 \ \&c.$$

which is *congruous* with 1, or of the form $mp+1$, is 2^{12}, and consequently, in this case $t=p-1$: but if the modulus be 23,

we find $2^{11} = 2048 = mp + 1$, where $t = \dfrac{p-1}{2} = \dfrac{23-1}{2}$: again,

if $a=3$ and $p=13$, we find $3^3 = mp+1$, where $t = 3 = \dfrac{13-1}{4}$;

and similarly in other cases.*

531. Those values of a, the least of whose powers, which is of the form $mp+1$, is a^{p-1}, have been called by Euler *primitive roots* of the *modulus p*, and are connected with some very important theories: the periods of remainders which they form are called *complete* periods, and include every number less than p: all other roots the least of whose powers of the form $mp+1$ are sub-multiples of $p-1$, are called *subordinate* roots and all other periods are called *incomplete* periods.

Primitive roots of the modulus p.

532. Since p is an odd number, $p-1 = 2n$, and therefore
$$a^{p-1} - 1 = a^{2n} - 1 = (a^n + 1)(a^n - 1):$$
and since $a^{p-1} - 1$ is divisible by p, it follows that one of the two factors $a^n - 1$ or $a^n + 1$ is divisible by p: and since $a^n - 1$

Connection between the first and the second half of the series of remainders of a primitive root.

---

* The proposition relative to the periods of circulating decimals noticed in a Note to Art. 162 is involved in this proposition: for if 10 be a primitive root (Art. 531) of a prime modulus n, then the number of places in each period of the decimal corresponding to $\dfrac{1}{n}$, will be equal to $n-1$: if not, it will be a sub-multiple of it. Thus 10 is a primitive root of 7 and 10^6 is the first term of the series
$$1, 10, 10^2 \ldots \ldots$$
which is of the form $7m+1$ and $\dfrac{1}{7}$ forms a recurring decimal of 6 places in each period: but if $n=11$, then $10^2 = 11m+1$ and $\dfrac{1}{11}$ forms a recurring decimal of 2 places in each period only.

is not divisible by p, (since a^{p-1} is the least power of a which makes $a^{p-1} - 1$ divisible by p) it follows that $a^n + 1$ is divisible by p, and that therefore the remainder from the division of a^n by p is $p - 1$: it will follow therefore that if the series of $p - 1$ or of $2n$ successive remainders be divided into two equal portions, the first term of the second portion will be equal to $p - 1$.

Again, if we take two terms $a^{n-\mu}$ and $a^{n+\mu}$, in the series of powers of the primitive root, which are equidistant from the *culminating* term a^n, their product is a^{2n} or a^{p-1}; and consequently, the remainder from the division of the product of these terms, or **Associated** *of their corresponding remainders* will be 1*: such terms are **terms.** said to be *associated* terms, and it is manifest that if the terms and their order of succession in the first half of the series be given, the terms and order of succession of the second half of the series may be determined.

Equally **533.** The same remark is applicable likewise to the series **true of** of remainders of any *incomplete* period, corresponding to an **complete** **and incom-** index t, which is an even number; for under such circum- **plete pe-** stances, **riods of an** **even num-** **ber of** $$a^t - 1 = a^{2r} - 1 = (a^r + 1)(a^r - 1) = mp:$$ **terms.**

and since a^t is the least power of a, which makes $a^t - 1$ a

---

* For if
$$a^{n-\mu} = mp + \alpha \quad \text{and} \quad a^{n+\mu} = m'p + \beta,$$
then $\qquad a^{n-\mu} \times a^{n+\mu} = a^{2n} = m''p + \alpha\beta$;

and consequently the remainder from the product of $a^{n-\mu}$ and $a^{n+\mu}$ is the same as the remainder from the product $\alpha\beta$ of their corresponding remainders α and β.

Thus 2 is a primitive root of 13, and the succession of remainders from the division of the terms of the series

$$1, \quad 2, \quad 2^2, \quad 2^3, \quad 2^4, \quad 2^5, \quad 2^6, \quad 2^7, \quad 2^8, \quad 2^9, \quad 2^{10}, \quad 2^{11}, \quad 2^{12}$$

by 13, is $\quad 1, \quad 2, \quad 4, \quad 8, \quad 3, \quad 6, \quad 12, \quad 11, \quad 9, \quad 5, \quad 10, \quad 7, \quad 1.$

The 7th term is $12 = 13 - 1$: also 3 and 9 are remainders equidistant from 12, and their product 27 divided by 13 gives a remainder 1: if the first associated term 3 be given, the second x may be found, by the solution of the equation $3x = 13m + 1$ or $3x - 13m = 1$: and since $3(13 - 4) - 13(3 - 1) = 1$, we find $x = 13 - 4 = 9$, which is the term required: in a similar manner the first associated term being 8, the second, x is found from the equation $8x - 13m = 1$, which gives $x = 5$.

multiple of p, and since p divides one of the two factors $a^r + 1$ or $a^r - 1$, it follows that it must be a divisor of $a^r + 1$, or that $a^r = m'p + p - 1$: it thus appears that the first term of the second half of the series of remainders of an *incomplete* period of an even number of terms, will be $p - 1$, and that the remaining terms of one half of this series will be *associated* terms with those of the first half of the series, which are severally equidistant from $p - 1$.*

534. PROP. If there be one primitive root of a modulus p, there are as many primitive roots of this modulus, as there are numbers less than $p - 1$ and prime to it.

If there be one primitive root of a modulus p, there are as many as there are numbers prime to $p - 1$, and less than $p - 1$.

For if a be a primitive root of p, then $a^{p-1} = mp + 1$: and if we suppose r to be prime to $p - 1$, then we get $a^r = m'p + \alpha$, where α is different from 1: then α or a^r is a primitive root of p, since no power of α or of a^r, which is less than $p - 1$ is of the form $mp + 1$†: and since the same remark applies to the remainder from the division of every power of a by p, whose index is prime to $p - 1$ and to such powers of a only ‡, it follows that there are as many primitive roots as there are numbers prime to $p - 1$ and less than $p - 1$ and no more.

535. A *subordinate* (Art. 531) root a of the modulus p, is one which makes $a^t = mp + 1$, where t is a *submultiple* of $p - 1$: and it may be proved, by the same process of reasoning as that employed in the last Article, that if there be one such subordinate root corresponding to t, there are as many such roots as there are numbers prime to t and less than t.

The same proposition extended to subordinate roots.

536. PROP. The whole number of *subordinate* and *primitive* roots of any prime modulus p is equal to $p - 1$.

The whole number of primitive and subordinate roots of p is equal to $p - 1$.

The whole number of numbers not greater than n and prime to n, or to some one of its divisors is equal to n.

* Thus if $a = 10$ and $p = 13$, in the incomplete series of remainders 1, 10, 9, 12, 3, 4, we find 12 or $13 - 1$ for the first term of the second half of the series.

† For the remainders from the division of a^{nr} and a^n by p, are the same, since all the terms in the series for $(m'p + \alpha)^n$ are multiples of p (Note, Art. 528) except the last, which is α^r: it is obvious likewise that if r be prime to $p - 1$, nr cannot be a multiple of $p - 1$, unless it is equal to $p - 1$ or to a multiple of it.

‡ For if r have a common divisor δ with $p - 1$, then $r \times \dfrac{p-1}{\delta} = \rho\,(p-1)$: or a power of a^r, which is less than $p - 1$, may be equal to $p - 1$, or to a multiple of it.

For every number less than p, is either a *subordinate* or a *primitive* root.

537. Prop. The whole number of numbers not greater than n and prime to n or to some one of its divisors, is equal to n.

For if a, b, c, &c. be the divisors of n, 1 and n being included, then if we multiply the numbers prime to a, b, c, &c. by $\frac{n}{a}$, $\frac{n}{b}$, $\frac{n}{c}$, respectively, the resulting products will not be greater than n.

All these products are different from each other: for if possible, let α and β be numbers prime to a and b respectively, and let $\frac{n}{a} \times \alpha = \frac{n}{b} \times \beta$, or $\frac{\alpha}{a} = \frac{\beta}{b}$: but since these fractions are equal to each other and in their lowest terms, it follows that $\alpha = \beta$ and $a = b$ (Art. 120), which is contrary to the hypothesis, since a and b are assumed to be *different* factors of n.

Again, every number between 1 and n inclusive, will be found amongst these products: for if t be any number not prime to n, and if x be the greatest common measure of t and n, then t will be prime to $\frac{n}{x}$, or in other words, t will be a number prime to one of the factors of n. It follows therefore that the whole series of numbers which are prime to some one of the factors of n, 1 and n included, will be equal to n.

538. There must be *primitive* as well as *subordinate* roots corresponding to every prime modulus p.

There must be primitive as well as subordinate roots corresponding to every prime modulus p.

For there are $p-1$ numbers and $p-1$ numbers *only*, which are prime to $p-1$ or to some one of its divisors (Art. 537): and there are also $p-1$ *primitive* and *subordinate* roots corresponding to every prime modulus p: it appears likewise that for any given factor of $p-1$, if there be one root corresponding to it, there are as many such roots as there are numbers prime to that factor and less than it (Arts. 534, 535): but inasmuch as the whole number of such roots is equal likewise to the greatest possible number of those numbers which are prime to the factors of $p - 1$, and less than $p - 1$, it follows that there must exist roots corresponding to every factor of $p - 1$, otherwise the number of them would *not* be equal to $p - 1$: it follows therefore that there must be as many roots corresponding to $p - 1$ (which are therefore primitive roots) as there are numbers less than $p - 1$ and prime to it.

539. PROP. *Wilson's Theorem.* If p be a prime number, the continued product of the natural numbers 1, 2, 3, &c. as far as $p - 1$, increased by 1, is divisible by p.

Wilson's Theorem.

For if a be a primitive root of p (and such primitive roots always exist, Art. 538) then the remainders from the division of the several terms of the series

$$1, \ a, \ a^2, \ \ldots a^{p-1},$$

will include all the natural numbers from 1 to $p - 1$; and consequently, the remainder from the division of their continued product by p, will be the same as from the division of the continued product of the natural numbers by p^*: but the continued product of the terms of the series

$$1, \ a, \ a^2, \ \ldots a^{p-1},$$

is equal to

$$a^{1+2+3+\cdots p-1} = a^{\frac{p(p-1)}{2}} = a^{2n^2+n} = a^{2n^2} \times a^n \dagger,$$

if we replace p (an odd number) by $2n + 1$ (Art. 516): but since the remainder from the division of $a^{2n} = a^{p-1}$ is 1, the remainder from the division of $a^{2n^2} = (a^{2n})^n$ is also 1: it follows therefore that the remainder from the division $a^{2n^2} \times a^n$ is the same as that from the division of a^n, which is $p - 1$ (Art. 532): it follows therefore that the remainder from the division of

* For if
$$a^m = rp + a, \ a^{m'} = r'p + a', \ a^{m''} = r''p + a'' \ \&c.$$
then
$$a^m \times a^{m'} \times a^{m''} \times \&c. = a^{m+m'+m''+\&c.} = \rho p + aa'a'' :$$

and consequently the remainder from the division of the product of a^m, $a^{m'}$, $a^{m''}$ &c. by p is the same as that from the division of the product of their remainders a, a', a'' ... by p.

† For the sum of the series of natural numbers
$$1 + 2 + 3 + \ldots n - 1 = \frac{n(n-1)}{2} \ (\text{Art. 422}).$$

$1 \times 2 \times \ldots (p-1)$ by p is $p-1$, and consequently, the remainder from the division of $1 \times 2 \times 3 \times \ldots (p-1)+1$ by p is 0, whenever p is a prime number*.

Extension of Wilson's Theorem to the terms of an *incomplete* period.

540. PROP. The product of all the remainders of an incomplete period, when divided by the prime modulus p, will give remainders which are 1 or $p-1$, according as the number of terms in that period is odd or even.

For if $a_1, a_2, \ldots a_t$ be the series of remainders of the period

$$a, a^2, a^3, \ldots a^t,$$

the remainder from the product of

$$a_1, a_2, a_3, \ldots a_t,$$

will be the same as from the product

$$a \times a^2 \times \ldots a^t = a^{1+2+3+\ldots t} = a^{\frac{t(t+1)}{2}}:$$

if we suppose t to be an even number or $2n$, then

$$a^{\frac{t(t+1)}{2}} = a^{nt+n} = a^{nt} \times a^n = mp + p - 1,$$

since the remainder from a^{nt}, divided by p, is 1, and from a^n, divided by p, is $p-1$ (Art. 533): but if t be an odd number equal to $2n+1$, then

$$a^{\frac{t(t+1)}{2}} = a^{(2n+1)(n+1)} = a^{(n+1)t} = mp + 1:$$

it follows therefore that the continued product of the terms of a subordinate period of t terms is of the form $mp+1$ or $mp+p-1$, according as t is odd cr event.

This Theorem obviously includes that of Wilson; for if $t = p-1$, when p is a prime number and therefore odd, t will be an even number, and therefore the continued product of the

---

* If p be a composite number, its factors are included amongst the factors of $1 \times 2 \times \ldots (p-1)$ which is therefore divisible by it: under such circumstances, therefore, $1 \times 2 \times 3 \times \ldots (p-1) + 2$ is not divisible by p.

† Thus, if a be 5 to the modulus 13, then the continued product of the terms of the incomplete period 1, 5, 12, 8 or 480 is $= 36 \times 13 + 12$: but, if a be 5 to the modulus 11, the continued product of the incomplete period 1, 5, 3, 4, 9 or $540 = 49 \times 11 + 1$.

natural numbers as far as t or $p-1$, will leave a remainder $p-1$ when divided by p.

541. PROP. The sum of all the terms of any period, whether complete or incomplete, to a prime modulus p, is a multiple of p.

For the sum of any period of remainders is of the same form, to the modulus p, with the remainder from the sum of the series

$$1 + a + a^2 + \ldots a^{t-1} = \frac{a^t - 1}{a - 1} = mp \;;$$

since $a^t - 1 = mp^*$:

Thus, if $p = 13$ and if $a = 5$, we find the period of remainders,

$$1, \; 5, \; 12, \; 8,$$

whose sum is $26 = 2 \times 13$.

542. Many other remarkable consequences may be deduced from the principles which have been employed in the establishment of the preceding Theorems: but the sketch which we have given of one important branch of the theory of numbers, which has already extended somewhat beyond the space which it should probably occupy in an elementary work of this nature, may be considered quite sufficient to illustrate and exemplify not merely the mode of conducting such investigations, but likewise some of the peculiar difficulties which attend them from the absence of general methods, and from the want of a continuous and deductive connection between the several propositions to be demonstrated.

* Unless $a - 1$ be divisible by p, or a be *congruous* to 1, in which case the period consists of one term only.

ADDITIONS AND CORRECTIONS.

Art. 88. This formation of indefinite quotients is strictly analogous to the formation of the quotients of division in common arithmetic: for we proceed generally to apply the rule for division, without previously knowing whether the process will terminate or not: thus if we are required to divide 11 by 13, we proceed as follows:

$$13) \ 11.00 \ (.846153$$

$$
\begin{array}{r}
104 \\
\hline
60 \\
52 \\
\hline
80 \\
78 \\
\hline
20 \\
13 \\
\hline
70 \\
65 \\
\hline
50 \\
39 \\
\hline
11
\end{array}
$$

The quotients now recur in the same order, and form therefore, if continued indefinitely, an indefinite series. In a similar manner if we are required to divide 11 by 16, we proceed as follows:

$$16) \ 11.0 \ (6875$$

$$
\begin{array}{r}
96 \\
\hline
140 \\
128 \\
\hline
120 \\
112 \\
\hline
80 \\
80
\end{array}
$$

In this case the quotient terminates, and under the enlarged view of numbers which is taken in Chapter 2, as including fractional as well as integral numbers, the divisor may be said to be contained a certain number of times exactly in the dividend.

Art. 112. This proposition, one of the most important in the theory of numbers, is demonstrated by Euclid, El. VII. Prop. 32: it is demonstrated by Gauss in his Disquisitiones Arithmeticæ, Art. 13, in conformity with his general method of treating the theory of numbers, of which a slight notice is given in Chap. x. Art. 514, and those which follow.

Art. 148, Note. The French have resumed since the 1st of January, 1841, their decimal system of weights and measures in all its integrity: it is universally adopted, though with different names, in Belgium.

It has recently been proposed, in a Report of a Commission on weights and measures, presented to Parliament in February, 1842, to introduce such changes in our monetary and metrical systems as may lead to the general adoption of the decimal scale in all written accounts, and to its extensive, though not exclusive, use in the ordinary transactions of life.

Art. 181. If a decimal coinage and system of weights and measures was adopted, this process of abridged multiplication would become not merely useful but necessary. Thus if the decimal coinage proceeded by sovereigns (20s.), *victorines* (2s.), *cents* (2¾d.), *millets* (²⁴⁄₅₅ farthing), and if the divisions of area proceeded by acres, *chains* ($\frac{1}{10}$th acre), *chainettes* ($\frac{1}{100}$th acre), and its decimal subdivisions, (in conformity with the existing practice of measuring by Gunter's chain), the value of 37 acres, 7 chains, 4 chainettes (37.74 acres), at £47. 7 vict. 9 cents (£47.79) per acre, would be found as follows: all values below cents being rejected:

$$
\begin{array}{r|l}
\multicolumn{2}{c}{37 \cdot 74} \\
\multicolumn{2}{c}{47 \cdot 79} \\
\hline
1509 & 6 \\
264 & 18 \\
26 & 42 \\
3 & 39 \\
\hline
\end{array}
$$

£1803 . 59

The same question, adapted to our existing coins and measures, and solved as a Rule of Three question, would assume the following form.

Required the value of 37 acres, 2 roods, and 38 poles of land at £47. 15s. 10d. per acre.

acre.		a. r. p.		£. s. d.	
1	:	37 . 2 . 38	::	47 . 15 . 10	: x
4		4		20	

4	150	955
40	40	12

160	6038	11470
		6038

91760
34410
68820

160) 69255760 (12) 432849
640
                        20) 36070.9

525
480
                        £1803 . 10 . 9

455
320

1357
1280

776
640

1360
1280

80

There are 134 figures to be written in this process, and only 34 in the former : the time consumed in performing the operations would be nearly in the same proportion, or as 4 to 1 nearly.

With a decimal metrical and monetary system, the distinction between simple and compound arithmetic would disappear, inasmuch as all quantities involved in arithmetical operations would be presented at once, without previous reduction, in the decimal scale: few metrical tables would be required, and those of the most simple kind: and it would rarely be necessary to incorporate in the fundamental rules, the processes of *decimal* as well as of *integral* arithmetic, which are now, in common books, most improperly and unphilosophically separated from each other.

The effect of the proposed change would be to lessen the labours of the schoolboy as much as those of the tradesman: and to introduce into all transactions of account a uniformity, clearness and brevity which would produce the most important benefits to trade and commerce.

Art. 232. The proof, however, of the following propositions, which are referred to in this Article, may be deduced from very simple and elementary considerations.

(1) The extreme limit of the values of a', a'', &c. in the successive complete quotients (Art. 190) $\dfrac{\sqrt{n}+a'}{r}$, $\dfrac{\sqrt{n}+a''}{r'}$, &c. is a, which is the greatest integer less than $\sqrt{n}$. For a'^2, a''^2, &c. in the expressions $r' = \dfrac{n-a'^2}{r}$, $r'' = \dfrac{n-a''^2}{r'}$, &c. (Art. 229), are always less than n, and therefore the values of a', a'', &c. cannot exceed a.

(2) The extreme limit of the values of the integral quotients b, b', &c. is $2a$.

For $a'' = r'b' - a'$ or $a'' + a' = r'b'$: and since the limit of the value of $a'' + a'$ is $2a$ (Prop. 1), and since r' is either a whole number or 1 (Art. 229, Note), it follows that the extreme limit of the value of b' is $2a$.

(3) The extreme limit of the values of r, r', r'', &c. is $2a$.

For since $a'' + a' = r'b'$, and since the extreme limit of the value of $a'' + a'$ is $2a$, and b' is either a whole number or 1, it follows that r' cannot exceed $2a$.

The value of $r = n - a^2$ cannot exceed $2a$; for if it did, a would not be the greatest integer less than $\sqrt{n}$.

(4) If any one of the series of quotients b', b'', &c. be equal to $2a$, then the corresponding values of a'' and a' are severally equal to a.

For if $b' = 2a$, then $a'' + a' = r'b' = 2a$, and therefore $a'' = a$ and $a' = a$: for neither a'' nor a' can exceed a.

(5) Every complete quotient in the series determines that which follows it.

For if $\dfrac{\sqrt{n} + a'}{r}$ and $\dfrac{\sqrt{n} + a''}{r'}$ be two successive complete quotients, and b' the integer quotient corresponding to the first, then we have $a'' = r'b' - a'$ and $r' = \dfrac{n - a'^2}{r}$, and consequently a'' and r' in the second complete quotient are entirely dependent upon the first.

(6) The quotients, both complete and integral, recur by periods, beginning with the first complete quotient $\dfrac{\sqrt{n} + a}{r}$.

The quotients $\dfrac{\sqrt{n} + a'}{r'}$, $\dfrac{\sqrt{n} + a''}{r''}$, &c. must recur within an interval of less than $2a^2$ terms: for the limits of the values of a' and r', which determine a'' and r'', are a and $2a$ respectively, and there cannot therefore be more than $a \times 2a$ combinations of them which are different from each other.

Again, this recurrence must begin with the first complete quotient $\dfrac{\sqrt{n} + a}{r}$: for if not, let

$$\frac{\sqrt{n} + a_1}{r_1}, \quad \frac{\sqrt{n} + a_2}{r_2}, \ldots \ldots \frac{\sqrt{n} + a_m}{r_m},$$

$$\frac{\sqrt{n} + a_1}{r_1}, \quad \frac{\sqrt{n} + a_2}{r_2}, \ldots \ldots \frac{\sqrt{n} + a_m}{r_m},$$

be the two first complete periods, and let $\dfrac{\sqrt{n} + a}{\rho}$ be the complete quotient preceding $\dfrac{\sqrt{n} + a_1}{r_1}$ or the first recurring quotient; then $\dfrac{\sqrt{n} + a}{\rho}$ determines $\dfrac{\sqrt{n} + a_1}{r_1}$ in the same manner that $\dfrac{\sqrt{n} + a_m}{r_m}$ determines the succeeding term $\dfrac{\sqrt{n} + a_1}{r_1}$: and inasmuch as

$$\frac{\sqrt{n+a}}{\rho} = b_1 + \cfrac{1}{\cfrac{\sqrt{n+a_1}}{r_1}}$$

and
$$\frac{\sqrt{n+a_m}}{r_m} = b_1 + \cfrac{1}{\cfrac{\sqrt{n+a_1}}{r_1}};$$

it follows that $\dfrac{\sqrt{n+a}}{\rho} = \dfrac{\sqrt{n+a_m}}{r_m}$,

and equating the irrational and rational parts*, we get

$$\frac{\sqrt{n}}{\rho} = \frac{\sqrt{n}}{r_m} \quad \text{or} \quad \rho = r_m,$$

and also $\dfrac{a}{\rho} = \dfrac{a_m}{r_m}$;

and therefore $a = a_m$.

(7) The last integral quotient of each recurring period is $2a$.

For the first complete quotient of each recurring period is the first complete quotient, and is therefore $= \dfrac{\sqrt{n+a}}{r}$, where $r = n - a^2$: let $\dfrac{\sqrt{n+x}}{y}$ be the last complete quotient of a period: then since $y = \dfrac{n-a^2}{r}$ and $r = n - a^2$, it follows that $y = 1$, and that $\sqrt{n+x}$ is therefore the last complete quotient of the recurring period: and since x, when $y = 1$, is the greatest number which makes $n - x^2$ positive, it follows that $x = a$; and therefore the integral quotient corresponding to $\sqrt{n+x}$ is $a + a$ or $2a$.

(8) In a note to this Article, we have referred to the solution, when it is possible, of the equation

$$x^2 - ny^2 \mp a = 0,$$

as dependent upon the formation of the fractions converging to $\sqrt{n}$: we shall now proceed to investigate the nature of this dependence.

---

* If $x + \sqrt{y} = a + \sqrt{b}$, where x and a are rational and $\sqrt{y}$ and $\sqrt{b}$ quadratic surds, we have $x = a$ and $y = b$: for if not, let $x = a + c$: then we get $a + c + \sqrt{y} = a + \sqrt{b}$, and therefore $c + \sqrt{y} = \sqrt{b}$, which is impossible (Art. 249): in a similar manner it may be shewn that x is not $= a - c$: it follows therefore that $x = a$ and $\sqrt{y} = \sqrt{b}$.

Let $\frac{p^0}{q^0}$, $\frac{p}{q}$, $\frac{p'}{q'}$ be three consecutive fractions converging to $\sqrt{n}$, corresponding to the quotients u^0, u, u': the theory of such fractions (Art. 190) gives us the equation

$$\frac{p'}{q'} = \frac{p\,u' + p^0}{q\,u' + q^0}:$$

let $\frac{\sqrt{n} + a}{r}$ be the complete quotient corresponding to u': if we replace u' by it, we get

$$\sqrt{n} = \frac{p\left(\dfrac{\sqrt{n}+a}{r}\right) + p^0}{q\left(\dfrac{\sqrt{n}+a}{r}\right) + q^0} *$$

$$= \frac{p\sqrt{n} + pa + p^0 r}{q\sqrt{n} + qa + q^0 r},$$

multiplying numerator and denominator by r: if we further multiply both sides of this equation by $q\sqrt{n} + qa + q^0 r$, we get

$$qn + (qa + q^0 r)\sqrt{n} = p\sqrt{n} + pa + p^0 r,$$

and equating rational and irrational parts (see Note, p. 391), we find

$$qn = pa + p^0 r \dots\dots\dots\dots(1),$$
$$\text{and } p\sqrt{n} = (qa + q^0 r)\sqrt{n}\,;$$

or dividing by $\sqrt{n}$,

$$p = qa + q^0 r \dots\dots\dots\dots(2).$$

If we multiply equation (1) by q and equation (2) by p, we get, by subtracting the first resulting equation from the second,

$$p^2 - nq^2 = (pq^0 - p^0 q)r,$$
$$\text{or } p^2 - n^2 q^2 - (pq^0 - p^0 q)r = 0\dots(3).$$

If $\frac{p}{q}$ be a fraction corresponding to an odd place in the first recurring period, and therefore to an even place in the entire series of fractions, we have $pq^0 - p^0 q = 1$† (Art. 193); therefore

$$p^2 - nq^2 - r = 0 \dots\dots\dots\dots(4).$$

---

* For if the imperfect quotient u' is replaced by the complete quotient, the converging fraction becomes equal to $\sqrt{n}$.

† It should be kept in mind that it is the reciprocals of the fractions formed by the general rule (Art. 191) from the series of quotients, which converge to $\sqrt{n}$; and therefore the series of such reciprocal fractions $\frac{p^0}{q^0}$, $\frac{p}{q}$, $\frac{p'}{q'}$ are alternately greater and less than $\sqrt{n}$, according as they occupy *even* or *odd* places in the series.

If $\frac{p}{q}$ be a fraction corresponding to an odd place in the first recurring period, and therefore to an even place in the entire series of fractions, we have $p^0 q - p q^0 = 1$ (Art. 193); and therefore

$$p^2 - n q^2 + r = 0 \ldots \ldots \ldots (5).$$

If. in the last case, the number of terms in each recurring period be odd, and if $\frac{p_1}{q_1}$ be the converging fraction corresponding to the divisor r in the second recurring period, and therefore to an odd place in the series of fractions, then we have

$$p_1^2 - n q_1^2 - r = 0 \ldots \ldots \ldots (6).$$

If the fraction $\frac{p}{q}$ correspond to the last term but one of a recurring period, then r in each of the equations (4), (5), (6) may be replaced by 1, which is the value of the corresponding divisor.

(9) The solution of the equation

$$x^2 + n y^2 - 1 = 0,$$

is always possible in whole numbers, if n be any whole number which is not a square.

If the number of terms in each recurring period of quotients corresponding to $\sqrt{n}$ be even, the converging fraction corresponding to the last term but one of the first and of every other succeeding period is even, and therefore greater than $\sqrt{n}$: it follows therefore that if $\frac{x}{y}$ be this converging fraction, we have

$$x^2 - n y^2 - 1 = 0.$$

The values of x and y thus found satisfy the proposed equation: and the same is the case with the values of x and y in the converging fraction $\frac{x}{y}$ corresponding to the last term but one of every succeeding period: the number of solutions is therefore unlimited.

Again, if the number of terms in each recurring period corresponding to $\sqrt{n}$ be odd, the last term but one of the *second* recurring period will be even: and if $\frac{x}{y}$ be the corresponding converging fraction, then we have

$$x^2 - ny^2 - 1 = 0.$$

The same character will apply to the converging fraction corresponding to the last term but one of every alternate period: and the number of solutions therefore of this equation is, in this case also, unlimited.

(10) The following are examples:

(1) To solve the equation

$$x^2 - 23y^2 - 1 = 0.$$

The quotients corresponding to $\sqrt{23}$ determined by the rule Art. 230, are

$$4, 1, 3, 1, 8, 1, 3, 1, 8 \ldots$$

The number of terms in each period (4) is even.

The converging fractions are

$$\frac{1}{4}, \frac{1}{5}, \frac{4}{19}, \frac{5}{24} \times, \frac{44}{211}, \frac{49}{235}, \frac{191}{916}, \frac{240}{1151} \times, \frac{2111}{10124}, \frac{2351}{11275},$$

$$\frac{9164}{43949}, \frac{11515}{55224} \times \ldots$$

The penultimate fractions in each period, whose reciprocals converge to $\sqrt{23}$, are

$$\frac{5}{24}, \frac{240}{1151}, \frac{11515}{55224}, \frac{552480}{2649601},$$

and the pairs of values of x and y are

$$x = 24, \quad 1151, \quad 55224, \quad 2649601, \quad \&c.$$
$$y = 5, \quad 240, \quad 11515, \quad 552480, \quad \&c.$$

(2) To solve the equation

$$x^2 - 23y^2 + 1 = 0.$$

The penultimate term of each recurring period of quotients being an even term, there is no solution of this equation in whole numbers: for the corresponding converging fractions, as we have seen, furnish the solution of the equation

$$x^2 - 23y^2 - 1 = 0.$$

(3) To solve the equations

$$x^2 - 23y^2 + 7 = 0,$$
$$x^2 - 23y^2 - 2 = 0.$$

The complete quotients for every recurring period of the integral quotients of $\sqrt{23}$, are

$$\frac{\sqrt{23}+4}{7}, \quad \frac{\sqrt{23}+2}{2}, \quad \frac{\sqrt{23}+3}{7}, \quad \frac{\sqrt{23}+4}{1},$$

and the recurring period of divisors is therefore

$$7, \quad 2, \quad 7, \quad 1.$$

The converging fractions are given in the solution of Ex. 1, which give for the solution of the first of the given equations, the pairs of values

$$x = 4, \quad 19, \quad 211, \quad 916, \ldots\ldots$$
$$y = 1, \quad 4, \quad 44, \quad 191, \ldots\ldots$$

and for the second equation

$$x = 5, \quad 235, \quad 11275,$$
$$y = 1, \quad 49, \quad 2351,$$

There is no solution in whole numbers of the equations

$$x^2 - 23y^2 - 7 = 0,$$
$$x^2 - 23y^2 + 2 = 0,$$

nor of the equation

$$x^2 - 23y^2 \pm a = 0,$$

when a is different from 1, 7 or 2.

(4) To solve the equation

$$x^2 - 13y^2 + 1 = 0.$$

The quotients corresponding to $\sqrt{13}$ are

$$3, \, 1, \, 1, \, 1, \, 1, \, 6, \, 1, \, 1, \, 1, \, 1, \, 6 \ldots\ldots$$

The number of terms in each recurring period is (5) an odd number, and the converging fractions are

$$\frac{1}{3}, \frac{1}{4}, \frac{2}{7}, \frac{3}{11}, \frac{5}{18} \times, \frac{33}{119}, \frac{38}{137}, \frac{71}{256}, \frac{109}{393}, \frac{180}{649} \times, \frac{1189}{4287}, \frac{1369}{4936},$$

$$\frac{2558}{9223}, \frac{3927}{14159}, \frac{6485}{23382} \times \cdots \cdots$$

The penultimate fractions in alternate periods, beginning with the first, are

$$\frac{5}{18}, \quad \frac{6485}{23382}, \cdots\cdots$$

and the pairs of values of x and y in the equation are

$$x = 18, \quad 23382, \ldots \ldots$$
$$y = 5, \quad 6485, \ldots \ldots$$

The first penultimate fraction in the alternate periods, beginning with the second, is $\dfrac{180}{649}$, and furnishes a solution of the equation

$$x^2 - 13y^2 - 1 = 0.$$

(5) To solve the equation

$$x^2 - 44y^2 + 1 = 0.$$

The series of quotients are

$$6, 1, 1, 1, 2, 1, 1, 1, 12 \ldots \ldots$$

The pairs of values of x and y are

$$x = 199, \quad 79201,$$
$$y = 30, \quad 11940.$$

The series of divisors for one period is

$$8, 5, 7, 4, 7, 5, 8, 1.$$

The pairs of values of x and y which solve the equations

(a) $\quad x^2 - 44y^2 + 8 = 0$, are $x = 6, \; 126, \; 2514, \; 50154,$
$$y = 1, \; 19, \quad 379, \quad 7561.$$

(b) $\quad x^2 - 44y^2 - 5 = 0$, are $x = 7, \quad 73, \; 2713, \; 29047,$
$$y = 1, \quad 11, \quad 409, \quad 4379.$$

(c) $\quad x^2 - 44y^2 + 7 = 0$, are $x = 13, \quad 53, \; 5227, \; 21107,$
$$y = 2, \quad 8, \quad 788, \quad 3182.$$

(d) $\quad x^2 - 44y^2 - 4 = 0$, are $x = 20, \; 7940, \ldots \ldots$
$$y = 3, \; 1197, \ldots \ldots$$

All forms of the equation

$$x^2 - 44y^2 \pm a = 0$$

different from the above, are incapable of solution in whole numbers.

(6) To solve the equation

$$x^2 - 26y^2 - 1 = 0.$$

The quotients are

$$5, 10, 10, 10, \ldots \ldots$$

The reciprocals of the converging fractions are

$$\frac{1}{5}, \quad \frac{10}{51}, \quad \frac{101}{515}, \quad \frac{1020}{5201}.$$

The pairs of values of x and y are

$$x = 51, \quad 5201, \quad 530451,$$
$$y = 10, \quad 1020, \quad 104030.$$

If the equation had been

$$x^2 - 26y^2 + 1 = 0,$$

the pairs of values of x and y would have been

$$x = 5, \quad 515, \quad 51525, \ldots \ldots$$
$$y = 1, \quad 101, \quad 10301, \ldots \ldots$$

More generally, if $n = a^2 + 1$, as in the equation

$$x^2 - (a^2 + 1)y^2 - 1 = 0,$$

the series of quotients will be

$$a, \ 2a, \ 2a, \ldots \ldots$$

where the recurring period consists of one term only.

Again, if $n = a^2 - 1$, or $a^2 + a$, or $a^2 - a$, as in the equations

$$x^2 - (a^2 - 1)y^2 - 1 = 0 \ldots \ldots (a),$$
$$x^2 - (a^2 + a)y^2 - 1 = 0 \ldots \ldots (b),$$
$$x^2 - (a^2 - a)y^2 - 1 = 0 \ldots \ldots (c),$$

the recurring period of quotients will consist of two terms only.

For the first equation (a) the quotients are

$$a - 1, \ 1, \ 2(a - 1), \ 1, \ 2(a - 1), \ldots \ldots$$

For the second equation (b) the quotients are

$$a, \ 2, \ 2a, \ 2, \ 2a, \ldots \ldots$$

For the third equation (c) the quotients are

$$a - 1, \ 2, \ 2(a - 1), \ 2, \ 2(a - 1).$$

The solution of the equation

$$x^2 - ny^2 - 1 = 0$$

is one of the most important problems in the Theory of Numbers.

Art. 404, p. 241. If the simultaneous equations involving two unknown symbols x and y be expressed generally by

$$ax + by = k \ldots \ldots \ldots (1),$$
$$a'x + b'y = k' \ldots \ldots \ldots (2),$$

we get, by the ordinary process of elimination (Art. 395), multiplying the first equation by b' and the second by b,

$$ab'x + bb'y = b'k \dots\dots (3),$$

$$a'bx + bb'y = bk' \dots\dots (4),$$

and subtracting (4) from (3), we find

$$(ab' - a'b)x = b'k - bk',$$

and $x = \dfrac{b'k - bk'}{ab' - a'b};$

and by a similar process we find

$$y = \frac{a'k - ak'}{ab' - a'b}.$$

If there be three simultaneous equations, involving three unknown symbols x, y and z, they may be expressed generally by

$$ax + by + cz = k \dots\dots (5),$$

$$a'x + b'y + c'z = k' \dots\dots (6),$$

$$a''x + b''y + c''z = k'' \dots\dots (7).$$

By transferring cz, $c'z$, $c''z$ severally to the right-hand side of these equations, we get

$$ax + by = k - cz = K \dots\dots (8),$$

$$a'x + b'y = k' - c'z = K' \dots\dots (9),$$

$$a''x + b''y = k'' - c''z = K'' \dots\dots (10),$$

replacing $k - cz$, $k' - c'z$, $k'' - c''z$ severally by K, K' and K''.

If we now solve equations (8) and (9) in the same manner as equations (1) and (2), we shall get

$$x = \frac{b'K - bK'}{ab' - a'b}, \qquad y = \frac{a'K - aK'}{ab' - a'b}.$$

Replacing in these expressions K by $k - cz$ and K' by $k' - c'z$, we get

$$x = \frac{b'(k - cz) - b(k' - c'z)}{ab' - a'b},$$

$$y = \frac{a'(k - cz) - a(k' - c'z)}{ab' - a'b}.$$

If we now substitute these values of x and y in equation (7), clearing the equation of fractions, we get

$$a''b'k - a''b'cz - a''bk' + a''bc'z + a'b''k - a'b''cz - ab''k' + ab''c'z$$
$$+ ab'c'' - a'bc''z = ab'k'' - a'bk''.$$

Transposing the known quantities to one side and the unknown to the other, and dividing both sides by the resulting coefficient of z, we get

$$z = \frac{ab'k'' - ab''k' - a'bk'' + a'b''k + a''bk' - a''b'k}{ab'c'' - ab''c' - a'bc'' + a'b''c + a''bc' - a''b'c}.$$

The same value of z would be obtained by beginning with the solutions of equations (8) and (10) or (9) and (10), instead of (8) and (9): or in other words, the result is necessarily the same, in whatever manner the equations are combined.

By a similar process we find

$$x = \frac{kb'c'' - kb''c' - k'bc'' + k'b''c + k''bc' - k''b'c}{ab'c'' - ab''c' - a'bc'' + a'b''c + a''bc' - a''b'c},$$

$$y = \frac{ak'c'' - ak''c' - a'kc'' + a'k''c + a''kc' - a''k'c}{ab'c'' - ab''c' - a'bc'' + a'b''c + a''bc' - a''b'c}.$$